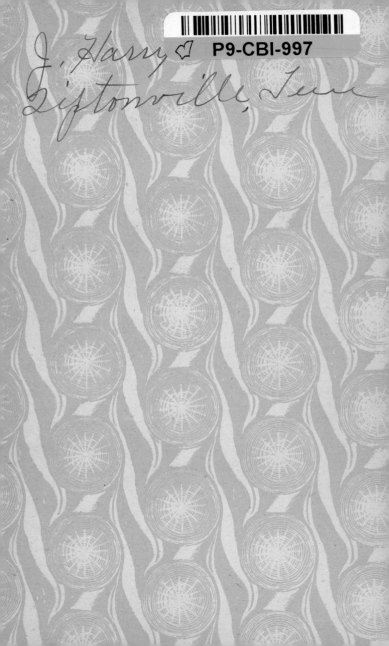

J. Harry ♡
Liftonville, Tenn

Everyman, I will go with thee, and be thy guide,
In thy most need to go by thy side.

This is No. 47 of Everyman's Library

EVERYMAN'S LIBRARY
EDITED BY ERNEST RHYS

SCIENCE

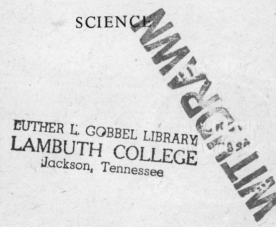
MAN'S PLACE
IN NATURE AND OTHER ESSAYS
BY THOMAS HENRY HUXLEY · INTRO-
DUCTION BY SIR OLIVER LODGE

THOMAS HENRY HUXLEY, born at Ealing in 1825. Medical apprentice at thirteen; entered Charing Cross Hospital, 1842; assistant-surgeon on H.M.S. *Rattlesnake*, 1846–50; F.R.S., 1850; President of the Royal Society, 1883; retired from public life, 1885. Died in 1895

MAN'S PLACE IN NATURE
AND OTHER ESSAYS

THOMAS HENRY HUXLEY

1787

LONDON: J. M. DENT & SONS LTD.
NEW YORK: E. P. DUTTON & CO. INC.

CONTENTS

Contents

INTRODUCTION

FORTY years ago the position of scientific studies was not so firmly established as it is to-day, and a conflict was necessary to secure their general recognition. The forces of obscurantism and of free and easy dogmatism were arrayed against them; and, just as in former centuries astronomy, and in more recent times geology, so in our own lifetime biology, has had to offer a harsh and fighting front, lest its progress be impeded by the hostility born of preconceived opinions, and by the bigotry of self-appointed guardians of conservative views.

The man who probably did as much as any to fight the battle of science in the nineteenth century, and secure the victory for free enquiry and progressive knowledge, is Thomas Henry Huxley; and it is an interesting fact that already the lapse of time is making it possible to bring his writings in cheap form to the notice of a multitude of interested readers. The pugnacious attitude, however, which, forty years ago, was appropriate, has become a little antique now; the conflict is not indeed over, but it has either totally shifted its ground, or is continued on the old battlefield chiefly by survivors, and by a few of a younger generation who have been brought up in the old spirit.

The truths of materialism now run but little risk of being denied or ignored, they run perhaps some danger of being exaggerated. Brilliantly true and successful in their own territory, they are occasionally pushed by enthusiastic disciples over the frontier line into regions where they can do nothing but break down. As if enthusiastic worshippers of motor-cars, proud of their performance on the good roads of France, should take them over into the Sahara or essay them on a Polar expedition.

That represents the mistake which, in modern times, by

careless thinkers, is being made. They tend to press the materialistic statements and scientific doctrines of a great man like Huxley, as if they were co-extensive with all existence. This is not really a widening of the materialistic aspect of things, it is a cramping of everything else ; it is an attempt to limit the universe to one of its aspects.

But the mistake is not made solely, nor even chiefly, by those eager disciples who are pursuing the delusive gleam of a materialistic philosophy—for these there is hope,—to attempt is a healthy exercise, and they will find out their mistake in time ; but the mistake is also made by those who are specially impressed with the spiritual side of things, who so delight to see guidance and management everywhere, that they wish to blind their eyes to the very mechanism whereby it is accomplished. They think that those who point out and earnestly study the mechanism are undermining the foundations of faith. Nothing of the kind. A traveller in the deck-cabin of an Atlantic liner may prefer to ignore the engines and the firemen, and all the machinery and toil which is urging him luxuriously forward over the waves in the sunshine ; he may try to imagine that he is on a sailing vessel propelled by the free air of heaven alone ; but there is just as much utilization of natural forces to a desired end in one case of navigation as in the other, and every detail of the steamship, down to the last drop of sweat from a fireman's grimy body, is an undeniable reality.

There are people who still resent the conclusions of biology as to man's place in nature, and try to counteract them ; but, as the late Professor Ritchie said (" Philosophical Studies," page 24)—

" It is a mistake, which has constantly been made in the past by those who are anxious for the spiritual interests of man, to interfere with the changes which are going on in scientific conceptions. Such interference has always ended in the defeat of the supporters of the quasi-scientific doctrines which the growing science of the time has discarded. Theology interfered with Galileo, and gained nothing in the end by its interference. Astronomy, geology, biology, anthropology, historical criticism, have at different periods raised alarm in the minds of those who dread a materialistic view of man's nature ; and with the very best intentions they have tried to fight the supposed enemy on his own ground, eagerly welcoming, for instance, every sign of disagreement between Darwinians and Lamarckians, or every dispute between different schools of historical critics, as if the spiritual well-being of mankind were bound up with the scientific beliefs of the seventeenth, or even earlier, century, as if *e.g.* it made all the difference in man's spiritual nature whether he was made directly out of inorganic dust or slowly ascended from lower organic forms. These are questions that must be settled by specialists. On the other hand, philosophic criticism is in place when the scientific specialist begins to dogmatize about the universe as a whole, when he speaks for example as if an accurate narrative of the various steps by which the lower forms of life have passed into the higher was a sufficient explanation to us of the mystery of existence."

Let it be understood, therefore, that science is one thing, and philosophy another : that science most properly concerns itself with matter and motion, and reduces phenomena, as far as it can, to mechanism. The more successfully it does that, the more it fulfils its end and aim ; but when, on the strength of that achievement, it seeks to blossom into a philosophy, when it endeavours to conclude that its scope is complete and all-inclusive, that nothing exists in the universe but mechanism, and that the aspect of things from a scientific point of view is their only aspect,—then it is becoming narrow and bigoted and deserving of rebuke. Such rebuke it received from Huxley, such rebuke it will always receive from scientific men who realize properly the magnitude of existence and the vast potentialities of the universe.

Our opportunities of exploration are good as far as they go, but they are not extensive ; we live as it were in the mortar of one of the stones of St. Paul's Cathedral ; and yet so assiduously have we cultivated our faculties that we can trace something of the outline of the whole design and have begun to realize the plan of the building—a surprising feat for insects of limited faculty. And—continuing the parable— two schools of thought have arisen : one saying that it was conceived in the mind of an architect and designed and built wholly by him, the other saying that it was put together stone by stone in accordance with the laws of mechanics and physics. Both statements are true, and those that emphasize the latter are not thereby denying the existence of Christopher Wren, though to the unwise enthusiasts on the side of design they may appear to be doing so. Each side is stating a truth, and neither side is stating the whole truth. Nor should we find it easy with all our efforts to state the whole truth exhaustively, even about such a thing as that. Those who deny any side of truth are to that extent unbelievers, and Huxley was righteously indignant with those short-sighted bigots who blasphemed against that aspect of divine truth which had been specially revealed to him. This is what he lived to preach, and to this he was faithful to the uttermost.

Let him be thought of as a devotee of truth, and a student of the more materialistic side of things, but never let him be thought of as a philosophical materialist or as one who abounded in cheap negations.

The objection which it is necessary to express concerning Materialism as a complete system is based not on its assertions but on its negations. In so far as it makes positive assertions, embodying the result of scientific discovery and even of scientific speculation based thereupon, there is no fault to find with it ; but when, on the strength of that, it sets up to be a philosophy of the universe—all inclusive, therefore, and shutting out a number of truths otherwise perceived, or which appeal to other faculties, or which are equally true and are not really contradictory of legitimately materialistic statements—then it is that its insufficiency and narrowness have to be displayed. As Professor Ritchie said :—" The 'legitimate materialism of the sciences' simply means temporary and convenient abstraction from the cognitive conditions under which there are 'facts' or 'objects' for us at all ; it is 'dogmatic materialism' which is metaphysics of the bad sort."

It will be probably instructive, and it may be sufficient, if I show that two great leaders in scientific thought (one the greatest of all men of science who have yet lived), though well aware of much that could be said positively on the materialistic side, and very willing to admit or even to extend the province of science or exact knowledge to the uttermost, yet were very far from being philosophic materialists or from imagining that other modes of regarding the universe were thereby excluded.

Great leaders of thought, in fact, are not accustomed to take a narrow view of existence, or to suppose that one mode of regarding it, or one set of formulæ expressing it, can possibly be sufficient and complete. Even a sheet of paper has two sides: a terrestrial globe presents different aspects from different points of view; a crystal has a variety of facets; and the totality of existence is not likely to be more simple than any of these—is not likely to be readily expressible in any form of words, or to be thoroughly conceivable by any human mind.

It may be well to remember that Sir Isaac Newton was a Theist of the most pronounced and thorough conviction, although he had a great deal to do with the reduction of the major Cosmos to mechanics, *i.e.*, with its explanation by the elaborated machinery of simple forces, and he conceived it possible that, in the progress of science, this process of reduction to mechanics would continue till it embraced nearly all the phenomena of nature. (See extract below.) That, indeed, has been the effort of science ever since, and therein lies the legitimate basis for materialistic statements, though not for a materialistic philosophy.

The following sound remarks concerning Newton are taken from Huxley's " Hume," p. 246 :—

" Newton demonstrated all the host of heaven to be but the elements of a vast mechanism, regulated by the same laws as those which express the falling of a stone to the ground. There is a passage in the preface to the first edition of the ' Principia ' which shows that Newton was penetrated, as completely as Descartes, with the belief that all the phenomena of nature are expressible in terms of matter and motion :—

" ' Would that the rest of the phenomena of nature could be deduced by a like kind of reasoning from mechanical prin-

ciples.   For many circumstances lead me to suspect that all
these phenomena may depend upon certain forces, in virtue
of which the particles of bodies, by causes not yet known, are
either mutually impelled against one another, and cohere into
regular figures, or repel and recede from one another ; which
forces being unknown, philosophers have as yet explored
nature in vain.   But I hope that, either by this method of
philosophizing, or by some other and better, the principles
here laid down may throw some light upon the matter.' "

Here is a full-blown anticipation of an intelligible exposition
of the Universe in terms of matter and force—the substantial
basis of what smaller men call materialism and develop into
what they consider to be a materialistic philosophy.   But
there is no necessity for any such scheme ; and Professor
Huxley himself, who is commonly spoken of by half-informed
people as if he were a philosophic materialist, was really
nothing of the kind ; for although, like Newton, fully imbued
with the mechanical doctrine, and of course far better informed concerning the biological departments of nature, and
the discoveries which have in the last century been made,—
and though he rightly regarded it as his mission to make the
scientific point of view clear to his benighted contemporaries,
and was full of enthusiasm for the facts on which materialists
take their stand,—he saw clearly that these alone were insuffi-
cient for a philosophy.   The following extracts from the
Hume volume will show that he entirely repudiated materialism as a satisfactory or complete philosophical system, and
that he was especially severe on gratuitous denials applied to
provinces beyond our scope :—

"While it is the summit of human wisdom to learn the
limit of our faculties, it may be wise to recollect that we have
no more right to make denials, than to put forth affirmatives,
about what lies beyond that limit.   Whether either mind or
matter has a 'substance' or not, is a problem which we are
incompetent to discuss : and it is just as likely that the
common notions upon the subject should be correct as any
others. . . . 'The same principles which, at first view, lead to
scepticism, pursued to a certain point, bring men back to
common sense' " (p. 282).

"Moreover, the ultimate forms of existence which we distinguish in our little speck of the universe are, possibly, only two out of infinite varieties of existence, not only analogous to matter and analogous to mind, but of kinds which we are not competent so much as to conceive,—in the midst of which, indeed, we might be set down, with no more notion of what was about us, than the worm in a flower-pot, on a London balcony, has of the life of the great city" (p. 286)

And again on pp. 251 and 279 :—

"It is worth any amount of trouble to . . . know by one's own knowledge the great truth . . . that the honest and rigorous following up of the argument which leads us to 'materialism' inevitably carries us beyond it."

"To sum up. If the materialist affirms that the universe and all its phenomena are resolvable into matter and motion, Berkeley replies, True ; but what you call matter and motion are known to us only as forms of consciousness ; their being is to be conceived or known ; and the existence of a state of consciousness apart from a thinking mind is a contradiction in terms.

"I conceive that this reasoning is irrefragable. And, therefore, if I were obliged to choose between absolute materialism and absolute idealism, I should feel compelled to accept the latter alternative."

Let the jubilant but uninstructed and comparatively ignorant amateur materialist therefore beware, and bethink himself twice or even thrice before he conceives that he understands the universe and is competent to pour scorn upon the intuitions and perceptions of great men in what may be to him alien regions of thought and experience.

Let him explain, if he can, what he means by his own identity, or the identity of any thinking or living being, which at different times consists of a totally different set of material particles. Something there clearly is which confers personal identity and constitutes an individual : it is a property characteristic of every form of life, even the humblest ; but it is not yet explained or understood, and it is no answer to assert gratuitously that there is some fundamental substance or material basis on which that identity depends, any more than it is an explanation to say that it depends upon a soul. These are all forms of words. As Hume says, quoted by Huxley with approval, in the work already cited, p. 194 :—

"It is impossible to attach any definite meaning to the word 'substance,' when employed for the hypothetical substratum of soul and matter. . . . If it be said that our personal identity requires the assumption of a substance which remains the same while the accidents of perception shift and change, the question arises what is meant by personal identity ? . . . A plant or an animal, in the course of its existence, from the condition of an egg or seed to the end of life, remains the same neither in form, nor in structure, nor in the matter of which it is composed : every attribute it possesses is constantly changing, and yet we say that it is always one and the same individual " (p. 194).

And in his own preface to the Hume volume Huxley expresses himself forcibly thus—equally antagonistic as was his wont to both ostensible friend and ostensible foe, as soon as they got off what he considered the straight path :—

"That which it may be well for us not to forget is, that the first-recorded judicial murder of a scientific thinker [Socrates] was compassed and effected, not by a despot, nor by priests, but was brought about by eloquent demagogues. . . . Clear knowledge of what one does not know is just as important as knowing what one does know. . . .

"The development of exact natural knowledge in all its vast range, from physics to history and criticism, is the consequence of the working out, in this province, of the resolution to 'take nothing for truth without clear knowledge that it is such'; to consider all beliefs open to criticism ; to regard the value of authority as neither greater nor less, than as much as it can prove itself to be worth. The modern spirit is not the spirit 'which always denies,' delighting only in destruction ; still less is it that which builds castles in the air rather than not construct; it is that spirit which works and will work 'without haste and without rest,' gathering harvest after har-

vest of truth into its barns, and devouring error with unquenchable fire " (p. viii).

The harvesting of truth is a fairly safe operation, for if some
falsehood be inadvertently harvested along with the grain we
may hope that, having a less robust and hardy nature, it will
before long be detected by its decaying odour ; but the rooting
up and devouring of error with unquenchable fire is a more
dangerous enterprise, inasmuch as flames are apt to spread
beyond our control; and the lack of infallibility in the selection
of error may to future generations become painfully apparent.

The phrase represents a good healthy energetic mood however, and in a world liable to become overgrown with weeds
and choked with refuse, the cleansing work of a firebrand
may from time to time be a necessity, in order that the free
wind of heaven and the sunlight may once more reach the
fertile soil.

But it is unfair to think of Huxley even when young as a
firebrand, though it is true that he was to some extent a man
of war, and though the fierce and consuming mood is rather
more prominent in his early writings than in his later work.

A fighting attitude was inevitable forty years ago, because
then the truths of biology were being received with hostility,
and the free science and philosophy of a later time seemed
likely to have a poor chance of life. But the world has
changed or is changing now, the wholesome influences of fire
have done their work, and it would be a rather barbarous
anachronism to apply the same agency among the young
green shoots of healthy learning which are springing up in
the cleared ground.

OLIVER LODGE.

1906.

AMONG the earlier published works of T. H. Huxley (1825–1895), and of the essays contained in this volume: "The Darwinian Hypothesis" first appeared in the *Times*, Dec. 26, 1859; "On the Educational Value of the Natural History Sciences" (Address given at St. Martin's Hall), was published in 1854; "Time and Life" (*Macmillan's Magazine*), Dec. 1859; "The Origin of Species" (*Westminster Review*), April 1860; "A Lobster: or, The Study of Zoology," 1861. "Geological Contemporaneity and Persistent Types of Life" (Address to Geological Society), 1862, was re-published in "Lay Sermons," vol. viii.; "Six Lectures to Working Men on the Phenomena of Organic Nature," 1863, in "Collected Essays," vol. vii. "Evidence as to Man's Place in Nature," 1863. Of his other works, the translation by Huxley and Busk of "Kölliker's Manual of Human Histology," appeared in 1853. "Lectures on the Elements of Comparative Anatomy," "Elementary Atlas of Comparative Osteology"; two Science Lectures, "The Circulation of the Blood" and "Corals and Coral Reefs," and "Lessons in Elementary Physiology," in 1866. "Introduction to the Classification of Animals," 1869. "Lay Sermons, Essays, and Reviews," 1870. "Critiques and Addresses," 1873. "On Yeast: A Lecture," 1872. "A Manual of the Anatomy of Vertebrated Animals," 1871. "Manual of the Anatomy of Invertebrated Animals," 1877. "American Addresses," 1877. "Physiography," 1877. "Hume" in "English Men of Letters," 1878. "The Crayfish: an Introduction to the Study of Zoology," 1880. "Science and Culture, and other Essays," 1881. "Essays upon some Controverted Questions," 1892. "Evolution and Ethics" (the Romanes Lecture), 1893. Huxley also assisted in editing the series of Science Primers published by Messrs. Macmillan, and contributed the introductory volume himself. The "Collected Essays," in nine vols., containing all that he cared to preserve, 1893. "The Scientific Memoirs of T. H. Huxley," edited by Professor Michael Foster and Professor E. Ray Lankester, in five vols., 1898–1903. His "Life and Letters," edited by his son, Leonard Huxley, was published in 1900.

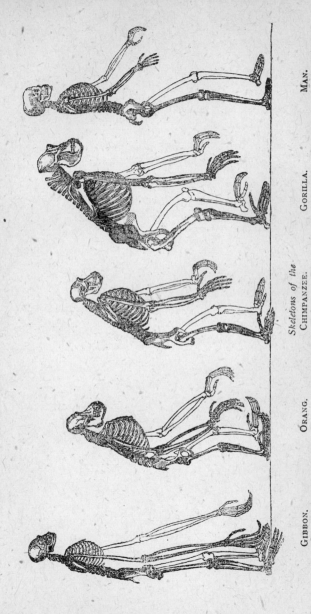

GIBBON.   ORANG.   CHIMPANZEE.   GORILLA.   MAN.

Skeletons of the

Photographically reduced from Diagrams of the natural size (except that of the Gibbon, which was twice as large as nature), drawn by Mr. Waterhouse Hawkins from specimens in the Museum of the Royal College of Surgeons.

HUXLEY'S ESSAYS

I

ON THE NATURAL HISTORY OF THE MAN-LIKE APES

ANCIENT traditions, when tested by the severe processes of modern investigation, commonly enough fade away into mere dreams : but it is singular how often the dream turns out to have been a half-waking one, presaging a reality. Ovid foreshadowed the discoveries of the geologist : the Atlantis was an imagination, but Columbus found a western world : and though the quaint forms of Centaurs and Satyrs have an existence only in the realms of art, creatures approaching man more nearly than they in essential structure, and yet as thoroughly brutal as the goat's or horse's half of the mythical compound, are now not only known, but notorious.

I have not met with any notice of one of these MAN-LIKE APES of earlier date than that contained in Pigafetta's "Description of the Kingdom of Congo," [1] drawn up from the notes of a Portuguese sailor, Eduardo Lopez, and published in 1598. The tenth chapter of this work is entitled "De Animalibus quæ in hac provincia re-

---

[1] REGNUM CONGO : hoc est VERA DESCRIPTIO REGNI AFRICANI QUOD TAM AB INCOLIS QUAM LUSITANIS CONGUS APPELLATUR, per Philippum Pigafettam, olim ex Edoardo Lopez acroamatis lingua Italica excerpta, num Latio sermone donata ab August. Cassiod. Reinio. Iconibus et imaginibus rerum memorabilium quasi vivis, opera et industria Joan. Theodori et Joan. Israelis de Bry, fratrum exornata. Francofurti, MDXCVIII.

periuntur," and contains a brief passage to the effect that
"in the Songan country, on the banks of the Zaire, there
are multitudes of apes, which afford great delight to the
nobles by imitating human gestures." As this might
apply to almost any kind of apes, I should have thought
little of it, had not the brothers De Bry, whose engravings
illustrate the work, thought fit, in their eleventh "Argumentum," to figure two of these "Simiæ magnatum deliciæ."
So much of the plate as contains these apes is faithfully

FIG. I.—Simiæ magnatum deliciæ.—De Bry, 1598.

copied in the woodcut (Fig. 1), and it will be observed
that they are tail-less, long-armed, and large-eared; and
about the size of Chimpanzees. It may be that these
apes are as much figments of the imagination of the
ingenious brothers as the winged, two-legged, crocodile-
headed dragon which adorns the same plate; or, on the
other hand, it may be that the artists have constructed
their drawings from some essentially faithful description
of a Gorilla or a Chimpanzee. And, in either case, though
these figures are worth a passing notice, the oldest trustworthy and definite accounts of any animal of this kind

date from the 17th century, and are due to an Englishman.

The first edition of that most amusing old book, "Purchas his Pilgrimage," was published in 1613, and therein are to be found many references to the statements of one whom Purchas terms "Andrew Battell (my neere neighbour, dwelling at Leigh in Essex) who served under Manuel Silvera Perera, Governor under the King of Spaine, at his city of Saint Paul, and with him went farre into the countrey of Angola"; and again, "my friend, Andrew Battle, who lived in the kingdom of Congo many yeares," and who, "upon some quarell betwixt the Portugals (among whom he was a sergeant of a band) and him, lived eight or nine moneths in the woodes." From this weather-beaten old soldier, Purchas was amazed to hear "of a kinde of Great Apes, if they might so bee termed, of the height of a man, but twice as bigge in feature of their limmes, with strength proportionable, hairie all over, otherwise altogether like men and women in their whole bodily shape.[1] They lived on such wilde fruits as the trees and woods yielded, and in the night time lodged on the trees."

This extract is, however, less detailed and clear in its statements than a passage in the third chapter of the second part of another work—"Purchas his Pilgrimes," published in 1625, by the same author—which has been often, though hardly ever quite rightly, cited. The chapter is entitled, "The strange adventures of Andrew Battell, of Leigh in Essex, sent by the Portugals prisoner to Angola, who lived there and in the adioining regions neere eighteene yeeres." And the sixth section of this chapter is headed—"Of the Provinces of Bongo, Calongo, Mayombe, Manikesocke, Motimbas: of the Ape Monster Pongo, their hunting: Idolatries; and divers other observations."

Bongo

Pongo

"This province (Calongo) toward the east bordereth upon Bongo, and toward the north upon Mayombe, which is nineteen leagues from Longo along the coast.

Longo

"This province of Mayombe is all woods and groves,

---

[1] "Except this that their legges had no calves."—[Ed. 1626.]
And in a marginal note, "These great apes are called Pongo's."

so overgrowne that a man may travaile twentie days in the shadow without any sunne or heat. Here is no kind of corne nor graine, so that the people liveth onely upon plantanes and roots of sundrie sorts, very good; and nuts; nor any kinde of tame cattell, nor hens.

"But they have great store of elephant's flesh, which they greatly esteeme, and many kinds of wild beasts; and great store of fish. Here is a great sandy bay, two leagues to the northward of Cape Negro,[1] which is the port of Mayombe. Sometimes the Portugals lade log-wood in this bay. Here is a great river, called Banna: in the winter it hath no barre, because the generall winds cause a great sea. But when the sunne hath his south declination, then a boat may goe in; for then it is smooth because of the raine. This river is very great, and hath many ilands and people dwelling in them. The woods are so covered with baboones, monkies, apes and parrots, that it will feare any man to travaile in them alone. Here are also two kinds of monsters, which are common in these woods, and very dangerous.

"The greatest of these two monsters is called Pongo in their language, and the lesser is called Engeco. This Pongo is in all proportion like a man; but that he is more like a giant in stature than a man; for he is very tall, and hath a man's face, hollow-eyed, with long haire upon his browes. His face and eares are without haire, and his hands also. His bodie is full of haire, but not very thicke; and it is of a dunnish colour.

"He differeth not from a man but in his legs; for they have no calfe. Hee goeth alwaies upon his legs, and carrieth his hands clasped in the nape of his necke when he goeth upon the ground. They sleepe in the trees, and build shelters for the raine. They feed upon fruit that they find in the woods, and upon nuts, for they eate no kind of flesh. They cannot speake, and have no under-standing more than a beast. The people of the countrie, when they travaile in the woods make fires where they sleepe in the night; and in the morning when they are gone, the Pongoes will come and sit about the fire till it goeth out; for they have no understanding to lay the

---

[1] *Purchas' note.*—Cape Negro is in 16 degrees south of the line.

wood together. They goe many together and kill many
negroes that travaile in the woods. Many times they fall
upon the elephants which come to feed where they be,
and so beate them with their clubbed fists, and pieces of
wood, that they will runne roaring away from them.
Those Pongoes are never taken alive because they are
so strong, that ten men cannot hold one of them; but
yet they take many of their young ones with poisoned
arrowes.

"The young Pongo hangeth on his mother's belly with
his hands fast clasped about her, so that when the
countrie people kill any of the females they take the
young one, which hangeth fast upon his mother.

"When they die among themselves, they cover the
dead with great heaps of boughs and wood, which is
commonly found in the forest." [1]

It does not appear difficult to identify the exact region
of which Battell speaks. Longo is doubtless the name of
the place usually spelled Loango on our maps. Mayombe
still lies some nineteen leagues northward from Loango,
along the coast; and Cilongo or Kilonga, Manikesocke,
and Motimbas are yet registered by geographers. The
Cape Negro of Battell, however, cannot be the modern
Cape Negro in 16° S., since Loango itself is in 4° S.
latitude. On the other hand, the "great river called
Banna" corresponds very well with the "Camma" and
"Fernand Vas," of modern geographers, which form a
great delta on this part of the African coast.

Now this "Camma" country is situated about a degree
and a-half south of the Equator, while a few miles to the
north of the line lies the Gaboon, and a degree or so
north of that, the Money River—both well known to

---

[1] Purchas' marginal note, p. 982 :—"The Pongo a giant ape. He
told me in conference with him, that one of these Pongoes tooke a
negro boy of his which lived a moneth with them. For they hurt
not those which they surprise at unawares, except they look on them;
which he avoyded. He said their highth was like a man's, but their
bignesse twice as great. I saw the negro boy. What the other
monster should be he hath forgotten to relate; and these papers
came to my hand since his death, which, otherwise, in my often con-
ferences, I might have learned. Perhaps he meaneth the Pigmy
Pongo killers mentioned."

modern naturalists as localities where the largest of man-like Apes has been obtained. Moreover, at the present day, the word Engeco, or N'schego, is applied by the natives of these regions to the smaller of the two great Apes which inhabit them; so that there can be no rational doubt that Andrew Battell spoke of that which he knew of his own knowledge, or, at any rate, by immediate report from the natives of Western Africa. The "Engeco," however, is that "other monster" whose nature Battell "forgot to relate," while the name "Pongo" —applied to the animal whose characters and habits are so fully and carefully described—seems to have died out, at least in its primitive form and signification. Indeed, there is evidence that not only in Battell's time, but up to a very recent date, it was used in a totally different sense from that in which he employs it.

For example, the second chapter of Purchas' work, which I have just quoted, contains "A Description and Historicall Declaration of the Golden Kingdom of Guinea, &c. &c. Translated from the Dutch, and compared also with the Latin," wherein it is stated (p. 986) that—

"The River Gaboon lyeth about fifteen miles northward from Rio de Angra, and eight miles northward from Cape de Lope Gonsalvez (Cape Lopez), and is right under the Equinoctial line, about fifteene miles from St. Thomas, and is a great land, well and easily to be knowne. At the mouth of the river there lieth a sand, three or foure fathoms deepe, whereon it beateth mightily with the streame which runneth out of the river into the sea. This river, in the mouth thereof, is at least foure miles broad; but when you are about the Iland called *Pongo,* it is not above two miles broad. . . . On both sides the river there standeth many trees. . . . The Iland called *Pongo,* which hath a monstrous high hill."

The French naval officers, whose letters are appended to the late M. Isidore Geoff. Saint Hilaire's excellent essay on the Gorilla,[1] note in similar terms the width of the Gaboon, the trees that line its banks down to the water's edge, and the strong current that sets out of it. They describe two islands in its estuary;—one low, called

[1] Archives du Museum, tome x.

Perroquet; the other high, presenting three conical hills, called Coniquet; and one of them, M. Franquet, expressly states that, formerly, the Chief of Coniquet was called *Meni-Pongo*, meaning thereby Lord of *Pongo ;* and that the *N'Pongues* (as, in agreement with Dr. Savage, he affirms the natives call themselves) term the estuary of the Gaboon itself *N'Pongo.*

It is so easy, in dealing with savages, to misunderstand their applications of words to things, that one is at first inclined to suspect Battell of having confounded the name of this region, where his "greater monster" still abounds, with the name of the animal itself. But he is so right about other matters (including the name of the "lesser monster") that one is loth to suspect the old traveller of error; and, on the other hand, we shall find that a voyager of a hundred years' later date speaks of the name "Boggoe," as applied to a great Ape, by the inhabitants of quite another part of Africa—Sierra Leone.

Homo Sylvestris. Orang Outang.

FIG. 2.—The Orang of Tulpius, 1641.

But I must leave this question to be settled by philologers and travellers; and I should hardly have dwelt so long upon it except for the curious part played by this word '*Pongo*' in the later history of the man-like Apes.

The generation which succeeded Battell saw the first of the man-like Apes which was ever brought to Europe, or, at any rate, whose visit found a historian. In the third book of Tulpius' "Observationes Medicæ," published in 1641, the 56th chapter or section is devoted to what he calls *Satyrus indicus,* "called by the Indians Orang-autang, or Man-of-the-Woods, and by the Africans Quoias Morrou." He gives a very good figure, evidently from the life, of the specimen of this animal, "nostra memoria ex

Angolâ delatum," presented to Frederick Henry Prince of Orange. Tulpius says it was as big as a child of three years old, and as stout as one of six years : and that its back was covered with black hair. It is plainly a young Chimpanzee.

In the meanwhile, the existence of other, Asiatic, man-like Apes became known, but at first in a very mythical fashion. Thus Bontius (1658) gives an altogether fabulous and ridiculous account and figure of an animal which he calls "Orang-outang"; and though he says, "vidi Ego cujus effigiem hic exhibeo," the said effigies (see Fig. 6 for Hoppius' copy of it) is nothing but a very hairy woman of rather comely aspect, and with proportions and feet wholly human. The judicious English anatomist, Tyson, was justified in saying of this description by Bontius, "I confess I do mistrust the whole representation."

It is to the last mentioned writer, and his coadjutor Cowper, that we owe the first account of a man-like ape which has any pretensions to scientific accuracy and completeness. The treatise entitled, "*Orang-outang, sive Homo Sylvestris ;* or the Anatomy of a Pygmie compared with that of a *Monkey*, an *Ape*, and a *Man*," published by the Royal Society in 1699, is, indeed, a work of remarkable merit, and has, in some respects, served as a model to subsequent inquirers. This "Pygmie," Tyson tells us, "was brought from Angola, in Africa ; but was first taken a great deal higher up the country."; its hair "was of a coal-black colour, and strait," and "when it went as a quadruped on all four, 'twas awkwardly ; not placing the palm of the hand flat to the ground, but it walk'd upon its knuckles, as I observed it to do when weak and had not strength enough to support its body."—"From the top of the head to the heel of the foot, in a strait line, it measured twenty-six inches."

These characters, even without Tyson's good figures (Figs. 3 and 4), would have been sufficient to prove his "Pygmie" to be a young Chimpanzee But the opportunity of examining the skeleton of the very animal Tyson anatomised having most unexpectedly presented itself to me, I am able to bear independent testimony to its being

a veritable *Troglodytes niger*,[1] though still very young.
Although fully appreciating the resemblances between his
Pygmie and Man, Tyson by no means overlooked the
differences between the two, and he concludes his memoir
by summing up first, the points in which "the Ourang-

FIGS. 3 and 4.—The 'Pygmie' reduced from Tyson's
figures 1 and 2, 1699.

outang or Pygmie more resembled a Man than Apes and
Monkeys do," under forty-seven distinct heads; and then
giving, in thirty-four similar brief paragraphs, the respects
in which "the Ourang-outang or Pygmie differ'd from a
Man and resembled more the Ape and Monkey kind."

[1] I am indebted to Dr. Wright, of Cheltenham, whose paleontological labours are so well known, for bringing this interesting relic
to my knowledge. Tyson's granddaughter, it appears, married
Dr. Allardyce, a physician of repute in Cheltenham, and brought, as
part of her dowry, the skeleton of the 'Pygmie.' Dr. Allardyce
presented it to the Cheltenham Museum, and, through the good
offices of my friend Dr. Wright, the authorities of the Museum have
permitted me to borrow, what is, perhaps, its most remarkable
ornament.

After a careful survey of the literature of the subject extant in his time, our author arrives at the conclusion that his "Pygmie" is identical neither with the Orangs of Tulpius and Bontius, nor with the Quoias Morrou of Dapper (or rather of Tulpius), the Barris of d'Arcos, nor with the Pongo of Battell; but that it is a species of ape probably identical with the Pygmies of the Ancients, and, says Tyson, though it "does so much resemble *a Man* in many of its parts, more than any of the ape kind, or any other *animal* in the world, that I know of: yet by no means do I look upon it as the product of a *mixt* generation—'tis a *Brute-Animal sui generis*, and a particular *species of Ape*."

The name of "Chimpanzee," by which one of the African Apes is now so well known, appears to have come into use in the first half of the eighteenth century, but the only important addition made, in that period, to our acquaintance with the man-like apes of Africa is contained in "A New Voyage to Guinea," by William Smith, which bears the date 1744.

In describing the animals of Sierra Leone, p. 51, this writer says :—

"I shall next describe a strange sort of animal, called by the white men in this country Mandrill,[1] but why it is so called I know not, nor did I ever hear the name before, neither can those who call them so tell, except it be for their near resemblance of a human creature, though nothing at all like an Ape. Their bodies, when full grown, are as big in circumference as a middle-sized man's—their legs much shorter, and their feet larger; their arms and hands in proportion. The head is

---

[1] "Mandrill" seems to signify a "man-like ape," the word "Drill" or "Dril" having been anciently employed in England to denote an Ape or Baboon. Thus in the fifth edition of Blount's "Glossographia, or a Dictionary interpreting the hard words of whatsoever language now used in our refined English tongue . . . very useful for all such as desire to understand what they read," published in 1681, I find, "Dril—a stone-cutter's tool wherewith he bores little holes in marble, &c. Also a large overgrown Ape and Baboon, so called." "Drill" is used in the same sense in Charleton's "Onomasticon Zoicon," 1668. The singular etymology of the word given by Buffon seems hardly a probable one.

monstrously big, and the face broad and flat, without any other hair but the eyebrows; the nose very small, the mouth wide, and the lips thin. The face, which is covered by a white skin, is monstrously ugly, being all over wrinkled as with old age; the teeth broad and yellow; the hands have no more hair than the face, but the same white skin, though all the rest of the body is covered with long black hair, like a bear. They never go upon all fours, like apes; but cry, when vexed or teased, just like children. . . .

FIG. 5.—Facsimile of William Smith's figure of the " Mandrill," 1744.

"When I was at Sherbro, one Mr. Cummerbus, whom I shall have occasion hereafter to mention, made me a present of one of these strange animals, which are called by the natives Boggoe: it was a she-cub, of six months' age, but even then larger than a Baboon. I gave it in charge to one of the slaves, who knew how to feed and nurse it, being a very tender sort of animal; but when-ever I went off the deck the sailors began to teaze it—some loved to see its tears and hear it cry; others hated its snotty-nose; one who hurt it, being checked by the negro that took care of it, told the slave he was very fond of his country-woman, and asked him if he should not

like her for a wife? To which the slave very readily
replied, 'No, this no my wife; this a white woman—
this fit wife for you.' This unlucky wit of the negro's,
I fancy, hastened its death, for next morning it was found
dead under the windlass."

William Smith's 'Mandrill,' or 'Boggoe,' as his description and figure testify, was, without doubt, a Chimpanzee.

Linnæus knew nothing, of his own observation, of the
man-like Apes of either Africa or Asia, but a dissertation

FIG. 6.—The Anthropomorpha of Linnæus.

by his pupil Hoppius in the "Amœnitates Academicæ"
(VI. 'Anthropomorpha') may be regarded as embodying
his views respecting these animals.

The dissertation is illustrated by a plate, of which the
accompanying woodcut, Fig. 6, is a reduced copy. The
figures are entitled (from left to right) 1. *Troglodyta
Bontii;* 2. *Lucifer Aldrovandi;* 3. *Satyrus Tulpii;* 4.
Pygmæus Edwardi. The first is a bad copy of Bontius'
fictitious 'Ourang-outang,' in whose existence, however,
Linnæus appears to have fully believed; for in the
standard edition of the "Systema Naturæ," it is enumerated as a second species of Homo; "H. nocturnus."
Lucifer Aldrovandi is a copy of a figure in Aldrovandus,
'De Quadrupedibus digitatis viviparis,' Lib. 2, p. 249
(1645), entitled "Cercopithecus formæ raræ *Barbilius*

vocatus et originem a china ducebat." Hoppius is of
opinion that this may be one of that cat-tailed people,
of whom Nicolaus Köping affirms that they eat a boat's
crew, "gubernator navis" and all! In the "Systema
Naturæ" Linnæus calls it in a note, *Homo caudatus*, and
seems inclined to regard it as a third species of man.
According to Temminck, *Satyrus Tulpii* is a copy of the
figure of a Chimpanzee published by Scotin in 1738,
which I have not seen. It is the *Satyrus indicus* of
the "Systema Naturæ," and is regarded by Linnæus as
possibly a distinct species from *Satyrus sylvestris*. The
last, named *Pygmæus Edwardi*, is copied from the figure
of a young "Man of the Woods," or true Orang-Utan,
given in Edwards' 'Gleanings of Natural History' (1758).

Buffon was more fortunate than his great rival. Not
only had he the rare opportunity of examining a young
Chimpanzee in the living state, but he became possessed
of an adult Asiatic man-like Ape—the first and the last
adult specimen of any of these animals brought to Europe
for many years. With the valuable assistance of Dau-
benton, Buffon gave an excellent description of this
creature, which, from its singular proportions, he termed
the long-armed Ape, or Gibbon. It is the modern
Hylobates lar.

Thus when, in 1766, Buffon wrote the fourteenth
volume of his great work, he was personally familiar with
the young of one kind of African man-like Ape, and with
the adult of an Asiatic species—while the Orang-Utan
and the Mandrill of Smith were known to him by report.
Furthermore, the Abbé Prevost had translated a good
deal of Purchas' Pilgrims into French, in his 'Histoire
générale des Voyages' (1748), and there Buffon found a
version of Andrew Battell's account of the Pongo and
the Engeco. All these data Buffon attempts to weld
together into harmony in his chapter entitled "Les
Orang-outangs ou le Pongo et le Jocko." To this title
the following note is appended:—

"Orang-outang nom de cet animal aux Indes orientales:
Pongo nom de cet animal à Lowando Province de Congo.
"Jocko, Enjocko, nom de cet animal à Congo que nous
avons adopté. *En* est l'article que nous avons retranché."

Thus it was that Andrew Battell's "Engeco" became metamorphosed into "Jocko," and, in the latter shape, was spread all over the world, in consequence of the extensive popularity of Buffon's works. The Abbé Prevost and Buffon between them, however, did a good deal more disfigurement to Battell's sober account than 'cutting off an article.' Thus Battell's statement that the Pongos "cannot speake, and have no understanding more than a beast," is rendered by Buffon " qu'il ne peut parler *quoiqu'il ait plus d'entendement que les autres animaux*"; and again, Purchas' affirmation, "He told me in conference with him, that one of these Pongos tooke a negro boy of his which lived a moneth with them," stands in the French version, "un pongo lui enleva un petit negre qui passa un *an* entier dans la societé de ces animaux."

After quoting the account of the great Pongo, Buffon justly remarks, that all the 'Jockos' and 'Orangs' hitherto brought to Europe were young; and he suggests that, in their adult condition, they might be as big as the Pongo or 'great Orang'; so that, provisionally, he regarded the Jockos, Orangs, and Pongos as all of one species. And perhaps this was as much as the state of knowledge at the time warranted. But how it came about that Buffon failed to perceive the similarity of Smith's 'Mandrill' to his own 'Jocko,' and confounded the former with so totally different a creature as the blue-faced Baboon, is not so easily intelligible.

Twenty years later Buffon changed his opinion,[1] and expressed his belief that the Orangs constituted a genus with two species,—a large one, the Pongo of Battell, and a small one, the Jocko : that the small one (Jocko) is the East Indian Orang ; and that the young animals from Africa, observed by himself and Tulpius, are simply young Pongos.

In the meanwhile, the Dutch naturalist, Vosmaer, gave, in 1778, a very good account and figure of a young Orang, brought alive to Holland, and his countryman, the famous anatomist, Peter Camper, published (1779) an essay on the Orang-Utan of similar value to that of

[1] Histoire Naturelle, Suppl. tome 7ème, 1789.

Tyson on the Chimpanzee. He dissected several females and a male, all of which, from the state of their skeleton and their dentition, he justly supposes to have been young. However, judging by the analogy of man, he concludes that they could not have exceeded four feet in height in the adult condition. Furthermore, he is very clear as to the specific distinctness of the true East Indian Orang.

"The Orang," says he, "differs not only from the Pigmy of Tyson and from the Orang of Tulpius by its peculiar colour and its long toes, but also by its whole external form. Its arms, its hands, and its feet are longer, while the thumbs, on the contrary, are much shorter, and the great toes much smaller in proportion."[1] And again, "The true Orang, that is to say, that of Asia, that of Borneo, is consequently not the Pithecus, or tailless Ape, which the Greeks, and especially Galen, have described. It is neither the Pongo nor the Jocko, nor the Orang of Tulpius, nor the Pigmy of Tyson,—*it is an animal of a peculiar species*, as I shall prove in the clearest manner by the organs of voice and the skeleton in the following chapters" (l. c. p. 64).

A few years later, M. Radermacher, who held a high office in the Government of the Dutch dominions in India, and was an active member of the Batavian Society of Arts and Sciences, published, in the second part of the Transactions of that Society,[2] a Description of the Island of Borneo, which was written between the years 1779 and 1781, and, among much other interesting matter, contains some notes upon the Orang. The small sort of Orang-Utan, viz. that of Vosmaer and of Edwards, he says, is found only in Borneo, and chiefly about Banjermassing, Mampauwa, and Landak. Of these he had seen some fifty during his residence in the Indies; but none exceeded $2\frac{1}{2}$ feet in length. The larger sort, often regarded as chimæra, continues Radermacher, would, perhaps long have remained so, had it not been for the exertions of the Resident at Rembang, M. Palm, who,

[1] Camper, Œuvres, i. p. 56.
[2] Verhandelingen van het Bataviaasch Genootschap. Tweede Deel. Derde Druk. 1826.

on returning from Landak towards Pontiana, shot one, and forwarded it to Batavia in spirit, for transmission to Europe.

Palm's letter describing the capture runs thus:— "Herewith I send your Excellency, contrary to all expectation (since long ago I offered more than a hundred ducats to the natives for an Orang-Utan of four or five feet high) an Orang which I heard of this morning about eight o'clock. For a long time we did our best to take the frightful beast alive in the dense forest about half way to Landak. We forgot even to eat, so anxious were we not to let him escape; but it was necessary to take care he did not revenge himself, as he kept continually breaking off heavy pieces of wood and green branches, and dashing them at us. This game lasted till four o'clock in the afternoon, when we determined to shoot him; in which I succeeded very well, and indeed better than I ever shot from a boat before; for the bullet went just into the side of his chest, so that he was not much damaged. We got him into the prow still living, and bound him fast, and next morning he died of his wounds. All Pontiana came on board to see him when we arrived." Palm gives his height from the head to the heel as 49 inches.

A very intelligent German officer, Baron Von Wurmb, who at this time held a post in the Dutch East India service, and was Secretary of the Batavian Society, studied this animal, and his careful description of it, entitled "Beschrijving van der Groote Borneosche Orang-outang of de Oost-Indische Pongo," is contained in the same volume of the Batavian Society's Transactions. After Von Wurmb had drawn up his description he states, in a letter dated Batavia, Feb. 18, 1781,[1] that the specimen was sent to Europe in brandy to be placed in the collection of the Prince of Orange; "unfortunately," he continues, "we hear that the ship has been wrecked." Von Wurmb died in the course of the year 1781, the letter in which this passage occurs being the last he wrote; but in his posthumous papers, published in the fourth part of

[1] "Briefe des Herrn v. Wurmb und des H. Baron von Wollzogen. Gotha, 1794."

the Transactions of the Batavian Society, there is a brief description, with measurements, of a female Pongo four feet high.

Did either of these original specimens, on which Von Wurmb's descriptions are based, ever reach Europe? It is commonly supposed that they did; but I doubt the fact. For, appended to the memoir "De l'Ourang-outang," in the collected edition of Camper's works, tome i., pp. 64-66, is a note by Camper himself, referring to Von Wurmb's papers, and continuing thus:—
"Heretofore, this kind of ape had never been known in

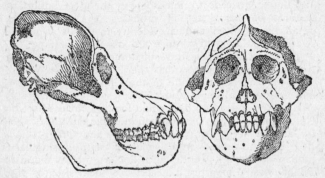

Fig. 7.—The Pongo Skull, sent by Radermacher to Camper, after Camper's original sketches, as reproduced by Lucæ.

Europe. Radermacher has had the kindness to send me the skull of one of these animals, which measured fifty-three inches, or four feet five inches, in height. I have sent some sketches of it to M. Soemmering at Mayence, which are better calculated, however, to give an idea of the form than of the real size of the parts."

These sketches have been reproduced by Fischer and by Lucæ, and bear date 1783, Soemmering having received them in 1784. Had either of Von Wurmb's specimens reached Holland, they would hardly have been unknown at this time to Camper, who, however, goes on to say:—"It appears that since this, some more of these monsters have been captured, for an entire skeleton, very badly set up, which had been sent to the Museum of the Prince of Orange, and which I saw only on the 27th of June, 1784, was more than four feet high. I examined this skeleton again on the 19th December, 1785, after it had been excellently put to rights by the ingenious Onymus."

It appears evident, then, that this skeleton, which is doubtless that which has always gone by the name of Wurmb's Pongo, is not that of the animal described by him, though unquestionably similar in all essential points.

Camper proceeds to note some of the most important features of this skeleton; promises to describe it in detail by-and-bye; and is evidently in doubt as to the relation of this great 'Pongo' to his "petit Orang."

The promised further investigations were never carried out; and so it happened that the Pongo of Von Wurmb took its place by the side of the Chimpanzee, Gibbon, and Orang as a fourth and colossal species of man-like Ape. And indeed nothing could look much less like the Chimpanzees or the Orangs, then known, than the Pongo; for all the specimens of Chimpanzee and Orang which had been observed were small of stature, singularly human in aspect, gentle and docile; while Wurmb's Pongo was a monster almost twice their size, of vast strength and fierceness, and very brutal in expression; its great projecting muzzle, armed with strong teeth, being further disfigured by the outgrowth of the cheeks into fleshy lobes.

Eventually, in accordance with the usual marauding habits of the Revolutionary armies, the 'Pongo' skeleton was carried away from Holland into France, and notices of it, expressly intended to demonstrate its entire distinctness from the Orang and its affinity with the baboons, were given, in 1798, by Geoffroy St. Hilaire and Cuvier.

Even in Cuvier's "Tableau Elementaire," and in the first edition of his great work, the "Regne Animal," the 'Pongo' is classed as a species of Baboon. However, so early as 1818, it appears that Cuvier saw reason to alter this opinion, and to adopt the view suggested several

years before by Blumenbach,[1] and after him by Tilesius,
that the Bornean Pongo is simply an adult Orang. In
1824, Rudolphi demonstrated, by the condition of the
dentition, more fully and completely than had been done
by his predecessors, that the Orangs described up to
that time were all young animals, and that the skull and
teeth of the adult would probably be such as those seen
in the Pongo of Wurmb. In the second edition of the
'Regne Animal' (1829), Cuvier infers, from the 'proportions of all the parts' and 'the arrangements of the
foramina and sutures of the head,' that the Pongo is
the adult of the Orang-Utan, 'at least of a very closely
allied species,' and this conclusion was eventually placed
beyond all doubt by Professor Owen's Memoir published in the 'Zoological Transactions' for 1835, and
by Temminck in his 'Monographies de Mammalogie.'
Temminck's memoir is remarkable for the completeness
of the evidence which it affords as to the modification
which the form of the Orang undergoes according to
age and sex. Tiedemann first published an account of
the brain of the young Orang, while Sandifort, Müller
and Schlegel, described the muscles and the viscera of
the adult, and gave the earliest detailed and trustworthy
history of the habits of the great Indian Ape in a state of
nature ; and as important additions have been made by
later observers, we are at this moment better acquainted
with the adult of the Orang-Utan, than with that of any
of the other greater man-like Apes.

It is certainly the Pongo of Wurmb ;[2] and it is as
certainly not the Pongo of Battell, seeing that the Orang-
Utan is entirely confined to the great Asiatic islands of
Borneo and Sumatra.

And while the progress of discovery thus cleared up
the history of the Orang, it also became established that
the only other man-like Apes in the eastern world were
the various species of Gibbon—Apes of smaller stature,

[1] See Blumenbach, "Abbildungen Naturhistorichen Gegenstände,"
No. 12, 1810 ; and Tilesius, "Naturhistoriche Früchte der ersten
Kaiserlich-Russischen Erdumsegelung," p. 115, 1813.
[2] Speaking broadly and without prejudice to the question, whether
there be more than one species of Orang.

and therefore attracting less attention than the Orangs, though they are spread over a much wider range of country, and are hence more accessible to observation.

Although the geographical area inhabited by the 'Pongo' and 'Engeco' of Battell is so much nearer to Europe than that in which the Orang and Gibbon are found, our acquaintance with the African Apes has been of slower growth; indeed, it is only within the last few years that the truthful story of the old English adventurer has been rendered fully intelligible. It was not until 1835 that the skeleton of the adult Chimpanzee became known, by the publication of Professor Owen's above-mentioned very excellent memoir "On the osteology of the Chimpanzee and Orang," in the Zoological Transactions—a memoir which, by the accuracy of its descriptions, the carefulness of its comparisons, and the excellence of its figures, made an epoch in the history of our knowledge of the bony framework, not only of the Chimpanzee, but of all the anthropoid Apes.

By the investigations herein detailed, it became evident that the old Chimpanzee acquired a size and aspect as different from those of the young known to Tyson, to Buffon, and to Traill, as those of the old Orang from the young Orang; and the subsequent very important researches of Messrs. Savage and Wyman, the American missionary and anatomist, have not only confirmed this conclusion, but have added many new details.[1]

One of the most interesting among the many valuable discoveries made by Dr. Thomas Savage is the fact, that the natives in the Gaboon country at the present day, apply to the Chimpanzee a name—"Enché-eko"—which is obviously identical with the "Engeko" of Battell; a discovery which has been confirmed by all later inquirers. Battell's "lesser monster," being thus proved to be a

---

[1] See "Observations on the external characters and habits of the Troglodytes niger, by Thomas N. Savage, M.D., and on its organization, by Jeffries Wyman, M.D.," Boston Journal of Natural History, vol, iv., 1843–4; and "External characters, habits, and osteology of Troglodytes Gorilla," by the same authors, ibid., vol. v., 1847.

veritable existence, of course a strong presumption arose that his " greater monster," the ' Pongo,' would sooner or later be discovered. And, indeed, a modern traveller, Bowdich, had, in 1819, found strong evidence, among the natives, of the existence of a second great Ape, called the ' Ingena,' " five feet high, and four across the shoulders," the builder of a rude house, on the outside of which it slept.

In 1847, Dr. Savage had the good fortune to make another and most important addition to our knowledge of the man-like Apes; for, being unexpectedly detained at the Gaboon river, he saw in the house of the Rev. Mr. Wilson, a missionary resident there, "a skull represented by the natives to be a monkey-like animal, remarkable for its size, ferocity, and habits." From the contour of the skull, and the information derived from several intelligent natives, " I was induced," says Dr. Savage (using the term Orang in its old general sense), " to believe that it belonged to a new species of Orang. I expressed this opinion to Mr. Wilson, with a desire for further investigation; and, if possible, to decide the point by the inspection of a specimen alive or dead." The result of the combined exertions of Messrs. Savage and Wilson was not only the ob- taining of a very full account of the habits of this new creature, but a still more important service to science, the enabling the excellent American anatomist already mentioned, Professor Wyman, to describe, from ample materials, the distinctive osteological characters of the new form. This animal was called by the natives of the Gaboon " Engé-ena," a name obviously identical with the " Ingena " of Bowdich; and Dr. Savage arrived at the conviction that this last discovered of all the great Apes was the long-sought " Pongo " of Battell.

The justice of this conclusion, indeed, is beyond doubt —for not only does the ' Engé-ena ' agree with Battell's " greater monster " in its hollow eyes, its great stature and its dun or iron-grey colour, but the only other man- like Ape which inhabits these latitudes—the Chimpanzee —is at once identified, by its smaller size, as the " lesser monster," and is excluded from any possibility of being the 'Pongo,' by the fact that it is black and not dun, to say nothing of the important circumstance already mentioned that it still retains the name of 'Engeko,' or 'Enché-eko,' by which Battell knew it.

In seeking for a specific name for the 'Enge-ena,' however, Dr. Savage wisely avoided the much misused 'Pongo'; but finding in the ancient Periplus of Hanno the word "Gorilla" applied to certain hairy savage people, discovered by the Carthaginian voyager in an island on the African coast, he attached the specific name " *Gorilla* " to his new ape, whence arises its present well-known appellation. But Dr. Savage, more cautious than some of his successors, by no means identifies his ape with Hanno's 'wild men.' He merely says that the latter were "probably one of the species of the Orang;" and I quite agree with M. Brullé that there is no ground for identifying the modern 'Gorilla' with that of the Carthaginian admiral.

Since the memoir of Savage and Wyman was published, the skeleton of the Gorilla has been investigated by Professor Owen and by the late Professor Duvernoy, of the Jardin des Plantes, the latter having further supplied a valuable account of the muscular system and of many of the other soft parts; while African missionaries and travellers have confirmed and expanded the account originally given of the habits of this great man-like Ape, which has had the singular fortune of being the first to be made known to the general world and the last to be scientifically investigated.

Two centuries and a half have passed away since Battell told his stories about the 'greater' and the 'lesser monsters' to Purchas, and it has taken nearly that time to arrive at the clear result that there are four distinct kinds of Anthropoids—in Eastern Asia, the Gibbons and the Orangs; in Western Africa, the Chimpanzees and the Gorilla.

The man-like Apes, the history of whose discovery has just been detailed, have certain characters of structure and of distribution in common. Thus they all have the same number of teeth as man—possessing four incisors,

two canines, four false molars, and six true molars in each
jaw, or 32 teeth in all, in the adult condition; while the
milk dentition consists of 20 teeth—or four incisors, two
canines, and four molars in each jaw. They are what are
called catarrhine Apes—that is, their nostrils have a
narrow partition and look downwards; and, furthermore,
their arms are always longer than their legs, the difference
being sometimes greater and sometimes less; so that if
the four were arranged in the order of the length of their
arms in proportion to that of their legs, we should have
this series—Orang $(1\frac{4}{9}$—1), Gibbon $(1\frac{1}{4}$—1), Gorilla
$(1\frac{1}{5}$—1), Chimpanzee $(1\frac{1}{16}$—1). In all, the fore limbs
are terminated by hands, provided with longer or shorter
thumbs; while the great toe of the foot, always smaller
than in Man, is far more moveable than in him and can
be opposed, like a thumb, to the rest of the foot. None
of these apes have tails, and none of them possess the
cheek-pouches common among monkeys. Finally, they
are all inhabitants of the old world.

The Gibbons are the smallest, slenderest, and longest-
limbed of the man-like apes; their arms are longer in
proportion to their bodies than those of any of the other
man-like Apes, so that they can touch the ground when
erect; their hands are longer than their feet, and they are
the only Anthropoids which possess callosities like the
lower monkeys. They are variously coloured. The
Orangs have arms which reach to the ankles in the erect
position of the animal; their thumbs and great toes are
very short, and their feet are longer than their hands.
They are covered with reddish-brown hair, and the sides
of the face, in adult males, are commonly produced into
two crescentic, flexible excrescences, like fatty tumours.
The Chimpanzees have arms which reach below the
knees; they have large thumbs and great toes, their
hands are longer than their feet, and their hair is black,
while the skin of the face is pale. The Gorilla, lastly,
has arms which reach to the middle of the leg, large
thumbs and great toes, feet longer than the hands, a
black face, and dark-grey or dun hair.

For the purpose which I have at present in view, it is
unnecessary that I should enter into any further minutiæ

respecting the distinctive characters of the genera and species into which these man-like Apes are divided by naturalists. Suffice it to say, that the Orangs and the Gibbons constitute the distinct genera, *Simia* and *Hylobates*; while the Chimpanzees and Gorillas are by some regarded simply as distinct species of one genus, *Troglodytes*; by others as distinct genera—*Troglodytes* being reserved for the Chimpanzees, and *Gorilla* for the Engéena or Pongo.

Sound knowledge respecting the habits and mode of life of the man-like Apes has been even more difficult of attainment than correct information regarding their structure.

Once in a generation, a Wallace may be found physically, mentally, and morally qualified to wander unscathed through the tropical wilds of America and of Asia; to form magnificent collections as he wanders; and withal to think out sagaciously the conclusions suggested by his collections: but, to the ordinary explorer or collector, the dense forests of equatorial Asia and Africa, which constitute the favourite habitation of the Orang, the Chimpanzee, and the Gorilla, present difficulties of no ordinary magnitude: and the man who risks his life by even a short visit to the malarious shores of those regions may well be excused if he shrinks from facing the dangers of the interior; if he contents himself with stimulating the industry of the better seasoned natives, and collecting and collating the more or less mythical reports and traditions with which they are too ready to supply him.

In such a manner most of the earlier accounts of the habits of the man-like Apes originated; and even now a good deal of what passes current must be admitted to have no very safe foundation. The best information we possess is that, based almost wholly on direct European testimony, respecting the Gibbons; the next best evidence relates to the Orangs; while our knowledge of the habits of the Chimpanzee and the Gorilla stands much in need of support and enlargement by additional testimony from instructed European eye-witnesses.

It will therefore be convenient in endeavouring to form a notion of what we are justified in believing about these

animals, to commence with the best known man-like
Apes, the Gibbons and Orangs; and to make use of the
perfectly reliable information respecting them as a sort of
criterion of the probable truth or falsehood of assertions
respecting the others.

Of the GIBBONS, half a dozen species are found scattered
over the Asiatic islands, Java, Sumatra, Borneo, and
through Malacca, Siam, Arracan, and an uncertain extent
of Hindostan, on the main land of Asia. The largest
attain a few inches above three feet in height, from the
crown to the heel, so that they are shorter than the other
man-like Apes; while the slenderness of their bodies
renders their mass far smaller in proportion even to this
diminished height.

Dr. Salomon Müller, an accomplished Dutch naturalist,
who lived for many years in the Eastern Archipelago, and
to the results of whose personal experience I shall frequently have occasion to refer, states that the Gibbons
are true mountaineers, loving the slopes and edges of the
hills, though they rarely ascend beyond the limit of the
fig-trees. All day long they haunt the tops of the tall
trees; and though, towards evening, they descend in
small troops to the open ground, no sooner do they spy
a man than they dart up the hill-sides, and disappear in
the darker valleys.

All observers testify to the prodigious volume of voice
possessed by these animals. According to the writer
whom I have just cited, in one of them, the Siamang, "the
voice is grave and penetrating, resembling the sounds
gōek, gōek, gōek, gōek, goek ha ha ha ha haaāāā, and may
easily be heard at a distance of half a league." While the
cry is being uttered, the great membranous bag under
the throat which communicates with the organ of voice,
the so-called "laryngeal sac," becomes greatly distended,
diminishing again when the creature relapses into silence.

M. Duvaucel, likewise, affirms that the cry of the
Siamang may be heard for miles—making the woods
ring again. So Mr. Martin[1] describes the cry of the
agile Gibbon as "overpowering and deafening" in
a room, and "from its strength, well calculated for

[1] "Man and Monkies," p. 423.

resounding through the vast forests." Mr. Waterhouse, an accomplished musician as well as zoologist, says, "The Gibbon's voice is certainly much more powerful than that of any singer I ever heard." And yet it is to be recollected that this animal is not half the height of, and far less bulky in proportion than, a man.

There is good testimony that various species of Gibbon readily take to the erect posture. Mr. George Bennett,[1] a very excellent observer, in describing the habits of a male *Hylobates syndactylus* which remained for some time in his possession, says: "He invariably walks in the erect posture when on a level surface; and then the arms either hang down, enabling him to assist himself with his knuckles; or what is more usual, he keeps his arms uplifted in nearly an erect position, with the hands pendent ready to seize a rope, and climb up on the approach of danger or on the obtrusion of strangers. He walks rather quick in the erect posture, but with a waddling gait, and is soon run down if, whilst pursued, he has no opportunity of escaping by climbing. . . . When he walks in the erect posture he turns the leg and foot outwards, which occasions him to have a waddling gait and to seem bow-legged."

Dr. Burrough states of another Gibbon, the Horlack or Hooluk:

"They walk erect; and when placed on the floor, or in an open field, balance themselves very prettily, by raising their hands over their head and slightly bending the arm at the wrist and elbow, and then run tolerably fast, rocking from side to side; and, if urged to greater speed, they let fall their hands to the ground, and assist themselves forward, rather jumping than running, still keeping the body, however, nearly erect."

Somewhat different evidence, however, is given by Dr. Winslow Lewis:[2]

"Their only manner of walking was on their posterior or inferior extremities, the others being raised upwards to preserve their equilibrium, as rope-dancers are assisted by long poles at fairs. Their progression was not by

[1] "Wanderings in New South Wales," vol. ii. chap. viii., 1834.
[2] Boston Journal of Natural History, vol. i., 1834.

FIG. 8.—A Gibbon (*H. pileatus*), after Wolf.

placing one foot before the other, but by simultaneously using both, as in jumping." Dr. Salomon Müller also states that the Gibbons progress upon the ground by a short series of tottering jumps, effected only by the hind limbs, the body being held altogether upright.

But Mr. Martin (l. c. p. 418), who also speaks from direct observation, says of the Gibbons generally :

" Pre-eminently qualified for arboreal habits, and displaying among the branches amazing activity, the Gibbons are not so awkward or embarrassed on a level surface as might be imagined. They walk erect, with a waddling or unsteady gait, but at a quick pace ; the equilibrium of the body requiring to be kept up, either by touching the ground with the knuckles, first on one side then on the other, or by uplifting the arms so as to poise it. As with the Chimpanzee, the whole of the narrow, long sole of the foot is placed upon the ground at once and raised at once, without any elasticity of step."

After this mass of concurrent and independent testimony, it cannot reasonably be doubted that the Gibbons commonly and habitually assume the erect attitude.

But level ground is not the place where these animals can display their very remarkable and peculiar locomotive powers, and that prodigious activity which almost tempts one to rank them among flying rather than among ordinary climbing mammals.

Mr. Martin (l. c. p. 430) has given so excellent and graphic an account of the movements of a *Hylobates agilis*, living in the Zoological Gardens, in 1840, that I will quote it in full :

" It is almost impossible to convey in words an idea of the quickness and graceful address of her movements : they may indeed be termed aerial, as she seems merely to touch in her progress the branches among which she exhibits her evolutions. In these feats her hands and arms are the sole organs of locomotion ; her body hanging as if suspended by a rope, sustained by one hand (the right, for example), she launches herself, by an energetic movement, to a distant branch, which she catches with the left hand ; but her hold is less than momentary : the impulse for the next launch is acquired : the branch then aimed at is attained by the right hand again, and quitted instantaneously, and so on, in alternate succession. In this manner spaces of twelve and eighteen feet are cleared, with the greatest ease and uninterruptedly, for hours together, without the slightest appearance of fatigue being manifested; and it is evident that, if more space could be allowed, distances very greatly exceeding eighteen feet would be as easily cleared; so that Duvaucel's assertion that he has seen these animals launch themselves from one branch to another, forty feet asunder, startling as it is, may be well credited. Sometimes, on seizing a branch in her progress, she will throw herself, by the power of one arm only, completely round it, making a revolution with such rapidity as almost to deceive the eye, and continue her progress with undiminished velocity. It is singular to observe how suddenly this Gibbon can stop, when the impetus given by the rapidity and distance of her swinging leaps would seem to require a gradual abatement of her movements. In the very midst of her flight a branch is seized, the body raised, and she is seen, as if by magic, quietly seated on it, grasping it with her feet. As suddenly she again throws herself into action.

"The following facts will convey some notion of her dexterity and quickness. A live bird was let loose in her apartment; she marked its flight, made a long swing to a distant branch, caught the bird with one hand in her passage, and attained the branch with her other hand; her aim, both at the bird and at the branch, being as successful as if one object only had engaged her attention. It may be added that she instantly bit off the head of the bird, picked its feathers, and then threw it down without attempting to eat it.

"On another occasion this animal swung herself from a perch, across a passage at least twelve feet wide, against a window which it was thought would be immediately broken: but not so; to the surprise of all, she caught the narrow framework between the panes with her hand, in an instant attained the proper impetus, and sprang back again to the cage she had left—a feat requiring not only great strength, but the nicest precision."

The Gibbons appear to be naturally very gentle, but

there is very good evidence that they will bite severely when irritated — a female *Hylobates agilis* having so severely lacerated one man with her long canines, that he died ; while she had injured others so much that, by way of precaution, these formidable teeth had been filed down; but, if threatened, she would still turn on her keeper. The Gibbons eat insects, but appear generally to avoid animal food. A Siamang, however, was seen by Mr. Bennett to seize and devour greedily a live lizard. They commonly drink by dipping their fingers in the liquid and then licking them. It is asserted that they sleep in a sitting posture.

Duvaucel affirms that he has seen the females carry their young to the waterside and there wash their faces, in spite of resistance and cries. They are gentle and affectionate in captivity—full of tricks and pettishness, like spoiled children, and yet not devoid of a certain conscience, as an anecdote, told by Mr. Bennett (l. c. p. 156), will show. It would appear that his Gibbon had a peculiar inclination for disarranging things in the cabin. Among these articles, a piece of soap would especially attract his notice, and for the removal of this he had been once or twice scolded. "One morning," says Mr. Bennett, "I was writing, the ape being present in the cabin, when casting my eyes towards him, I saw the little fellow taking the soap. I watched him without his perceiving that I did so : and he occasionally would cast a furtive glance towards the place where I sat. I pretended to write ; he, seeing me busily occupied, took the soap, and moved away with it in his paw. When he had walked half the length of the cabin, I spoke quietly, without frightening him. The instant he found I saw him, he walked back again, and deposited the soap nearly in the same place from whence he had taken it. There was certainly something more than instinct in that action : he evidently betrayed a consciousness of having done wrong both by his first and last actions— and what is reason if that is not an exercise of it?"

The most elaborate account of the natural history of the ORANG-UTAN extant, is that given in the "Verhande-

lingen over de Natuurlijke Geschiedenis der Nederland-
sche overzeesche Bezittingen (1839–45)," by Dr. Salomon
Müller and Dr. Schlegel, and I shall base what I have to

FIG. 9.—An adult male Orang-Utan, after Müller and Schlegel.

say upon this subject almost entirely on their statements,
adding, here and there, particulars of interest from the
writings of Brooke, Wallace, and others.

The Orang-Utan would rarely seem to exceed four feet

in height, but the body is very bulky, measuring two-thirds of the height in circumference.[1]

The Orang-Utan is found only in Sumatra and Borneo, and is common in neither of these islands—in both of which it occurs always in low, flat plains, never in the mountains. It loves the densest and most sombre of the forests, which extend from the sea-shore inland, and thus is found only in the eastern half of Sumatra, where alone such forests occur, though, occasionally, it strays over to the western side.

On the other hand, it is generally distributed through Borneo, except in the mountains, or where the population is dense. In favourable places, the hunter may, by good fortune, see three or four in a day.

Except in the pairing time, the old males usually live by themselves. The old females, and the immature males, on the other hand, are often met with in twos and threes; and the former occasionally have young with them, though the pregnant females usually separate themselves, and sometimes remain apart after they have given birth to their offspring. The young Orangs seem to remain unusually long under their mother's protection, probably in consequence of their slow growth. While climbing, the mother always carries her young against her bosom, the young holding on by his mother's hair.[2] At

---

[1] The largest Orang-Utan, cited by Temminck, measured, when standing upright, 4 ft.; but he mentions having just received news of the capture of an Orang 5 ft. 3 in. high. Schlegel and Müller say that their largest old male measured, upright, 1.25 Netherlands "el"; and from the crown to the end of the toes, 1.5 el; the circumference of the body being about 1 el. The largest old female was 1.09 el high, when standing. The adult skeleton in the College of Surgeons' Museum, if set upright, would stand 3 ft. 6–8 in. from crown to sole. Dr. Humphry gives 3 ft. 8 in. as the mean height of two Orangs. Of seventeen Orangs examined by Mr. Wallace, the largest was 4 ft. 2 in. high, from the heel to the crown of the head. Mr. Spencer St. John, however, in his "Life in the Forests of the Far East," tells us of an Orang of "5 ft. 2 in., measuring fairly from the head to the heel," 15 in. across the face, and 12 in. round the wrist. It does not appear, however, that Mr. St. John measured this Orang himself.

[2] See Mr. Wallace's account of an infant "Orang-utan," in the "Annals of Natural History" for 1856. Mr. Wallace provided his interesting charge with an artificial mother of buffalo-skin, but the

what time of life the Orang-Utan becomes capable of propagation, and how long the females go with young, is
unknown, but it is probable that they are not adult until
they arrive at ten or fifteen years of age. A female which
lived for five years at Batavia, had not attained one-third
the height of the wild females. It is probable that, after
reaching adult years, they go on growing, though slowly,
and that they live to forty or fifty years. The Dyaks tell
of old Orangs, which have not only lost all their teeth,
but which find it so troublesome to climb, that they
maintain themselves on windfalls and juicy herbage.

The Orang is sluggish, exhibiting none of that marvellous activity characteristic of the Gibbons. Hunger alone
seems to stir him to exertion, and when it is stilled he
relapses into repose. When the animal sits, it curves its
back and bows its head, so as to look straight down on
the ground; sometimes it holds on with its hands by a
higher branch, sometimes lets them hang phlegmatically
down by its side—and in these positions the Orang will
remain, for hours together, in the same spot, almost without stirring, and only now and then giving utterance to
its deep, growling voice. By day, he usually climbs from
one tree-top to another, and only at night descends to the
ground, and if then threatened with danger, he seeks
refuge among the underwood. When not hunted, he
remains a long time in the same locality, and sometimes
stops for many days on the same tree—a firm place
among its branches serving him for a bed. It is rare for
the Orang to pass the night in the summit of a large tree,
probably because it is too windy and cold there for him;
but, as soon as night draws on, he descends from the
height and seeks out a fit bed in the lower and darker
part, or in the leafy top of a small tree, among which he
prefers Nibong Palms, Pandani, or one of those parasitic
Orchids which give the primæval forests of Borneo so
characteristic and striking an appearance. But wherever
he determines to sleep, there he prepares himself a sort
of nest: little boughs and leaves are drawn together round

cheat was too successful. The infant's entire experience led it to
associate teats with hair, and feeling the latter, it spent its existence
in vain endeavours to discover the former.

the selected spot, and bent crosswise over one another; while to make the bed soft, great leaves of Ferns, of Orchids, of *Pandanus fascicularis, Nipa fruticans,* &c., are laid over them. Those which Müller saw, many of them being very fresh, were situated at a height of ten to twenty-five feet above the ground, and had a circumference, on the average, of two or three feet. Some were packed many inches thick with *Pandanus* leaves; others were remarkable only for the cracked twigs, which, united in a common centre, formed a regular platform. "The rude *hut,*" says Sir James Brooke, "which they are stated to build in the trees, would be more properly called a seat or nest, for it has no roof or cover of any sort. The facility with which they form this nest is curious, and I had an opportunity of seeing a wounded female weave the branches together and seat herself, within a minute."

According to the Dyaks, the Orang rarely leaves his bed before the sun is well above the horizon and has dissipated the mists. He gets up about nine, and goes to bed again about five; but sometimes not till late in the twilight. He lies sometimes on his back; or, by way of change, turns on one side or the other, drawing his limbs up to his body, and resting his head on his hand. When the night is cold, windy, or rainy, he usually covers his body with a heap of *Pandanus, Nipa,* or Fern leaves, like those of which his bed is made, and he is especially careful to wrap up his head in them. It is this habit of covering himself up which has probably led to the fable that the Orang builds huts in the trees.

Although the Orang resides mostly amid the boughs of great trees, during the daytime, he is very rarely seen squatting on a thick branch, as other apes, and particularly the Gibbons, do. The Orang, on the contrary, confines himself to the slender leafy branches, so that he is seen right at the top of the trees, a mode of life which is closely related to the constitution of his hinder limbs, and especially to that of his seat. For this is provided with no callosities, such as are possessed by many of the lower apes, and even by the Gibbons; and those bones of the pelvis, which are termed the ischia, and which form the solid framework of the surface on which the body rests in the sitting posture, are not expanded like those of the apes which possess callosities, but are more like those of man.

An Orang climbs so slowly and cautiously,[1] as, in this act, to resemble a man more than an ape, taking great care of his feet, so that injury of them seems to affect him far more than it does other apes. Unlike the Gibbons, whose forearms do the greater part of the work, as they swing from branch to branch, the Orang never makes even the smallest jump. In climbing, he moves alternately one hand and one foot, or, after having laid fast hold with the hands, he draws up both feet together. In passing from one tree to another, he always seeks out a place where the twigs of both come close together, or interlace. Even when closely pursued, his circumspection is amazing : he shakes the branches to see if they will bear him, and then bending an overhanging bough down by throwing his weight gradually along it, he makes a bridge from the tree he wishes to quit to the next.[2]

On the ground the Orang always goes laboriously and shakily, on all fours. At starting he will run faster than a man, though he may soon be overtaken. The very long arms which, when he runs, are but little bent, raise the body of the Orang remarkably, so that he assumes much the posture of a very old man bent down by age, and making his way along by the help of a stick. In walking, the body is usually directed straight forward, unlike the other apes, which run more or less obliquely ; except the Gibbons, who in these, as in so many other respects, depart remarkably from their fellows.

The Orang cannot put its feet flat on the ground, but is supported upon their outer edges, the heel resting more on the ground, while the curved toes partly rest upon the ground by the upper side of their first joint, the two outermost toes of each foot completely resting on this surface. The hands are held in the opposite manner,

---

[1] "They are the slowest and least active of all the monkey tribe, and their motions are surprisingly awkward and uncouth."—Sir James Brooke, in the " Proceedings of the Zoological Society," 1841.

[2] Mr. Wallace's account of the progression of the Orang almost exactly corresponds with this.

their inner edges serving as the chief support. The fingers are then bent out in such a manner that their foremost joints, especially those of the two innermost fingers, rest upon the ground by their upper sides, while the point of the free and straight thumb serves as an additional fulcrum.

The Orang never stands on its hind legs, and all the pictures, representing it as so doing, are as false as the assertion that it defends itself with sticks, and the like.

The long arms are of especial use, not only in climbing, but in the gathering of food from boughs to which the animal could not trust his weight. Figs, blossoms, and young leaves of various kinds, constitute the chief nutriment of the Orang; but strips of bamboo two or three feet long were found in the stomach of a male. They are not known to eat living animals.

Although, when taken young, the Orang-Utan soon becomes domesticated, and indeed seems to court human society, it is naturally a very wild and shy animal, though apparently sluggish and melancholy. The Dyaks affirm, that when the old males are wounded with arrows only, they will occasionally leave the trees and rush raging upon their enemies, whose sole safety lies in instant flight, as they are sure to be killed if caught.[1]

But, though possessed of immense strength, it is rare for the Orang to attempt to defend itself, especially when attacked with fire-arms. On such occasions he endeavours to hide himself, or to escape along the topmost branches of the trees, breaking off and throwing down

---

[1] Sir James Brooke, in a letter to Mr. Waterhouse, published in the proceedings of the Zoological Society for 1841, says:—"On the habits of the Orangs, as far as I have been able to observe them, I may remark that they are as dull and slothful as can well be conceived, and on no occasion, when pursuing them, did they move so fast as to preclude my keeping pace with them easily through a moderately clear forest; and even when obstructions below (such as wading up to the neck) allowed them to get away some distance, they were sure to stop and allow me to come up. I never observed the slightest attempt at defence, and the wood which sometimes rattled about our ears was broken by their weight, and not thrown, as some persons represent. If pushed to extremity, however, the *Pappan* could not be otherwise than formidable, and one unfortunate man, who, with a party, was trying to catch a large one alive, lost

the boughs as he goes. When wounded he betakes himself to the highest attainable point of the tree, and emits a singular cry, consisting at first of high notes, which at length deepen into a low roar, not unlike that of a panther. While giving out the high notes the Orang thrusts out his lips into a funnel shape; but in uttering the low notes he holds his mouth wide open, and at the same time the great throat bag, or laryngeal sac, becomes distended.

According to the Dyaks, the only animal the Orang measures his strength with is the crocodile, who occasionally seizes him on his visits to the water side. But they say that the Orang is more than a match for his enemy, and beats him to death, or rips up his throat by pulling the jaws asunder!

Much of what has been here stated was probably derived by Dr. Müller from the reports of his Dyak hunters; but a large male, four feet high, lived in captivity, under his observation, for a month, and receives a very bad character.

"He was a very wild beast," says Müller, "of prodigious strength, and false and wicked to the last degree. If any one approached he rose up slowly with a low growl, fixed his eyes in the direction in which he meant to make his attack, slowly passed his hand between the bars of his cage, and then extending his long arm, gave a sudden grip — usually at the face." He never tried to bite

two of his fingers, besides being severely bitten on the face, whilst the animal finally beat off his pursuers and escaped."

Mr. Wallace, on the other hand, affirms that he has several times observed them throwing down branches when pursued. "It is true he does not throw them *at* a person, but casts them down vertically; for it is evident that a bough cannot be thrown to any distance from the top of a lofty tree. In one case a female Mias, on a durian tree, kept up for at least ten minutes a continuous shower of branches and of the heavy, spined fruits, as large as 32-pounders, which most effectually kept us clear of the tree she was on. She could be seen breaking them off and throwing them down with every appearance of rage, uttering at intervals a loud pumping grunt, and evidently meaning mischief."—"On the Habits of the Orang-Utan," Annals of Nat. History, 1856. This statement, it will be observed, is quite in accordance with that contained in the letter of the Resident Palm quoted above (p. 16).

(though Orangs will bite one another), his great weapons of offence and defence being his hands.

His intelligence was very great; and Müller remarks, that though the faculties of the Orang have been estimated too highly, yet Cuvier, had he seen this specimen, would not have considered its intelligence to be only a little higher than that of the dog.

His hearing was very acute, but the sense of vision seemed to be less perfect. The under lip was the great organ of touch, and played a very important part in drinking, being thrust out like a trough, so as either to catch the falling rain, or to receive the contents of the half cocoa-nut shell full of water with which the Orang was supplied, and which, in drinking, he poured into the trough thus formed.

In Borneo the Orang-Utan of the Malays goes by the name of "*Mias*" among the Dyaks, who distinguish several kinds as *Mias Pappan*, or *Zimo, Mias Kassu*, and *Mias Rambi.* Whether these are distinct species, however, or whether they are mere races, and how far any of them are identical with the Sumatran Orang, as Mr. Wallace thinks the Mias Pappan to be, are problems which are at present undecided; and the variability of these great apes is so extensive, that the settlement of the question is a matter of great difficulty. Of the form called "Mias Pappan," Mr. Wallace [1] observes, "It is known by its large size, and by the lateral expansion of the face into fatty protuberances, or ridges, over the temporal muscles, which have been mis-termed *callosities*, as they are perfectly soft, smooth, and flexible. Five of this form, measured by me, varied only from 4 feet 1 inch to 4 feet 2 inches in height, from the heel to the crown of the head, the girth of the body from 3 feet to 3 feet 7½ inches, and the extent of the outstretched arms from 7 feet 2 inches to 7 feet 6 inches; the width of the face from 10 to 13¼ inches. The colour and length of the hair varied in different individuals, and in different parts of the same individual; some possessed a rudimentary nail on the great toe, others none at all; but they otherwise present no external differences on which to establish even varieties of a species.

[1] On the Orang-Utan, or Mias of Borneo, Annals of Natural History, 1856.

Yet, when we examine the crania of these individuals, we find remarkable differences of form, proportion, and dimension, no two being exactly alike. The slope of the profile, and the projection of the muzzle, together with the size of the cranium, offer differences as decided as those existing between the most strongly marked forms of the Caucasian and African crania in the human species. The orbits vary in width and height, the cranial ridge is either single or double, either much or little developed, and the zygomatic aperture varies considerably in size. This variation in the proportions of the crania enables us satisfactorily to explain the marked difference presented by the single-crested and double-crested skulls, which have been thought to prove the existence of two large species of Orang. The external surface of the skull varies considerably in size, as do also the zygomatic aperture and the temporal muscle; but they bear no necessary relation to each other, a small muscle often existing with a large cranial surface, and *vice versâ.* Now, those skulls which have the largest and strongest jaws and the widest zygomatic aperture, have the muscles so large that they meet on the crown of the skull, and deposit the bony ridge which separates them, and which is the highest in that which has the smallest cranial surface. In those which combine a large surface with comparatively weak jaws, and small zygomatic aperture, the muscles, on each side, do not extend to the crown, a space of from 1 to 2 inches remaining between them, and along their margins small ridges are formed. Intermediate forms are found, in which the ridges meet only in the hinder part of the skull. The form and size of the ridges are therefore independent of age, being sometimes more strongly developed in the less aged animal. Professor Temminck states that the series of skulls in the Leyden Museum shows the same result."

Mr. Wallace observed two male adult Orangs (Mias Kassu of the Dyaks), however, so very different from any of these that he concludes them to be specifically distinct; they were respectively 3 feet 8½ inches and 3 feet 9½ inches high, and possessed no sign of the cheek excrescences, but otherwise resembled the larger kinds.   The skull has no crest, but two bony ridges, 1¾ inches to 2 inches apart, as in the *Simia morio* of Professor Owen.   The teeth, however, are immense, equalling or surpassing those of the other species.   The females of both these kinds, according to Mr. Wallace, are devoid of excrescences, and resemble the smaller males, but are shorter by 1½ to 3 inches, and their canine teeth are comparatively small, subtruncated and dilated at the base, as in the so-called *Simia morio*, which is, in all probability, the skull of a female of the same species as the smaller males.   Both males and females of this smaller species are distinguishable, according to Mr. Wallace, by the comparatively large size of the middle incisors of the upper jaw.

So far as I am aware, no one has attempted to dispute the accuracy of the statements which I have just quoted regarding the habits of the two Asiatic man-like Apes; and if true, they must be admitted as evidence, that such an Ape—

1stly, May readily move along the ground in the erect, or semi-erect, position, and without direct support from its arms.

2ndly, That it may possess an extremely loud voice, so loud as to be readily heard one or two miles.

3rdly, That it may be capable of great viciousness and violence when irritated: and this is especially true of adult males.

4thly, That it may build a nest to sleep in.

Such being well-established facts respecting the Asiatic Anthropoids, analogy alone might justify us in expecting the African species to offer similar peculiarities, separately or combined; or, at any rate, would destroy the force of any attempted *à priori* argument against such direct testimony as might be adduced in favour of their existence.   And, if the organization of any of the African Apes could be demonstrated to fit it better than either of its Asiatic allies for the erect position and for efficient attack, there would be still less reason for doubting its occasional adoption of the upright attitude or of aggressive proceedings.

From the time of Tyson and Tulpius downwards, the habits of the young CHIMPANZEE in a state of captivity have been abundantly reported and commented upon. But trustworthy evidence as to the manners and customs of adult anthropoids of this species, in their native woods, was almost wanting up to the time of the publication of the paper by Dr. Savage, to which I have already referred ; containing notes of the observations which he made, and of the information which he collected from sources which he considered trustworthy, while resident at Cape Palmas, at the north-western limit of the Bight of Benin.

The adult Chimpanzees, measured by Dr. Savage, never exceeded, though the males may almost attain, five feet in height.

"When at rest, the sitting posture is that generally assumed. They are sometimes seen standing and walking, but when thus detected, they immediately take to all fours, and flee from the presence of the observer. Such is their organization that they cannot stand erect, but lean forward. Hence they are seen, when standing, with the hands clasped over the occiput, or the lumbar region, which would seem necessary to balance or ease of posture.

" The toes of the adult are strongly flexed and turned inwards, and cannot be perfectly straightened. In the attempt the skin gathers into thick folds on the back, shewing that the full expansion of the foot, as is necessary in walking, is unnatural. The natural position is on all fours, the body anteriorly resting upon the knuckles. These are greatly enlarged, with the skin protuberant and thickened like the sole of the foot.

"They are expert climbers, as one would suppose from their organization. In their gambols they swing from limb to limb to a great distance, and leap with astonishing agility. It is not unusual to see the 'old folks' (in the language of an observer) sitting under a tree regaling themselves with fruit and friendly chat, while their 'children' are leaping around them, and swinging from tree to tree with boisterous merriment.

" As seen here, they cannot be called *gregarious*, seldom more than five, or ten at most, being found together. It has been said, on good authority, that they occasionally assemble in large numbers, in gambols. My informant asserts that he saw once not less than fifty so engaged; hooting, screaming, and drumming with sticks upon old logs, which is done in the latter case with equal facility by the four extremities. They do not appear ever to act on the offensive, and seldom, if ever really, on the defensive. When about to be captured, they resist by throwing their arms about their opponent, and attempting to draw him into contact with their teeth." (Savage, l. c. p. 384.)

With respect to this last point Dr. Savage is very explicit in another place:

"*Biting* is their principal art of defence. I have seen one man who had been thus severely wounded in the feet.

"The strong development of the canine teeth in the adult would seem to indicate a carnivorous propensity; but in no state save that of domestication do they manifest it. At first they reject flesh, but easily acquire a fondness for it. The canines are early developed, and evidently designed to act the important part of weapons of defence. When in contact with man almost the first effort of the animal is—*to bite*.

"They avoid the abodes of men, and build their habitations in trees. Their construction is more that of *nests* than *huts*, as they have been erroneously termed by some naturalists. They generally build not far above the ground. Branches or twigs are bent, or partly broken, and crossed, and the whole supported by the body of a limb or a crotch. Sometimes a nest will be found near the *end* of a *strong leafy branch* twenty or thirty feet from the ground. One I have lately seen that could not be less than forty feet, and more probably it was fifty. But this is an unusual height.

"Their dwelling-place is not permanent, but changed in pursuit of food and solitude, according to the force of circumstances. We more often see them in elevated places; but this arises from the fact that the low grounds, being more favourable for the natives' rice-farms, are the oftener cleared, and hence are almost always wanting in suitable trees for their nests. . . . It is seldom that more than one or two nests are seen upon the same tree, or in the same neighbourhood : five have been found, but it was an unusual circumstance." . . .

"They are very filthy in their habits. . . . It is a tradition with the natives generally here, that they were once members of their own tribe : that for their depraved habits they were expelled from all human society, and, that through an obstinate indulgence of their vile propensities, they have degenerated into their present state and organization. They are, however, eaten by them, and when cooked with the oil and pulp of the palm-nut considered a highly palatable morsel.

"They exhibit a remarkable degree of intelligence in their habits, and, on the part of the mother, much affection for their young. The second female described was upon a tree when first discovered, with her mate and two young ones (a male and a female). Her first impulse was to descend with great rapidity, and make off into the thicket, with her mate and female offspring. The young male remaining behind, she soon returned to the rescue. She ascended and took him in her arms, at which moment she was shot, the ball passing through the forearm of the young one, on its way to the heart of the mother. . . .

"In a recent case, the mother, when discovered, remained upon the tree with her offspring, watching intently the movements of the hunter. As he took aim, she motioned with her hand, precisely in the manner of a human being, to have him desist and go away. When the wound has not proved instantly fatal, they have been known to stop the flow of blood by pressing with the hand upon the part, and when this did not succeed, to apply leaves and grass. . . . When shot, they give a sudden screech, not unlike that of a human being in sudden and acute distress."

The ordinary voice of the Chimpanzee, however, is affirmed to be hoarse, guttural, and not very loud, somewhat like "whoo-whoo" (l. c. p. 365).

The analogy of the Chimpanzee to the Orang, in its nest-building habit and in the mode of forming its nest, is exceedingly interesting; while, on the other hand, the activity of this ape, and its tendency to bite, are particulars in which it rather resembles the Gibbons. In extent of geographical range, again, the Chimpanzees—which are found from Sierra Leone to Congo—remind one of the Gibbons, rather than of either of the other man-like apes; and it seems not unlikely that, as is the case with the Gibbons, there may be several species spread over the geographical area of the genus.

The same excellent observer, from whom I have borrowed the preceding account of the habits of the adult Chimpanzee, published, fifteen years ago,[1] an account of the GORILLA, which has, in its most essential points, been confirmed by subsequent observers, and to which so very little has really been added, that in justice to Dr. Savage I give it almost in full.

"It should be borne in mind that my account is based upon the statements of the aborigines of that region (the Gaboon). In this connection, it may also be proper for me to remark, that having been a missionary resident for several years, studying, from habitual intercourse, the African mind and character, I felt myself prepared to discriminate and decide upon the probability of their statements. Besides, being familiar with the history and habits of its interesting congener (*Trog. niger*, Geoff.), I was able to separate their accounts of the two animals, which, having the same locality and a similarity of habit, are confounded in the minds of the mass, especially as but few—such as traders to the interior and huntsmen—have ever seen the animal in question.

"The tribe from which our knowledge of the animal is derived, and whose territory forms its habitat, is the *Mpongwe*, occupying both banks of the River Gaboon, from its mouth to some fifty or sixty miles upward. . . .

"If the word 'Pongo' be of African origin, it is probably a corruption of the word *Mpongwe*, the name of the tribe on the banks of the Gaboon, and hence applied to the region they inhabit. Their local name for the Chimpanzee is *Enché-eko*, as near as it can be Anglicized, from

[1] Notice of the external characters and habits of Troglodytes Gorilla. Boston Journal of Natural History, 1847.

which the common term 'Jocko' probably comes. The Mpongwe appellation for its new congener is *Engé-ena*, prolonging the sound of the first vowel, and slightly sounding the second.

FIG. 1C.—The Gorilla (after Wolff).

"The habitat of the *Engé-ena* is the interior of lower Guinea, whilst that of the *Enché-eko* is nearer the sea-board.

"Its height is about five feet; it is disproportionately broad across the shoulders, thickly covered with coarse black hair, which is said to be similar in its arrangement to that of the *Enché-eko;* with age it becomes grey, which fact has given rise to the report that both animals are seen of different colours.

"*Head.*—The prominent features of the head are, the great width and elongation of the face, the depth of the molar region, the branches of the lower jaw being very deep and extending far backward, and the comparative smallness of the cranial portion; the eyes are very large, and said to be like those of the Enché-eko, a bright hazel; nose broad and flat, slightly elevated towards the root; the muzzle broad, and prominent lips and chin, with scattered grey hairs; the under lip highly mobile, and capable of great elongation when the animal is enraged, then hanging over the chin; skin of the face and ears naked, and of a dark brown, approaching to black.

"The most remarkable feature of the head is a high ridge, or crest of hair, in the course of the sagittal suture, which meets posteriorly with a transverse ridge of the same, but less prominent, running round from the back of one ear to the other. The animal has the power of moving the scalp freely forward and back, and when enraged is said to contract it strongly over the brow, thus bringing down the hairy ridge and pointing the hair forward, so as to present an indescribably ferocious aspect.

"Neck short, thick, and hairy; chest and shoulders very broad, said to be fully double the size of the Enché-ekos; arms very long, reaching some way below the knee—the fore-arm much the shortest; hands very large, the thumbs much larger than the fingers. . . .

"The gait is shuffling; the motion of the body, which is never upright as in man, but bent forward, is somewhat rolling, or from side to side. The arms being longer than the Chimpanzee, it does not stoop as much in walking; like that animal, it makes progression by thrusting its arms forward, resting the hands on the ground, and then giving the body a half jumping half swinging motion between them. In this act it is said not to flex the fingers, as does the Chimpanzee, resting on its knuckles,

but to extend them, making a fulcrum of the hand.
When it assumes the walking posture, to which it is said
to be much inclined, it balances its huge body by flexing
its arms upward.

"They live in bands, but are not so numerous as the
Chimpanzees: the females generally exceed the other
sex in number. My informants all agree in the assertion
that but one adult male is seen in a band; that when the
young males grow up, a contest takes place for mastery,
and the strongest, by killing and driving out the others,
establishes himself as the head of the community."

Dr. Savage repudiates the stories about the Gorillas
carrying off women and van-
quishing elephants, and then
adds:

"Their dwellings, if they
may be so called, are similar
to those of the Chimpanzee,
consisting simply of a few
sticks and leafy branches,
supported by the crotches
and limbs of trees: they
afford no shelter, and are occupied only at night.

FIG. 11.—Gorilla walking (after
Wolff).

"They are exceedingly
ferocious, and always offensive in their habits, never
running from man, as does the Chimpanzee. They are
objects of terror to the natives, and are never encountered
by them except on the defensive. The few that have
been captured were killed by elephant-hunters and native
traders, as they came suddenly upon them while passing
through the forests.

"It is said that when the male is first seen he gives
a terrific yell, that resounds far and wide through the
forest, something like kh—ah! kh—ah! prolonged and
shrill. His enormous jaws are widely opened at each
expiration, his under lip hangs over the chin, and the
hairy ridge and scalp are contracted upon the brow,
presenting an aspect of indescribable ferocity.

"The females and young, at the first cry, quickly
disappear. He then approaches the enemy in great fury,

pouring out his horrid cries in quick succession. The hunter awaits his approach with his gun extended : if his aim is not sure, he permits the animal to grasp the barrel, and as he carries it to his mouth (which is his habit) he fires. Should the gun fail to go off, the barrel (that of the ordinary musket, which is thin) is crushed between his teeth, and the encounter soon proves fatal to the hunter.

"In the wild state, their habits are in general like those of the *Troglodytes niger*, building their nests loosely in trees, living on similar fruits, and changing their place of resort from force of circumstances."

Dr. Savage's observations were confirmed and supplemented by those of Mr. Ford, who communicated an interesting paper on the Gorilla to the Philadelphian Academy of Sciences, in 1852. With respect to the geographical distribution of this greatest of all the man-like Apes, Mr. Ford remarks :

"This animal inhabits the range of mountains that traverse the interior of Guinea, from the Cameroon in the north, to Angola in the south, and about 100 miles inland, and called by the geographers Crystal Mountains. The limit to which this animal extends, either north or south, I am unable to define. But that limit is doubtless some distance north of this river [Gaboon]. I was able to certify myself of this fact in a late excursion to the head-waters of the Mooney (Danger) River, which comes into the sea some sixty miles from this place. I was informed (credibly, I think) that they were numerous among the mountains in which that river rises, and far north of that.

"In the south, this species extends to the Congo River, as I am told by native traders who have visited the coast between the Gaboon and that river. Beyond that, I am not informed. This animal is only found at a distance from the coast in most cases, and, according to my best information, approaches it nowhere so nearly as on the south side of this river, where they have been found within ten miles of the sea. This, however, is only of late occurrence. I am informed by some of the oldest Mpongwe men that formerly he was only found on the sources of the river, but that at present he may be found within half-a-day's walk of its mouth. Formerly he inhabited the mountainous ridge where Bushmen alone inhabited, but now he boldly approaches the Mpongwe plantations. This is doubtless the reason of the scarcity of information in years past, as the opportunities for receiving a knowledge of the animal have not been wanting; traders having for one hundred years frequented this river, and specimens, such as have been brought here within a year, could not have been exhibited without having attracted the attention of the most stupid."

One specimen Mr. Ford examined weighed 170 lbs., without the thoracic, or pelvic, viscera, and measured four feet four inches round the chest. This writer describes so minutely and graphically the onslaught of the Gorilla—though he does not for a moment pretend to have witnessed the scene—that I am tempted to give this part of his paper in full, for comparison with other narratives:

"He always rises to his feet when making an attack, though he approaches his antagonist in a stooping posture.

"Though he never lies in wait, yet, when he hears, sees, or scents a man, he immediately utters his characteristic cry, prepares for an attack, and always acts on the offensive. The cry he utters resembles a grunt more than a growl, and is similar to the cry of the Chimpanzee, when irritated, but vastly louder. It is said to be audible at a great distance. His preparation consists in attending the females and young ones, by whom he is usually accompanied, to a little distance. He, however, soon returns, with his crest erect and projecting forward, his nostrils dilated, and his under-lip thrown down; at the same time uttering his characteristic yell, designed, it would seem, to terrify his antagonist. Instantly, unless he is disabled by a well-directed shot, he makes an onset, and, striking his antagonist with the palm of his hands, or seizing him with a grasp from which there is no escape, he dashes him upon the ground, and lacerates him with his tusks.

"He is said to seize a musket, and instantly crush the barrel between his teeth. . . . This animal's savage nature is very well shewn by the implacable desperation of a young one that was brought here. It was taken very young, and kept four months, and many means were used to tame it; but it was incorrigible, so that it bit me an hour before it died."

Mr. Ford discredits the house-building and elephant-driving stories, and says that no well-informed natives believe them. They are tales told to children.

I might quote other testimony to a similar effect, but, as it appears to me, less carefully weighed and sifted, from the letters of MM. Franquet and Gautier Laboullay, appended to the memoir of M. I. G. St. Hilaire, which I have already cited.

Bearing in mind what is known regarding the Orang and the Gibbon, the statements of Dr. Savage and Mr. Ford do not appear to me to be justly open to criticism on *à priori* grounds. The Gibbons, as we have seen, readily assume the erect posture, but the Gorilla is far better fitted by its organization for that attitude than are the Gibbons: if the laryngeal pouches of the Gibbons, as is very likely, are important in giving volume to a voice which can be heard for half a league, the Gorilla, which has similar sacs, more largely developed, and whose bulk is fivefold that of a Gibbon, may well be audible for twice that distance. If the Orang fights with its hands, the Gibbons and Chimpanzees with their teeth, the Gorilla may, probably enough, do either or both; nor is there anything to be said against either Chimpanzee or Gorilla building a nest, when it is proved that the Orang-Utan habitually performs that feat.

With all this evidence, now ten to fifteen years old, before the world, it is not a little surprising that the assertions of a recent traveller, who, so far as the Gorilla is concerned, really does very little more than repeat, on his own authority, the statements of Savage and of Ford, should have met with so much and such bitter opposition. If subtraction be made of what was known before, the sum and substance of what M. Du Chaillu has affirmed as a matter of his own observation respecting the Gorilla, is, that, in advancing to the attack, the great brute beats his chest with his fists. I confess I see nothing very improbable, or very much worth disputing about, in this statement.

With respect to the other man-like Apes of Africa, M. Du Chaillu tells us absolutely nothing, of his own knowledge, regarding the common Chimpanzee; but he informs us of a bald-headed species or variety, the *nschiego mbouve*, which builds itself a shelter, and of another rare kind with a comparatively small face, large facial angle, and peculiar note, resembling "Kooloo."

As the Orang shelters itself with a rough coverlet of leaves, and the common Chimpanzee, according to that eminently trustworthy observer Dr. Savage, makes a sound like "Whoo-whoo,"—the grounds of the summary repudiation with which M. Du Chaillu's statements on these matters have been met is not obvious.

If I have abstained from quoting M. Du Chaillu's work, then, it is not because I discern any inherent improbability in his assertions respecting the man-like Apes; nor from any wish to throw suspicion on his veracity; but because, in my opinion, so long as his narrative remains in its present state of unexplained and apparently inexplicable confusion, it has no claim to original authority respecting any subject whatsoever.

It may be truth, but it is not evidence.

II

ON THE RELATIONS OF MAN TO THE LOWER ANIMALS

Multis videri poterit, majorem esse differentiam Simiæ et Hominis, quam diei et noctis; verum tamen hi, comparatione instituta inter summos Europæ Heroës et Hottentottos ad Caput bonæ spei degentes, difficillime sibi persuadebunt, has eosdem habere natales; vel si virginem nobilem aulicam, maxime comtam et humanissimam, conferre vellent cum homine sylvestri et sibi relicto, vix augurari possent, hunc et illam ejusdem esse speciei.—*Linnæi Amœnitates Acad. "Anthropomorpha."*

THE question of questions for mankind—the problem which underlies all others, and is more deeply interesting than any other—is the ascertainment of the place which Man occupies in nature and of his relations to the universe of things. Whence our race has come; what are the limits of our power over nature, and of nature's power over us; to what goal we are tending; are the problems which present themselves anew and with undiminished interest to every man born into the world. Most of us, shrinking from the difficulties and dangers which beset the seeker after original answers to these riddles, are contented to ignore them altogether, or to smother the investigating spirit under the featherbed of respected and respectable tradition. But, in every age, one or two restless spirits, blessed with that constructive genius, which can only build on a secure foundation, or cursed with the mere spirit of scepticism, are unable to follow in the well-worn and comfortable track of their forefathers and contemporaries, and unmindful of thorns and stumbling-blocks, strike out into paths of their own. The sceptics end in the infidelity which asserts the problem to be insoluble, or in the atheism which denies the existence of any orderly progress and governance of things : the men of genius propound solutions which grow into systems of Theology or of Philosophy, or veiled in musical language which suggests more than it asserts, take the shape of the Poetry of an epoch.

Each such answer to the great question, invariably asserted by the followers of its propounder, if not by himself, to be complete and final, remains in high authority and esteem, it may be for one century, or it may be for twenty : but, as invariably, Time proves each reply to have been a mere approximation to the truth— tolerable chiefly on account of the ignorance of those by whom it was accepted, and wholly intolerable when tested by the larger knowledge of their successors.

In a well-worn metaphor, a parallel is drawn between the life of man and the metamorphosis of the caterpillar into the butterfly ; but the comparison may be more just as well as more novel, if for its former term we take the mental progress of the race. History shows that the human mind, fed by constant accessions of knowledge, periodically grows too large for its theoretical coverings, and bursts them asunder to appear in new habiliments, as the feeding and growing grub, at intervals, casts its too narrow skin and assumes another, itself but temporary. Truly the imago state of Man seems to be terribly distant, but every moult is a step gained, and of such there have been many.

Since the revival of learning, whereby the Western races of Europe were enabled to enter upon that progress towards true knowledge, which was commenced by the philosophers of Greece, but was almost arrested in subsequent long ages of intellectual stagnation, or, at most, gyration, the human larva has been feeding vigorously, and moulting in proportion. A skin of some dimension was cast in the 16th century, and another towards the end of the 18th, while, within the last fifty years, the extraordinary growth of every department of physical science has spread among us mental food of so nutritious and stimulating a character that a new ecdysis seems imminent. But this is a process not unusually accompanied by many throes and some sickness and debility, or, it may be, by graver disturbances; so that every good citizen must feel bound to facilitate the process, and even if he have nothing but a scalpel to work withal, to ease the cracking integument to the best of his ability.

In this duty lies my excuse for the publication of these essays. For it will be admitted that some knowledge of man's position in the animate world is an indispensable preliminary to the proper understanding of his relations to the universe—and this again resolves itself, in the long run, into an inquiry into the nature and the closeness of the ties which connect him with those singular creatures whose history [1] has been sketched in the preceding pages.

The importance of such an inquiry is indeed intuitively manifest. Brought face to face with these blurred copies of himself, the least thoughtful of men is conscious of a certain shock, due perhaps, not so much to disgust at the aspect of what looks like an insulting caricature, as to the awakening of a sudden and profound mistrust of time-honoured theories and strongly-rooted prejudices regarding his own position in nature, and his relations to the under-world of life; while that which remains a dim suspicion for the unthinking, becomes a vast argument, fraught with the deepest consequences, for all who are acquainted with the recent progress of the anatomical and physiological sciences.

I now propose briefly to unfold that argument, and to set forth, in a form intelligible to those who possess no special acquaintance with anatomical science, the chief facts upon which all conclusions respecting the nature and the extent of the bonds which connect man with the brute world must be based: I shall then indicate the one immediate conclusion which, in my judgment, is justified by those facts, and I shall finally discuss the bearing of that conclusion upon the hypotheses which have been entertained respecting the Origin of Man.

[1] It will be understood that, in the preceding Essay, I have selected for notice from the vast mass of papers which have been written upon the man-like Apes, only those which seem to me to be of special moment.

The facts to which I would first direct the reader's attention, though ignored by many of the professed instructors of the public mind, are easy of demonstration and are universally agreed to by men of science; while their significance is so great, that whoso has duly pondered over them will, I think, find little to startle him in the other revelations of Biology. I refer to those facts which have been made known by the study of Development.

It is a truth of very wide, if not of universal, application, that every living creature commences its existence under a form different from, and simpler than, that which it eventually attains.

The oak is a more complex thing than the little rudimentary plant contained in the acorn; the caterpillar is more complex than the egg; the butterfly than the caterpillar; and each of these beings, in passing from its rudimentary to its perfect condition, runs through a series of changes, the sum of which is called its Development. In the higher animals these changes are extremely complicated; but, within the last half-century, the labours of such men as Von Baer, Rathke, Reichert, Bischof, and Remak have almost completely unravelled them, so that the successive stages of development which are exhibited by a Dog, for example, are now as well known to the embryologist as are the steps of the metamorphosis of the silkworm moth to the school-boy. It will be useful to consider with attention the nature and the order of the stages of canine development, as an example of the process in the higher animals generally.

The Dog, like all animals, save the very lowest (and further inquiries may not improbably remove the apparent exception), commences its existence as an egg: as a body which is, in every sense, as much an egg as that of a hen, but is devoid of that accumulation of nutritive matter which confers upon the bird's egg its exceptional size and domestic utility; and wants the shell, which would not only be useless to an animal incubated within the body of its parent, but would cut it off from access to the source of that nutriment which the young creature requires, but which the minute egg of the mammal does not contain within itself.

The Dog's egg is, in fact, a little spheroidal bag (Fig. 12), formed of a delicate transparent membrane called the *vitelline membrane*, and about $\frac{1}{130}$ to $\frac{1}{120}$th of an inch in diameter. It contains a mass of viscid nutritive matter—the '*yelk*'—within which is inclosed a second much more delicate spheroidal bag, called the '*germinal vesicle*' (*a*). In this, lastly, lies a more solid rounded body, termed the '*germinal spot*' (*b*).

The egg, or 'Ovum,' is originally formed within a gland, from which, in due season, it becomes detached,

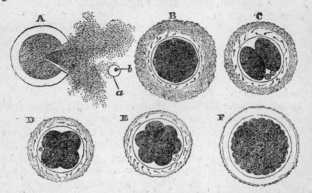

FIG. 12.—A. Egg of the Dog, with the vitelline membrane burst, so as to give exit to the yelk, the germinal vesicle (*a*), and its included spot (*b*).

B. C. D. E. F. Successive changes of the yelk indicated in the text. After Bischoff.

and passes into the living chamber fitted for its protection and maintenance during the protracted process of gestation. Here, when subjected to the required conditions, this minute and apparently insignificant particle of living matter becomes animated by a new and mysterious activity. The germinal vesicle and spot cease to be discernible (their precise fate being one of the yet unsolved problems of embryology), but the yelk becomes circumferentially indented, as if an invisible knife had been drawn round it, and thus appears divided into two hemispheres (Fig. 12, C).

By the repetition of this process in various planes, these hemispheres become subdivided, so that four segments are produced (D); and these, in like manner, divide and subdivide again, until the whole yelk is converted into a mass of granules, each of which consists of a minute spheroid of yelk-substance, inclosing a central particle, the so-called '*nucleus*' (F). Nature, by this process, has attained much the same result as that at which a human artificer arrives by his operations in a brickfield. She takes the rough plastic material of the yelk and breaks it up into well-shaped, tolerably even-sized masses, handy for building up into any part of the living edifice.

Next, the mass of organic bricks, or '*cells*' as they are technically called, thus formed, acquires an orderly arrangement, becoming converted into a hollow spheroid with double walls. Then, upon one side of this spheroid, appears a thickening, and, by and bye, in the centre of the area of thickening, a straight shallow groove (Fig. 13, A) marks the central line of the edifice which is to be raised, or, in other words, indicates the position of the middle line of the body of the future dog. The substance bounding the groove on each side next rises up into a fold, the rudiment of the side wall of that long cavity, which will eventually lodge the spinal marrow and the brain ; and in the floor of this chamber appears a solid cellular cord, the so-called '*notochord*.' One end of the inclosed cavity dilates to form the head (Fig. 13, B), the other remains narrow, and eventually becomes the tail ; the side walls of the body are fashioned out of the downward continuation of the walls of the groove ; and from them, by and bye, grow out little buds which, by degrees, assume the shape of limbs. Watching the fashioning process stage by stage, one is forcibly reminded of the modeller in clay. Every part, every organ, is at first, as it were, pinched up rudely, and sketched out in the rough ; then shaped more accurately ; and only, at last, receives the touches which stamp its final character.

Thus, at length, the young puppy assumes such a form as is shown in Fig. 13, C. In this condition it has a disproportionately large head, as dissimilar to that of a dog as the bud-like limbs are unlike his legs.

The remains of the yelk, which have not yet been applied to the nutrition and growth of the young animal, are contained in a sac attached to the rudimentary intestine, and termed the yelk-sac, or '*umbilical vesicle*.' Two membranous bags, intended to subserve respectively the protection and nutrition of the young creature, have been developed from the skin and from the under and hinder surface of the body; the former, the so-called '*amnion*,' is a sac filled with fluid, which invests the

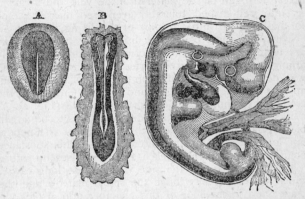

FIG. 13.—A. Earliest rudiment of the Dog. B. Rudiment further advanced, showing the foundations of the head, tail, and vertebral column. C. The very young puppy, with attached ends of the yelk-sac and allantois, and invested in the amnion.

whole body of the embryo, and plays the part of a sort of water-bed for it; the other, termed the '*allantois*,' grows out, loaded with blood-vessels, from the ventral region, and eventually applying itself to the walls of the cavity, in which the developing organism is contained, enables these vessels to become the channel by which the stream of nutriment, required to supply the wants of the offspring, is furnished to it by the parent.

The structure which is developed by the interlacement of the vessels of the offspring with those of the parent, and by means of which the former is enabled to receive nourishment and to get rid of effete matters, is termed the '*Placenta*.'

It would be tedious, and it is unnecessary for my present purpose, to trace the process of development further; suffice it to say, that, by a long and gradual series of changes, the rudiment here depicted and described becomes a puppy, is born, and then, by still slower and less perceptible steps, passes into the adult Dog.

There is not much apparent resemblance between a barndoor Fowl and the Dog who protects the farm-yard. Nevertheless the student of development finds, not only that the chick commences its existence as an egg, primarily identical, in all essential respects, with that of the Dog, but that the yelk of this egg undergoes division—that the primitive groove arises, and that the contiguous parts of the germ are fashioned, by precisely similar methods, into a young chick, which, at one stage of its existence, is so like the nascent Dog, that ordinary inspection would hardly distinguish the two.

The history of the development of any other vertebrate animal, Lizard, Snake, Frog, or Fish, tells the same story. There is always, to begin with, an egg having the same essential structure as that of the Dog :—the yelk of that egg always undergoes division, or '*segmentation*' as it is often called : the ultimate products of that segmentation constitute the building materials for the body of the young animal; and this is built up round a primitive groove, in the floor of which a notochord is developed. Furthermore, there is a period in which the young of all these animals resemble one another, not merely in outward form, but in all essentials of structure, so closely, that the differences between them are inconsiderable, while, in their subsequent course, they diverge more and more widely from one another. And it is a general law, that, the more closely any animals resemble one another in adult structure, the longer and the more intimately do their embryos resemble one another : so that, for example, the embryos of a Snake and of a Lizard remain like one another longer than do those of a Snake and of a Bird ; and the embryo of a Dog and of a Cat remain like one another for a far longer period than do those of a Dog and a Bird; or of a Dog and an Opossum; or even than those of a Dog and a Monkey.

Thus the study of development affords a clear test of closeness of structural affinity, and one turns with impatience to inquire what results are yielded by the study of the development of Man. Is he something apart? Does he originate in a totally different way from Dog, Bird, Frog, and Fish, thus justifying those who assert him to have no place in nature and no real affinity with the lower world of animal life? Or does he originate in a similar germ, pass through the same slow and gradually progressive modifications,—depend on the same contrivances for protection and nutrition, and finally enter the world by the help of the same mechanism? The reply is not doubtful for a moment, and has not been doubtful any time these thirty years. Without question, the mode of origin and the early stages of the development of man are identical with those of the animals immediately below him in the scale:—without a doubt, in these respects, he is far nearer the Apes, than the Apes are to the Dog.

The Human ovum is about $\frac{1}{125}$ of an inch in diameter, and might be described in the same terms as that of the Dog, so that I need only refer to the figure illustrative (14 A.) of its structure. It leaves the organ in which it is formed in a similar fashion and enters the organic chamber prepared for its reception in the same way, the conditions of its development being in all respects the same. It has not yet been possible (and only by some rare chance can it ever be possible) to study the human ovum in so early a developmental stage as that of yelk division, but there is every reason to conclude that the changes it undergoes are identical with those exhibited by the ova of other vertebrated animals; for the formative materials of which the rudimentary human body is composed, in the earliest conditions in which it has been observed, are the same as those of other animals. Some of these earliest stages are figured below and, as will be seen, they are strictly comparable to the very early states of the Dog; the marvellous correspondence between the two which is kept up, even for some time, as development advances, becoming apparent by the simple comparison of the figures with those on page 58.

Indeed, it is very long before the body of the young human being can be readily discriminated from that of the young puppy; but, at a tolerably early period, the two become distinguishable by the different form of their adjuncts, the yelk-sac and the allantois. The former, in the Dog, becomes long and spindle-shaped, while in Man it remains spherical; the latter, in the Dog, attains an extremely large size, and the vascular processes which are developed from it and eventually give rise to the

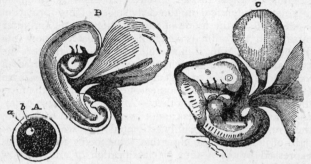

FIG. 14.—A. Human ovum (after Kölliker). *a.* germinal vesicle.
      b. germinal spot.
   B. A very early condition of Man, with yelk-sac, allantois, and amnion (original).
   C. A more advanced stage (after Kölliker), compare fig. 13, C.

formation of the placenta (taking root, as it were, in the parental organism, so as to draw nourishment therefrom, as the root of a tree extracts it from the soil) are arranged in an encircling zone, while in Man, the allantois remains comparatively small, and its vascular rootlets are eventually restricted to one disk-like spot. Hence, while the placenta of the Dog is like a girdle, that of Man has the cake-like form, indicated by the name of the organ.

But, exactly in those respects in which the developing Man differs from the Dog, he resembles the ape, which, like man, has a spheroidal yelk-sac and a discoidal— sometimes partially lobed—placenta.

So that it is only quite in the later stages of development that the young human being presents marked differences from the young ape, while the latter departs as much from the dog in its development, as the man does.

Startling as the last assertion may appear to be, it is demonstrably true, and it alone appears to me sufficient to place beyond all doubt the structural unity of man with the rest of the animal world, and more particularly and closely with the apes.

Thus, identical in the physical processes by which he originates—identical in the early stages of his formation—identical in the mode of his nutrition before and after birth, with the animals which lie immediately below him in the scale—Man, if his adult and perfect structure be compared with theirs, exhibits, as might be expected, a marvellous likeness of organization. He resembles them as they resemble one another—he differs from them as they differ from one another.—And, though these differences and resemblances cannot be weighed and measured, their value may be readily estimated; the scale or standard of judgment, touching that value, being afforded and expressed by the system of classification of animals now current among zoologists.

A careful study of the resemblances and differences presented by animals has, in fact, led naturalists to arrange them into groups, or assemblages, all the members of each group presenting a certain amount of definable resemblance, and the number of points of similarity being smaller as the group is larger and *vice versâ*. Thus, all creatures which agree only in presenting the few distinctive marks of animality form the 'Kingdom' ANIMALIA. The numerous animals which agree only in possessing the special characters of Vertebrates form one 'Sub-kingdom' of this Kingdom. Then the Sub-kingdom VERTEBRATA is subdivided into the five 'Classes,' Fishes, Amphibians, Reptiles, Birds, and Mammals, and these into smaller groups called 'Orders'; these into 'Families' and 'Genera'; while the last are finally broken up into the smallest assemblages, which are distinguished by the possession of constant, not-sexual, characters. These ultimate groups are Species.

Every year tends to bring about a greater uniformity of opinion throughout the zoological world as to the limits and characters of these groups, great and small. At present, for example, no one has the least doubt regarding the characters of the classes Mammalia, Aves, or Reptilia ; nor does the question arise whether any thoroughly well-known animal should be placed in one class or the other. Again, there is a very general agreement respecting the characters and limits of the orders of Mammals, and as to the animals which are structurally necessitated to take a place in one or another order.

No one doubts, for example, that the Sloth and the Ant-eater, the Kangaroo and the Opossum, the Tiger and the Badger, the Tapir and the Rhinoceros, are respectively members of the same orders. These successive pairs of animals may, and some do, differ from one another immensely, in such matters as the proportions and structure of their limbs ; the number of their dorsal and lumbar vertebræ ; the adaptation of their frames to climbing, leaping, or running ; the number and form of their teeth ; and the characters of their skulls and of the contained brain. But, with all these differences, they are so closely connected in all the more important and fundamental characters of their organization, and so distinctly separated by these same characters from other animals, that zoologists find it necessary to group them together as members of one order. And if any new animal were discovered, and were found to present no greater difference from the Kangaroo and the Opossum, for example, than these animals do from one another, the zoologist would not only be logically compelled to rank it in the same order with these, but he would not think of doing otherwise.

Bearing this obvious course of zoological reasoning in mind, let us endeavour for a moment to disconnect our thinking selves from the mask of humanity ; let us imagine ourselves scientific Saturnians, if you will, fairly acquainted with such animals as now inhabit the Earth,

and employed in discussing the relations they bear to a
new and singular 'erect and featherless biped,' which
some enterprising traveller, overcoming the difficulties of
space and gravitation, has brought from that distant
planet for our inspection, well preserved, may be, in a
cask of rum.   We should all, at once, agree upon placing
him among the mammalian vertebrates; and his lower
jaw, his molars, and his brain, would leave no room for
doubting the systematic position of the new genus among
those mammals, whose young are nourished during
gestation by means of a placenta, or what are called the
'placental mammals.'

Further, the most superficial study would at once convince us that, among the orders of placental mammals,
neither the Whales nor the hoofed creatures, nor the
Sloths and Ant-eaters, nor the carnivorous Cats, Dogs,
and Bears, still less the Rodent Rats and Rabbits, or the
Insectivorous Moles and Hedgehogs, or the Bats, could
claim our '*Homo*' as one of themselves.

There would remain then, but one order for comparison, that of the Apes (using that word in its broadest
sense), and the question for discussion would narrow
itself to this—is Man so different from any of these Apes
that he must form an order by himself? Or does he
differ less from them than they differ from one another,
and hence must take his place in the same order with
them?

Being happily free from all real, or imaginary, personal
interest in the results of the inquiry thus set afoot, we
should proceed to weigh the arguments on one side and
on the other, with as much judicial calmness as if the
question related to a new Opossum. We should endeavour to ascertain, without seeking either to magnify
or diminish them, all the characters by which our new
Mammal differed from the Apes; and if we found that
these were of less structural value, than those which distinguish certain members of the Ape order from others
universally admitted to be of the same order, we should
undoubtedly place the newly discovered tellurian genus
with them.

I now proceed to detail the facts which seem to me

to leave us no choice but to adopt the last mentioned course.

It is quite certain that the Ape which most nearly approaches man, in the totality of its organization, is either the Chimpanzee or the Gorilla ; and as it makes no practical difference, for the purposes of my present argument, which is selected for comparison, on the one hand, with Man, and on the other hand, with the rest of the Primates,[1] I shall select the latter (so far as its organization is known)—as a brute now so celebrated in prose and verse, that all must have heard of him, and have formed some conception of his appearance.   I shall take up as many of the most important points of difference between man and this remarkable creature, as the space at my disposal will allow me to discuss, and the necessities of the argument demand ; and I shall inquire into the value and magnitude of these differences, when placed side by side with those which separate the Gorilla from other animals of the same order.

In the general proportions of the body and limbs there is a remarkable difference between the Gorilla and Man, which at once strikes the eye.   The Gorilla's brain-case is smaller, its trunk larger, its lower limbs shorter, its upper limbs longer in proportion than those of Man.

I find that the vertebral column of a full-grown Gorilla, in the Museum of the Royal College of Surgeons, measures 27 inches along its anterior curvature, from the upper edge of the atlas, or first vertebra of the neck, to the lower extremity of the sacrum ; that the arm, without the hand, is $31\frac{1}{2}$ inches long; that the leg, without the foot, is $26\frac{1}{2}$ inches long; that the hand is $9\frac{3}{4}$ inches long; the foot $11\frac{1}{4}$ inches long.

In other words, taking the length of the spinal column as 100, the arm equals 115, the leg 96, the hand 36, and the foot 41.

In the skeleton of a male Bosjesman, in the same collection, the proportions, by the same measurement, to

[1] We are not at present thoroughly acquainted with the brain of the Gorilla, and therefore, in discussing cerebral characters, I shall take that of the Chimpanzee as my highest term among the Apes.

the spinal column, taken as 100, are—the arm 78, the leg 110, the hand 26, and the foot 32. In a woman of the same race the arm is 83, and the leg 120, the hand and foot remaining the same. In a European skeleton I find the arm to be 80, the leg 117, the hand 26, the foot 35.

Thus the leg is not so different as it looks at first sight, in its proportions to the spine in the Gorilla and in the Man—being very slightly shorter than the spine in the former, and between $\frac{1}{10}$ and $\frac{1}{6}$ longer than the spine in the latter. The foot is longer and the hand much longer in the Gorilla; but the great difference is caused by the arms, which are very much longer than the spine in the Gorilla, very much shorter than the spine in the Man.

The question now arises how are the other Apes related to the Gorilla in these respects—taking the length of the spine, measured in the same way, at 100. In an adult Chimpanzee, the arm is only 96, the leg 90, the hand 43, the foot 39—so that the hand and the leg depart more from the human proportion and the arm less, while the foot is about the same as in the Gorilla.

In the Orang, the arms are very much longer than in the Gorilla (122), while the legs are shorter (88); the foot is longer than the hand (52 and 48), and both are much longer in proportion to the spine.

In the other man-like Apes again, the Gibbons, these proportions are still further altered; the length of the arms being to that of the spinal column as 19 to 11; while the legs are also a third longer than the spinal column, so as to be longer than in Man, instead of shorter. The hand is half as long as the spinal column, and the foot, shorter than the hand, is about $\frac{5}{11}$ths of the length of the spinal column.

Thus *Hylobates* is as much longer in the arms than the Gorilla, as the Gorilla is longer in the arms than Man; while, on the other hand, it is as much longer in the legs than the Man, as the Man is longer in the legs than the Gorilla, so that it contains within itself the extremest deviations from the average length of both pairs of limbs (see the Frontispiece).

The Mandrill presents a middle condition, the arms and legs being nearly equal in length, and both being shorter than the spinal column; while hand and foot have nearly the same proportions to one another and to the spine, as in Man.

In the Spider monkey (*Ateles*) the leg is longer than the spine, and the arm than the leg; and, finally, in that remarkable Lemurine form, the Indri (*Lichanotus*), the leg is about as long as the spinal column, while the arm is not more than $\frac{11}{18}$ of its length; the hand having rather less and the foot rather more, than one-third the length of the spinal column.

These examples might be greatly multiplied, but they suffice to show that, in whatever proportion of its limbs the Gorilla differs from Man, the other Apes depart still more widely from the Gorilla, and that, consequently, such differences of proportion can have no ordinal value.

We may next consider the differences presented by the trunk, consisting of the vertebral column, or backbone, and the ribs and pelvis, or bony hip-basin, which are connected with it, in Man and in the Gorilla respectively.

In Man, in consequence partly of the disposition of the articular surfaces of the vertebræ, and largely of the elastic tension of some of the fibrous bands, or ligaments, which connect these vertebræ together, the spinal column, as a whole, has an elegant S-like curvature, being convex forwards in the neck, concave in the back, convex in the loins, or lumbar region, and concave again in the sacral region; an arrangement which gives much elasticity to the whole backbone, and diminishes the jar communicated to the spine, and through it to the head, by locomotion in the erect position.

Furthermore, under ordinary circumstances, Man has seven vertebræ in his neck, which are called *cervical;* twelve succeed these, bearing ribs and forming the upper part of the back, whence they are termed *dorsal;* five lie in the loins, bearing no distinct, or free, ribs, and are called *lumbar;* five, united together into a great bone, excavated in front, solidly wedged in between the hip bones, to form the back of the pelvis, and known by the name of the *sacrum,* succeed these; and finally, three or four little more or less moveable bones, so small as to be insignificant, constitute the *coccyx* or rudimentary tail.

In the Gorilla, the vertebral column is similarly divided into cervical, dorsal, lumbar, sacral and coccygeal vertebræ, and the total number of cervical and dorsal vertebræ, taken together, is the same as in Man; but the development of a pair of ribs to the first lumbar vertebra, which is an exceptional occurrence in Man, is the rule in the Gorilla; and hence, as lumbar are distinguished from dorsal vertebræ only by the presence or absence of free ribs, the seventeen "dorso-lumbar" vertebræ of the Gorilla are divided into thirteen dorsal and four lumbar, while in Man they are twelve dorsal and five lumbar.

Not only, however, does Man occasionally possess thirteen pair of ribs,[1] but the Gorilla sometimes has fourteen pairs, while an Orang-Utan skeleton in the Museum of the Royal College of Surgeons has twelve dorsal and five lumbar vertebræ, as in Man. Cuvier notes the same number in a *Hylobates*. On the other hand, among the lower Apes, many possess twelve dorsal and six or seven lumbar vertebræ; the Douroucouli has fourteen dorsal and eight lumbar, and a Lemur (*Stenops tardigradus*) has fifteen dorsal and nine lumbar vertebræ.

The vertebral column of the Gorilla, as a whole, differs from that of Man in the less marked character of its curves, especially in the slighter convexity of the lumbar region. Nevertheless, the curves are present, and are quite obvious in young skeletons of the Gorilla and Chimpanzee which have been prepared without removal of the ligaments. In young Orangs similarly preserved, on the other hand, the spinal column is either straight, or even concave forwards, throughout the lumbar region.

Whether we take these characters then, or such minor ones as those which are derivable from the proportional

[1] "More than once," says Peter Camper, "have I met with more than six lumbar vertebræ in man. . . . Once I found thirteen ribs and four lumbar vertebræ." Fallopius noted thirteen pair of ribs and only four lumbar vertebræ; and Eustachius once found eleven dorsal vertebræ and six lumbar vertebræ.— 'Œuvres de Pierre Camper,' T. I, p. 42. As Tyson states, his 'Pygmie' had thirteen pair of ribs and five lumbar vertebræ. The question of the curves of the spinal column in the Apes requires further investigation.

length of the spines of the cervical vertebræ, and the like, there is no doubt whatsoever as to the marked

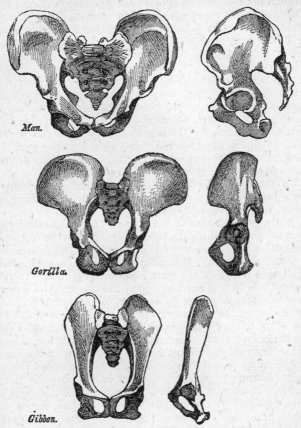

FIG. 15.—Front and side views of the bony pelvis of Man, the Gorilla and Gibbon : reduced from drawings made from nature, of the same absolute length, by Mr. Waterhouse Hawkins.

difference between Man and the Gorilla ; but there is as little, that equally marked differences, of the very same order, obtain between the Gorilla and the lower apes.

*D 47

The Pelvis, or bony girdle of the hips, of Man is a strikingly human part of his organization; the expanded haunch bones affording support for his viscera during his habitually erect posture, and giving space for the attachment of the great muscles which enable him to assume and to preserve that attitude. In these respects the pelvis of the Gorilla differs very considerably from his (Fig. 15). But go no lower than the Gibbon, and see how vastly more he differs from the Gorilla than the latter does from Man, even in this structure. Look at the flat, narrow haunch bones—the long and narrow passage—the coarse, outwardly curved, ischiatic prominences on which the Gibbon habitually rests, and which are coated by the so-called "callosities," dense patches of skin, wholly absent in the Gorilla, in the Chimpanzee, and in the Orang, as in Man!

In the lower Monkeys and in the Lemurs the difference becomes more striking still, the pelvis acquiring an altogether quadrupedal character.

But now let us turn to a nobler and more characteristic organ—that by which the human frame seems to be, and indeed is, so strongly distinguished from all others,— I mean the skull. The differences between a Gorilla's skull and a Man's are truly immense (Fig. 16). In the former, the face, formed largely by the massive jaw-bones, predominates over the brain case, or cranium proper: in the latter, the proportions of the two are reversed. In the Man, the occipital foramen, through which passes the great nervous cord connecting the brain with the nerves of the body, is placed just behind the centre of the base of the skull, which thus becomes evenly balanced in the erect posture; in the Gorilla, it lies in the posterior third of that base. In the Man, the surface of the skull is comparatively smooth, and the supraciliary ridges or brow prominences usually project but little—while, in the Gorilla, vast crests are developed upon the skull, and the brow ridges overhang the cavernous orbits, like great penthouses.

Sections of the skulls, however, show that some of the apparent defects of the Gorilla's cranium arise, in fact, not so much from deficiency of brain case as from excessive development of the parts of the face. The cranial cavity is not ill-shaped, and the forehead is not truly flattened or very retreating, its really well-formed curve being simply disguised by the mass of bone which is built up against it (Fig. 16).

But the roofs of the orbits rise more obliquely into the cranial cavity, thus diminishing the space for the lower part of the anterior lobes of the brain, and the absolute capacity of the cranium is far less than that of Man. So far as I am aware, no human cranium belonging to an adult man has yet been observed with a less cubical capacity than 62 cubic inches, the smallest cranium observed in any race of men by Morton, measuring 63 cubic inches; while, on the other hand, the most capacious Gorilla skull yet measured has a content of not more than $34\frac{1}{2}$ cubic inches. Let us assume, for simplicity's sake, that the lowest Man's skull has twice the capacity of that of the highest Gorilla.[1]

No doubt, this is a very striking difference, but it loses much of its apparent systematic value, when viewed by the light of certain other equally indubitable facts respecting cranial capacities.

The first of these is, that the difference in the volume of the cranial cavity of different races of mankind is far greater, absolutely, than that between the lowest Man and the highest Ape, while, relatively, it is about the same. For the largest human skull measured by Morton contained 114 cubic inches, that is to say, had very nearly double

---

[1] It has been affirmed that Hindoo crania sometimes contain as little as 27 ounces of water, which would give a capacity of about 46 cubic inches. The minimum capacity which I have assumed above, however, is based upon the valuable tables published by Professor R. Wagner in his "Vorstudien zu einer wissenschaftlichen Morphologie und Physiologie des menschlichen Gehirns." As the result of the careful weighing of more than 900 human brains, Professor Wagner states that one-half weighed between 1200 and 1400 grammes, and that about two-ninths, consisting for the most part of male brains, exceed 1400 grammes. The lightest brain of an adult male, with sound mental faculties, recorded by Wagner, weighed 1020 grammes. As a gramme equals 15.4 grains, and a cubic inch of water contains 252.4 grains, this is equivalent to 62 cubic inches of water; so that as brain is heavier than water, we are perfectly safe against erring on the side of diminution in taking

the capacity of the smallest; while its absolute preponderance, of 52 cubic inches—is far greater than that by which the lowest adult male human cranium surpasses the largest of the Gorillas ($62 - 34\frac{1}{2} = 27\frac{1}{2}$). Secondly, the adult crania of Gorillas which have as yet been measured differ among themselves by nearly one-third, the maximum capacity being 34.5 cubic inches, the minimum 24 cubic inches; and, thirdly, after making all due allowance for difference of size, the cranial capacities of some of the lower Apes fall nearly as much, relatively, below those of the higher Apes as the latter fall below Man.

Thus, even in the important matter of cranial capacity, Men differ more widely from one another than they do from the Apes; while the lowest Apes differ as much, in proportion, from the highest, as the latter does from Man. The last proposition is still better illustrated by the study of the modifications which other parts of the cranium undergo in the Simian series.

It is the large proportional size of the facial bones and the great projection of the jaws which confers upon the Gorilla's skull its small facial angle and brutal character.

But if we consider the proportional size of the facial bones to the skull proper only, the little *Chrysothrix* (Fig. 16) differs very widely from the Gorilla, and in the same way as Man does; while the Baboons (*Cynocephalus*, Fig. 16) exaggerate the gross proportions of the muzzle of the great Anthropoid, so that its visage looks mild and human by comparison with theirs. The difference

this as the smallest capacity of any adult male human brain. The only adult male brain, weighing as little as 970 grammes, is that of an idiot; but the brain of an adult woman, against the soundness of whose faculties nothing appears, weighed as little as 907 grammes (55.3 cubic inches of water); and Reid gives an adult female brain of still smaller capacity. The heaviest brain (1872 grammes, or about 115 cubic inches) was, however, that of a woman; next to it comes the brain of Cuvier (1861 grammes), then Byron (1807 grammes), and then an insane person (1783 grammes). The lightest adult brain recorded (720 grammes) was that of an idiotic female. The brains of five children, four years old, weighed between 1275 and 992 grammes. So that it may be safely said, that an average European child of four years old has a brain twice as large as that of an adult Gorilla.

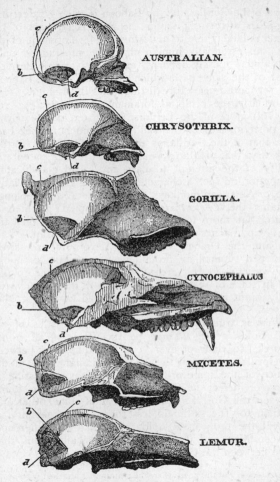

AUSTRALIAN.

CHRYSOTHRIX.

GORILLA.

CYNOCEPHALUS

MYCETES.

LEMUR.

FIG. 16.—Sections of the skulls of Man and various Apes, drawn so as to give the cerebral cavity the same length in each case, thereby displaying the varying proportions of the facial bones. The line *b* indicates the plane of the tentorium, which separates the cerebrum from the cerebellum ; *d*, the axis of the occipital outlet of the skull. The extent of cerebral cavity behind *c*, which is a perpendicular

between the Gorilla and the Baboon is even greater than it appears at first sight; for the great facial mass of the former is largely due to a downward development of the jaws; an essentially human character, superadded upon that almost purely forward, essentially brutal, development of the same parts which characterizes the Baboon, and yet more remarkably distinguishes the Lemur.

Similarly, the occipital foramen of *Mycetes* (Fig. 16), and still more of the Lemurs, is situated completely in the posterior face of the skull, or as much further back than that of the Gorilla, as that of the Gorilla is further back than that of Man; while, as if to render patent the futility of the attempt to base any broad classificatory distinction on such a character, the same group of Platyr- hine, or American monkeys, to which the *Mycetes* belongs, contains the *Chrysothrix*, whose occipital foramen is situated far more forward than in any other ape, and nearly approaches the position it holds in Man.

Again, the Orang's skull is as devoid of excessively developed supraciliary prominences as a Man's, though some varieties exhibit great crests elsewhere (see p. 39); and in some of the Cebine apes and in the *Chrysothrix*, the cranium is as smooth and rounded as that of Man himself.

What is true of these leading characteristics of the skull, holds good, as may be imagined, of all minor features; so that for every constant difference between the Gorilla's skull and the Man's, a similar constant dif- ference of the same order (that is to say, consisting in excess or defect of the same quality) may be found between the Gorilla's skull and that of some other ape. So that, for the skull, no less than for the skeleton in general, the proposition holds good, that the differences between Man and the Gorilla are of smaller value than those between the Gorilla and some other Apes.

erected on *b* at the point where the tentorium is attached posteriorly, indicates the degree to which the cerebrum overlaps the cerebellum —the space occupied by which is roughly indicated by the dark shading. In comparing these diagrams, it must be recollected, that figures on so small a scale as these simply exemplify the statements in the text, the proof of which is to be found in the objects them- selves.

In connection with the skull, I may speak of the teeth —organs which have a peculiar classificatory value, and whose resemblances and differences of number, form, and succession, taken as a whole, are usually regarded as more trustworthy indicators of affinity than any others.

Man is provided with two sets of teeth—milk teeth and permanent teeth. The former consist of four incisors, or cutting teeth ; two canines, or eye-teeth ; and four molars, or grinders, in each jaw—making twenty in all. The latter (Fig. 17) comprise four incisors, two canines, four small grinders, called premolars or false molars, and six large grinders, or true molars, in each jaw—making thirty-two in all. The internal incisors are larger than the external pair, in the upper jaw, smaller than the external pair, in the lower jaw. The crowns of the upper molars exhibit four cusps, or blunt-pointed elevations, and a ridge crosses the crown obliquely, from the inner, anterior, cusp to the outer, posterior cusp (Fig. 17 m^2). The anterior lower molars have five cusps, three external and two internal. The premolars have two cusps, one internal and one external, of which the outer is the higher.

In all these respects the dentition of the Gorilla may be described in the same terms as that of Man ; but in other matters it exhibits many and important differences (Fig. 17).

Thus the teeth of man constitute a regular and even series—without any break and without any marked projection of one tooth above the level of the rest; a peculiarity which, as Cuvier long ago showed, is shared by no other mammal save one—as different a creature from man as can well be imagined—namely, the long extinct *Anoplotherium*. The teeth of the Gorilla, on the contrary, exhibit a break, or interval, termed the *diastema*, in both jaws : in front of the eye-tooth, or between it and the outer incisor, in the upper jaw ; behind the eye-tooth, or between it and the front false molar, in the lower jaw. Into this break in the series, in each jaw, fits the canine of the opposite jaw ; the size of the eye-tooth in the Gorilla being so great that it projects, like a tusk, far beyond the general level of the other teeth. The roots of the false molar teeth of the Gorilla, again, are more complex than in Man, and the proportional size of the molars is different. The Gorilla has the crown of the hindmost grinder of the lower jaw more complex, and the order of eruption of the permanent teeth is different; the permanent canines making their appearance before the second and third molars in Man, and after them in the Gorilla.

Thus, while the teeth of the Gorilla closely resemble those of Man in number, kind, and in the general pattern of their crowns, they exhibit marked differences from those of Man in secondary respects, such as relative size, number of fangs, and order of appearance.

But, if the teeth of the Gorilla be compared with those of an Ape, no further removed from it than a *Cynocephalus*, or Baboon, it will be found that differences and resemblances of the same order are easily observable; but that many of the points in which the Gorilla resembles Man are those in which it differs from the Baboon; while various respects in which it differs from Man are exaggerated in the *Cynocephalus*. The number and the nature of the teeth remain the same in the Baboon as in the Gorilla and in Man. But the pattern of the Baboon's upper molars is quite different from that described above (Fig. 17), the canines are proportionally longer and more knife-like; the anterior premolar in the lower jaw is specially modified; the posterior molar of the lower jaw is still larger and more complex than in the Gorilla.

Passing from the old-world Apes to those of the new world, we meet with a change of much greater importance than any of these. In such a genus as *Cebus*, for example (Fig. 17), it will be found that while in some secondary points, such as the projection of the canines and the diastema, the resemblance to the great ape is preserved; in other and most important respects, the dentition is extremely different. Instead of 20 teeth in the milk set, there are 24: instead of 32 teeth in the permanent set, there are 36, the false molars being increased from eight to twelve. And in form, the crowns of the molars are very unlike those of the Gorilla, and differ far more widely from the human pattern.

The Marmosets, on the other hand, exhibit the same number of teeth as Man and the Gorilla; but, notwithstanding this, their dentition is very different, for they

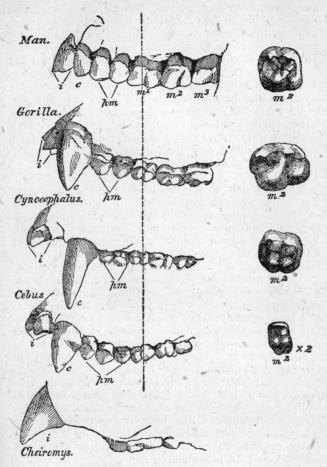

FIG. 17.—Lateral views, of the same length, of the upper jaws of various Primates. *i*, incisors; *c*, canines; *pm*, premolars; *m*, molars. A line is drawn through the first molar of Man, *Gorilla*, *Cynocephalus*, and *Cebus*, and the grinding surface of the second molar is shown in each, its anterior and internal angle being just above the *m* of *m²*.

have four more false molars, like the other American monkeys—but as they have four fewer true molars, the total remains the same.   And passing from the American apes to the Lemurs, the dentition becomes still more completely and essentially different from that of the Gorilla. The incisors begin to vary both in number and in form. The molars acquire, more and more, a many-pointed, insectivorous character, and in one Genus, the Aye-Aye (*Cheiromys*), the canines disappear, and the teeth completely simulate those of a Rodent (Fig. 17).

Hence it is obvious that, greatly as the dentition of the highest Ape differs from that of Man, it differs far more widely from that of the lower and lowest Apes.

Whatever part of the animal fabric—whatever series of muscles, whatever viscera might be selected for comparison—the result would be the same—the lower Apes and the Gorilla would differ more than the Gorilla and the Man.   I cannot attempt in this place to follow out all these comparisons in detail, and indeed it is unnecessary I should do so.   But certain real, or supposed, structural distinctions between man and the apes remain, upon which so much stress has been laid, that they require careful consideration, in order that the true value may be assigned to those which are real, and the emptiness of those which are fictitious may be exposed.   I refer to the characters of the hand, the foot, and the brain.

Man has been defined as the only animal possessed of two hands terminating his fore limbs, and of two feet ending his hind limbs, while it has been said that all the apes possess four hands; and he has been affirmed to differ fundamentally from all the apes in the characters of his brain, which alone, it has been strangely asserted and re-asserted, exhibits the structures known to anatomists as the posterior lobe, the posterior cornu of the lateral ventricle, and the hippocampus minor.

That the former proposition should have gained general acceptance is not surprising—indeed, at first sight, appearances are much in its favour : but, as for the second, one can only admire the surpassing courage of its enunciator, seeing that it is an innovation which is not only opposed to generally and justly accepted doctrines, but which is directly negatived by the testimony of all original inquirers, who have specially investigated the matter: and that it neither has been, nor can be, supported by a single anatomical preparation. It would, in fact, be unworthy of serious refutation, except for the general and natural belief that deliberate and reiterated assertions must have some foundation.

Before we can discuss the first point with advantage we must consider with some attention, and compare together, the structure of the human hand and that of the human foot, so that we may have distinct and clear ideas of what constitutes a hand and what a foot.

The external form of the human hand is familiar enough to every one. It consists of a stout wrist followed by a broad palm, formed of flesh, and tendons, and skin, binding together four bones, and dividing into four long and flexible digits, or fingers, each of which bears on the back of its last joint a broad and flattened nail. The longest cleft between any two digits is rather less than half as long as the hand. From the outer side of the base of the palm a stout digit goes off, having only two joints instead of three; so short, that it only reaches to a little beyond the middle of the first joint of the finger next it; and further remarkable by its great mobility, in consequence of which it can be directed outwards, almost at a right angle to the rest. This digit is called the '*pollex*,' or thumb; and, like the others, it bears a flat nail upon the back of its terminal joint. In consequence of the proportions and mobility of the thumb, it is what is termed "opposable"; in other words, its extremity can, with the greatest ease, be brought into contact with the extremities of any of the fingers; a property upon which the possibility of our carrying into effect the conceptions of the mind so largely depends.

The external form of the foot differs widely from that of the hand; and yet, when closely compared, the two present some singular resemblances. Thus the ankle corresponds in a manner with the wrist; the sole with the palm; the toes with the fingers; the great toe with the thumb. But the toes, or digits of the foot, are far shorter in proportion than the digits of the hand, and are less moveable, the want of mobility being most striking in the great toe—which, again, is very much larger in proportion to the other toes than the thumb to the fingers. In considering this point, however, it must not be forgotten that the civilized great toe, confined and cramped from childhood upwards, is seen to a great disadvantage, and that in uncivilized and barefooted people it retains a great amount of mobility, and even some sort of opposability. The Chinese boatmen are said to be able to pull an oar, the artisans of Bengal to weave, and the Carajas to steal fishhooks, by its help; though, after all, it must be recollected that the structure of its joints and the arrangement of its bones, necessarily render its prehensile action far less perfect than that of the thumb.

But to gain a precise conception of the resemblances and differences of the hand and foot, and of the distinctive characters of each, we must look below the skin, and compare the bony framework and its motor apparatus in each (Fig. 18).

The skeleton of the hand exhibits, in the region which we term the wrist, and which is technically called the *carpus*—two rows of closely fitted polygonal bones, four in each row, which are tolerably equal in size. The bones of the first row with the bones of the forearm form the wrist joint, and are arranged side by side, no one greatly exceeding or overlapping the rest.

The four bones of the second row of the carpus bear the four long bones which support the palm of the hand. The fifth bone of the same character is articulated in a much more free and moveable manner than the others, with its carpal bone, and forms the base of the thumb. These are called *metacarpal* bones, and they carry the *phalanges*, or bones of the digits, of which there are two in the thumb, and three in each of the fingers.

The skeleton of the foot is very like that of the hand in some respects. Thus there are three phalanges in each of the lesser toes, and only two in the great toe, which answers to the thumb. There is a long bone, termed *metatarsal*, answering to the metacarpal, for each digit;

and the *tarsus*, which corresponds with the carpus, presents four short polygonal bones in a row, which correspond very closely with the four carpal bones of the second row

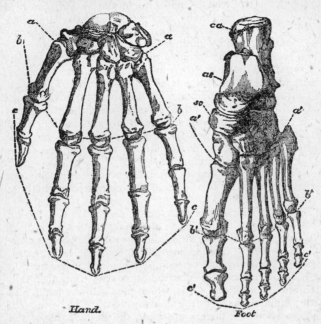

Hand.   *Foot*

FIG. 18.—The skeleton of the Hand and Foot of Man reduced from Dr. Carter's drawings in Gray's 'Anatomy.' The hand is drawn to a larger scale than the foot. The line *a a* in the hand indicates the boundary between the carpus and the metacarpus; *b b* that between the latter and the proximal phalanges; *c c* marks the ends of the distal phalanges. The line *a' a'* in the foot indicates the boundary between the tarsus and metatarsus; *b' b'* marks that between the metatarsus and the proximal phalanges; and *c' c'* bounds the ends of the distal phalanges; *ca*, the calcaneum; *as*, the astragalus; *sc*, the scaphoid bone in the tarsus.

of the hand. In other respects the foot differs very widely from the hand. Thus the great toe is the longest digit but one; and its metatarsal is far less moveably articulated with the tarsus, than the metacarpal of the thumb with the carpus. But a far more important distinction lies in the fact that, instead of four more tarsal bones there are only three; and that these three are not arranged side by side, or in one row. One of them, the *os calcis* or heel bone (*ca*), lies externally, and sends back the large projecting heel; another, the *astragalus* (*as*), rests on this by one face, and by another, forms, with the bones of the leg, the ankle joint; while a third face, directed forwards, is separated from the three inner tarsal bones of the row next the metatarsus by a bone called the *scaphoid* (*sc*).

Thus there is a fundamental difference in the structure of the foot and the hand, observable when the carpus and the tarsus are contrasted; and there are differences of degree noticeable when the proportions and the mobility of the metacarpals and metatarsals, with their respective digits, are compared together.

The same two classes of differences become obvious when the muscles of the hand are compared with those of the foot.

Three principal sets of muscles, called "flexors," bend the fingers and thumb, as in clenching the fist, and three sets—the extensors—extend them, as in straightening the fingers. These muscles are all "long muscles"; that is to say, the fleshy part of each, lying in and being fixed to the bones of the arm, is, at the other end, continued into tendons, or rounded cords, which pass into the hand, and are ultimately fixed to the bones which are to be moved. Thus, when the fingers are bent, the fleshy parts of the flexors of the fingers, placed in the arm, contract, in virtue of their peculiar endowment as muscles; and pulling the tendinous cords, connected with their ends, cause them to pull down the bones of the fingers towards the palm.

Not only are the principal flexors of the fingers and of the thumb long muscles, but they remain quite distinct from one another throughout their whole length.

In the foot, there are also three principal flexor muscles of the digits or toes, and three principal extensors; but one extensor and one flexor are short muscles; that is to say, their fleshy parts are not situated in the leg (which corresponds with the arm), but in the back and in the sole of the foot—regions which correspond with the back and the palm of the hand.

Again, the tendons of the long flexor of the toes, and of the long flexor of the great toe, when they reach the sole of the foot, do not remain distinct from one another, as the flexors in the palm of the hand do, but they become united and commingled in a very curious manner—while their united tendons receive an accessory muscle connected with the heel-bone.

But perhaps the most absolutely distinctive character about the muscles of the foot is the existence of what is termed the *peronæus longus*, a long muscle fixed to the outer bone of the leg, and sending its tendon to the outer ankle, behind and below which it passes, and then crosses the foot obliquely to be attached to the base of the great toe. No muscle in the hand exactly corresponds with this, which is eminently a foot muscle.

To resume—the foot of man is distinguished from his hand by the following absolute anatomical differences :—

1. By the arrangement of the tarsal bones.
2. By having a short flexor and a short extensor muscle of the digits.
3. By possessing the muscle termed *peronæus longus*.

And if we desire to ascertain whether the terminal division of a limb, in other Primates, is to be called a foot or a hand, it is by the presence or absence of these characters that we must be guided, and not by the mere proportions and greater or lesser mobility of the great toe, which may vary indefinitely without any fundamental alteration in the structure of the foot.

Keeping these considerations in mind, let us now turn to the limbs of the Gorilla. The terminal division of the fore limb presents no difficulty—bone for bone and muscle for muscle, are found to be arranged essentially as in man, or with such minor differences as are found as varieties in man. The Gorilla's hand is clumsier, heavier, and has a thumb somewhat shorter in proportion than that of man ; but no one has ever doubted its being a true hand.

At first sight, the termination of the hind limb of the Gorilla looks very hand-like, and as it is still more so in many of the lower apes, it is not wonderful that the appellation "Quadrumana," or four-handed creatures, adopted from the older anatomists[1] by Blumenbach, and unfortunately rendered current by Cuvier, should have gained such wide acceptance as a name for the Simian group.   But the most cursory anatomical investigation at once proves that the resemblance of the so-called "hind hand" to a true hand, is only skin deep, and that, in all essential respects, the hind limb of the Gorilla is as truly terminated by a foot as that of man.   The tarsal bones, in all important circumstances of number, disposition, and form, resemble those of man (Fig. 19).   The metatarsals and digits, on the other hand, are proportionally longer and more slender, while the great toe is not only proportionally shorter and weaker, but its metatarsal bone is united by a more moveable joint with the tarsus. At the same time, the foot is set more obliquely upon the leg than in man.

As to the muscles, there is a short flexor, a short extensor, and a *peronæus longus*, while the tendons of the long flexors of the great toe and of the other toes are united together and with an accessory fleshy bundle.

The hind limb of the Gorilla, therefore, ends in a true foot, with a very moveable great toe.   It is a prehensile foot, indeed, but is in no sense a hand : it is a foot which differs from that of man not in any fundamental character, but in mere proportions, in the degree of mobility, and in the secondary arrangement of its parts.

It must not be supposed, however, because I speak

---

[1] In speaking of the foot of his "Pygmie," Tyson remarks, p. 13 :—

"But this part in the formation and in its function too, being liker a Hand than a Foot : for the distinguishing this sort of animals from others, I have thought whether it might not be reckoned and called rather Quadru-manus than Quadrupes, *i.e.* a four-handed rather than a four-footed animal."

As this passage was published in 1699, M. I. G. St. Hilaire is clearly in error in ascribing the invention of the term "quadrumanous" to Buffon, though "bimanous" may belong to him. Tyson uses "Quadrumanus" in several places, as at p. 91. . . . "Our *Pygmie* is no Man, nor yet the *common Ape*, but a sort of *Animal* between both ; and though a *Biped*, yet of the *Quadrumanus*-kind : though some *Men* too have been observed to use their *Feet* like *Hands*, as I have seen several."

of these differences as not fundamental, that I wish to underrate their value. They are important enough in their way, the structure of the foot being in strict correlation with that of the rest of the organism in each case. Nor can it be doubted that the greater division of physiological labour in Man, so that the function of support is thrown wholly on the leg and foot, is an advance in

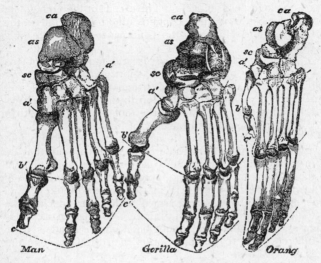

FIG. 19.—Foot of Man, Gorilla, and Orang-Utan of the same absolute length, to show the differences in proportion of each. Letters as in Fig. 18. Reduced from original drawings by Mr. Waterhouse Hawkins.

organization of very great moment to him; but, after all, regarded anatomically, the resemblances between the foot of Man and the foot of the Gorilla are far more striking and important than the differences.

I have dwelt upon this point at length, because it is one regarding which much delusion prevails; but I might have passed it over without detriment to my argument, which only requires me to show that, be the differences between the hand and foot of Man and those of the Gorilla what they may—the differences between those of the Gorilla and those of the lower Apes are much greater.

It is not necessary to descend lower in the scale than the Orang for conclusive evidence on this head.

The thumb of the Orang differs more from that of the Gorilla than the thumb of the Gorilla differs from that of Man, not only by its shortness, but by the absence of any special long flexor muscle. The carpus of the Orang, like that of most lower apes, contains nine bones, while in the Gorilla, as in Man and the Chimpanzee, there are only eight.

The Orang's foot (Fig. 19) is still more aberrant; its very long toes and short tarsus, short great toe, short and raised heel, great obliquity of articulation in the leg, and absence of a long flexor tendon to the great toe, separating it far more widely from the foot of the Gorilla than the latter is separated from that of Man.

But, in some of the lower apes, the hand and foot diverge still more from those of the Gorilla, than they do in the Orang. The thumb ceases to be opposable in the American monkeys; is reduced to a mere rudiment covered by the skin in the Spider Monkey; and is directed forwards and armed with a curved claw like the other digits, in the Marmosets—so that, in all these cases, there can be no doubt but that the hand is more different from that of the Gorilla than the Gorilla's hand is from Man's.

And as to the foot, the great toe of the Marmoset is still more insignificant in proportion than that of the Orang—while in the Lemurs it is very large, and as completely thumb-like and opposable as in the Gorilla— but in these animals the second toe is often irregularly modified, and in some species the two principal bones of the tarsus, the *astragalus* and the *os calcis*, are so immensely elongated as to render the foot, so far, totally unlike that of any other mammal.

So with regard to the muscles. The short flexor of the toes of the Gorilla differs from that of Man by the circumstance that one slip of the muscle is attached, not to the heel bone, but to the tendons of the long flexors. The lower Apes depart from the Gorilla by an exaggeration of the same character, two, three, or more, slips becoming fixed to the long flexor tendons—or by a multiplication of the slips.—Again, the Gorilla differs slightly from Man in the mode of interlacing of the long flexor tendons: and the lower apes differ from the Gorilla in exhibiting yet other, sometimes very complex, arrangements of the same parts, and occasionally in the absence of the accessory fleshy bundle.

Throughout all these modifications it must be recollected that the foot loses no one of its essential characters. Every Monkey and Lemur exhibits the characteristic arrangement of tarsal bones, possesses a short flexor and short extensor muscle, and a *peronæus longus*. Varied as the proportions and appearance of the organ may be, the terminal division of the hind limb remains, in plan and principle of construction, a foot, and never, in those respects, can be confounded with a hand.

Hardly any part of the bodily frame, then, could be found better calculated to illustrate the truth that the structural differences between Man and the highest Ape are of less value than those between the highest and the lower Apes, than the hand or the foot, and yet, perhaps, there is one organ the study of which enforces the same conclusion in a still more striking manner—and that is the Brain.

But before entering upon the precise question of the amount of difference between the Ape's brain and that of Man, it is necessary that we should clearly understand what constitutes a great, and what a small difference in cerebral structure; and we shall be best enabled to do this by a brief study of the chief modifications which the brain exhibits in the series of vertebrate animals.

The brain of a fish is very small, compared with the spinal cord into which it is continued, and with the nerves which come off from it: of the segments of which it is composed—the olfactory lobes, the cerebral hemisphere, and the succeeding divisions—no one predominates so much over the rest as to obscure or cover them; and the so-called optic lobes are, frequently, the largest masses of all. In Reptiles, the mass of the brain, relatively to the spinal cord, increases and the cerebral hemispheres begin to predominate over the other parts; while in Birds this predominance is still more marked. The brain of the lowest Mammals, such as the duck-billed Platypus and the Opossums and Kangaroos, exhibits a still more definite advance in the same direction. The cerebral hemispheres have now so much increased in size as, more or less, to hide the representatives of the optic lobes, which remain comparatively small, so that the brain of a Marsupial is extremely different from that of a Bird, Reptile, or Fish. A step higher in the scale, among the placental Mammals, the structure of the brain acquires a vast modification—not that it appears much altered externally, in a Rat or in a Rabbit, from what it is in a Marsupial—nor that the proportions of its parts are much changed, but an apparently new structure is found between the cerebral hemispheres, connecting them together, as what is called the 'great commissure' or 'corpus callosum.' The subject requires careful re-investigation, but if the currently received statements are correct, the appearance of the 'corpus callosum' in the placental mammals is the greatest and most sudden modification exhibited by the brain in the whole series of vertebrated animals—it is the greatest leap anywhere made by Nature in her brain work. For the two halves of the brain being once thus knit together, the progress of cerebral complexity is traceable through a complete series of steps from the lowest Rodent, or Insectivore, to Man; and that complexity consists, chiefly, in the disproportionate development of the cerebral hemispheres and of the cerebellum, but especially of the former, in respect to the other parts of the brain.

In the lower placental mammals, the cerebral hemispheres leave the proper upper and posterior face of the cerebellum completely visible, when the brain is viewed from above, but, in the higher forms, the hinder part of each hemisphere, separated only by the tentorium (p. 92) from the anterior face of the cerebellum, inclines backwards and downwards, and grows out, as the so-called "posterior lobe," so as at length to overlap and hide the cerebellum. In all Mammals, each cerebral hemisphere contains a cavity which is termed the 'ventricle,' and as this ventricle is prolonged, on the one hand, forwards, and on the other downwards, into the substance of the hemisphere, it is said to have two horns or 'cornua,' an 'anterior cornu,' and a 'descending cornu.' When the posterior lobe is well developed, a third prolongation of the ventricular cavity extends into it, and is called the "posterior cornu."

In the lower and smaller forms of placental Mammals the surface of the cerebral hemispheres is either smooth or evenly rounded, or exhibits a very few grooves, which are technically termed 'sulci,' separating ridges or 'convolutions' of the substance of the brain; and the smaller species of all orders tend to a similar smoothness of brain. But, in the higher orders, and especially the larger members of these orders, the grooves, or sulci, become extremely numerous, and the intermediate convolutions proportionately more complicated in their meanderings, until, in the Elephant, the Porpoise, the higher Apes, and Man, the cerebral surface appears a perfect labyrinth of tortuous foldings.

Where a posterior lobe exists and presents its customary cavity—the posterior cornu—it commonly happens that a particular sulcus appears upon the inner and under surface of the lobe, parallel with and beneath the floor of the cornu—which is, as it were, arched over the roof of the sulcus. It is as if the groove had been formed by indenting the floor of the posterior horn from without with a blunt instrument, so that the floor should rise as a convex eminence. Now this eminence is what has been termed the 'Hippocampus minor'; the 'Hippocampus major' being a larger eminence in the floor of the descending cornu. What may be the functional importance of either of these structures we know not.

As if to demonstrate, by a striking example, the impossibility of erecting any cerebral barrier between man and the apes, Nature has provided us, in the latter animals, with an almost complete series of gradations from brains little higher than that of a Rodent, to brains little lower than that of Man. And it is a remarkable circumstance that though, so far as our present knowledge extends, there *is* one true structural break in the series of forms of Simian brains, this hiatus does not lie between Man and the man-like apes, but between the lower and the lowest Simians ; or, in other words, between the old and new world apes and monkeys, and the Lemurs. Every Lemur which has yet been examined, in fact, has its cerebellum partially visible from above, and its posterior lobe, with the contained posterior cornu and hippocampus minor, more or less rudimentary. Every Marmoset, American monkey, old world monkey, Baboon, or Man-like ape, on the contrary, has its cerebellum entirely hidden, posteriorly, by the cerebral lobes, and possesses a large posterior cornu, with a well-developed hippocampus minor.

In many of these creatures, such as the Saimiri (*Chrysothrix*), the cerebral lobes overlap and extend much further behind the cerebellum, in proportion, than they do in man (Fig. 16)—and it is quite certain that, in all, the cerebellum is completely covered behind, by well-developed posterior lobes. The fact can be verified by every one who possesses the skull of any old or new world monkey. For, inasmuch as the brain in all mammals completely fills the cranial cavity, it is obvious that a cast of the interior of the skull will reproduce the general form of the brain, at any rate with such minute and, for the present purpose, utterly unimportant differences as may result from the absence of the enveloping membranes of the brain in the dry skull. But if such a cast be made in plaster, and compared with a similar cast of the interior of a human skull, it will be obvious that the cast of the cerebral chamber, representing the cerebrum of the ape, as completely covers over and overlaps the cast of the cerebellar chamber, representing the cerebellum, as it does in the man (Fig. 20). A careless observer, forgetting that a soft structure like the brain loses its proper shape the moment it is taken out of the skull, may indeed mistake the uncovered condition of the cerebellum of an extracted and distorted brain for the natural relations of the parts ; but his error must become patent even to himself if he try to replace the brain

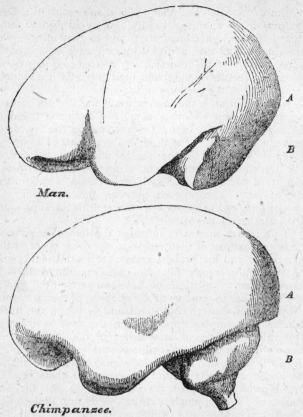

FIG. 20.—Drawings of the internal casts of a Man's and of a Chimpanzee's skull, of the same absolute length, and placed in corresponding positions, *A.* Cerebrum; *B.* Cerebellum. The former drawing is taken from a cast in the Museum of the Royal College of Surgeons, the latter from the photograph of the cast of a Chimpanzee's skull, which illustrates the paper by Mr. Marshall ' On the Brain of the Chimpanzee' in the Natural History Review for July, 1861. The sharper definition of the lower edge of the cast of the cerebral chamber in the Chimpanzee arises from the circumstance that the tentorium remained in that skull and not in the Man's. The cast more accurately represents the brain in Chimpanzee than in the Man; and the great backward projection of the posterior lobes of the cerebrum of the former, beyond the cerebellum, is conspicuous.

within the cranial chamber. To suppose that the cerebellum of an ape is naturally uncovered behind is a miscomprehension comparable only to that of one who should imagine that a man's lungs always occupy but a small portion of the thoracic cavity—because they do so when the chest is opened, and their elasticity is no longer neutralized by the pressure of the air.

And the error is the less excusable, as it must become apparent to every one who examines a section of the skull of any ape above a Lemur, without taking the trouble to make a cast of it. For there is a very marked groove in every such skull, as in the human skull—which indicates the line of attachment of what is termed the *tentorium*— a sort of parchment-like shelf, or partition, which, in the recent state, is interposed between the cerebrum and cerebellum, and prevents the former from pressing upon the latter (see Fig. 16).

This groove, therefore, indicates the line of separation between that part of the cranial cavity which contains the cerebrum, and that which contains the cerebellum ; and as the brain exactly fills the cavity of the skull, it is obvious that the relations of these two parts of the cranial cavity at once informs us of the relations of their contents. Now in man, in all the old world, and in all the new world Simiæ, with one exception, when the face is directed forwards, this line of attachment of the tentorium, or impression for the lateral sinus, as it is technically called, is nearly horizontal, and the cerebral chamber invariably overlaps or projects behind the cerebellar chamber. In the Howler Monkey or *Mycetes* (see Fig. 16), the line passes obliquely upwards and backwards, and the cerebral overlap is almost nil ; while in the Lemurs, as in the lower mammals, the line is much more inclined in the same direction, and the cerebellar chamber projects considerably beyond the cerebral.

When the gravest errors respecting points so easily settled as this question respecting the posterior lobes can be authoritatively propounded, it is no wonder that matters of observation, of no very complex character, but still requiring a certain amount of care, should have fared worse. Any one who cannot see the posterior lobe in an ape's brain is not likely to give a very valuable opinion respecting the posterior cornu or the hippocampus minor. If a man cannot see a church, it is preposterous to take his opinion about its altar-piece or painted window—so that I do not feel bound to enter upon any discussion of these points, but content myself with assuring the reader that the posterior cornu and the hippocampus minor, have now been seen—usually, at least as well developed as in man, and often better—not only in the Chimpanzee, the Orang, and the Gibbon, but in all the genera of the old world baboons and monkeys, and in most of the new world forms, including the Marmosets.[1]

In fact, all the abundant and trustworthy evidence (consisting of the results of careful investigations directed to the determination of these very questions, by skilled anatomists) which we now possess, leads to the conviction that, so far from the posterior lobe, the posterior cornu, and the hippocampus minor, being structures peculiar to and characteristic of man, as they have been over and over again asserted to be, even after the publication of the clearest demonstration of the reverse, it is precisely these structures which are the most marked cerebral characters common to man with the apes. They are among the most distinctly Simian peculiarities which the human organism exhibits.

As to the convolutions, the brains of the apes exhibit every stage of progress, from the almost smooth brain of the Marmoset, to the Orang and the Chimpanzee, which fall but little below Man. And it is most remarkable that, as soon as all the principal sulci appear, the pattern according to which they are arranged is identical with that of the corresponding sulci of man. The surface of the brain of a monkey exhibits a sort of skeleton map of man's, and in the man-like apes the details become more and more filled in, until it is only in minor characters, such as the greater excavation of the anterior lobes, the constant presence of fissures usually absent in man, and the different disposition and proportions of some

---

[1] See the note at the end of this essay for a succinct history of the controversy to which allusion is here made.

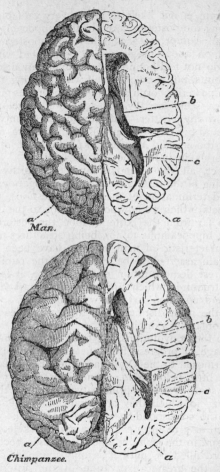

FIG. 21.—Drawings of the cerebral hemispheres of a Man and of a
    Chimpanzee of the same length, in order to show the relative pro-
    portions of the parts : the former taken from a specimen, which Mr.
    Flower, Conservator of the Museum of the Royal College of Surgeons,
    was good enough to dissect for me ; the latter, from the photograph
    of a similarly dissected Chimpanzee's brain, given in Mr. Marshall's
    paper above referred to.   *a*, posterior lobe ; *b*, lateral ventricle ; *c*,
    posterior cornu ; *x*, the hippocampus minor.

convolutions, that the Chimpanzee's or the Orang's brain can be structurally distinguished from Man's.

So far as cerebral structure goes, therefore, it is clear that Man differs less from the Chimpanzee or the Orang, than these do even from the Monkeys, and that the difference between the brains of the Chimpanzee and of Man is almost insignificant, when compared with that between the Chimpanzee brain and that of a Lemur.

It must not be overlooked, however, that there is a very striking difference in the absolute mass and weight between the lowest human brain and that of the highest ape—a difference which is all the more remarkable when we recollect that a full grown Gorilla is probably pretty nearly twice as heavy as a Bosjes man, or as many an European woman. It may be doubted whether a healthy human adult brain ever weighed less than thirty-one or two ounces, or that the heaviest Gorilla brain has exceeded twenty ounces.

This is a very noteworthy circumstance, and doubtless will one day help to furnish an explanation of the great gulf which intervenes between the lowest man and the highest ape in intellectual power;[1] but it has little

[1] I say *help* to furnish : for I by no means believe that it was any original difference of cerebral quality, or quantity, which caused that divergence between the human and the pithecoid stirpes, which has ended in the present enormous gulf between them. It is no doubt perfectly true, in a certain sense, that all difference of function is a result of difference of structure ; or, in other words, of difference in the combination of the primary molecular forces of living substance ; and, starting from this undeniable axiom, objectors occasionally, and with much seeming plausibility, argue that the vast intellectual chasm between the Ape and Man implies a corresponding structural chasm in the organs of the intellectual functions ; so that, it is said, the non-discovery of such vast differences proves, not that they are absent, but that Science is incompetent to detect them. A very little consideration, however, will, I think, show the fallacy of this reasoning. Its validity hangs upon the assumption, that intellectual power depends altogether on the brain—whereas the brain is only one condition out of many on which intellectual manifestations depend ; the others being, chiefly, the organs of the senses and the motor apparatuses, especially those which are concerned in prehension and in the production of articulate speech.

A man born dumb, notwithstanding his great cerebral mass and his inheritance of strong intellectual instincts, would be capable of few higher intellectual manifestations than an Orang or a Chimpanzee,

systematic value, for the simple reason that, as may be
concluded from what has been already said respecting
cranial capacity, the difference in weight of brain between
the highest and the lowest men is far greater, both
relatively and absolutely, than that between the lowest
man and the highest ape. The latter, as has been seen,
is represented by, say twelve, ounces of cerebral substance
absolutely, or by 32 : 20 relatively; but as the largest
recorded human brain weighed between 65 and 66 ounces,
the former difference is represented by more than 33
ounces absolutely, or by 65 : 32 relatively. Regarded
systematically the cerebral differences, of man and apes,
are not of more than generic value—his Family distinction
resting chiefly on his dentition, his pelvis, and his lower
limbs.

Thus, whatever system of organs be studied, the comparison of their modifications in the ape series leads to
one and the same result—that the structural differences
which separate Man from the Gorilla and the Chimpanzee
are not so great as those which separate the Gorilla from
the lower apes.

if he were confined to the society of dumb associates. And yet there
might not be the slightest discernible difference between his brain
and that of a highly intelligent and cultivated person. The dumbness
might be the result of a defective structure of the mouth, or of the
tongue, or a mere defective innervation of these parts; or it might
result from congenital deafness, caused by some minute defect of the
internal ear, which only a careful anatomist could discover.

The argument, that because there is an immense difference between a Man's intelligence and an Ape's, therefore, there must be an
equally immense difference between their brains, appears to me to be
about as well based as the reasoning by which one should endeavour
to prove that, because there is a "great gulf" between a watch that
keeps accurate time and another that will not go at all, there is
therefore a great structural hiatus between the two watches. A hair
in the balance-wheel, a little rust on a pinion, a bend in a tooth of
the escapement, a something so slight that only the practised eye of
the watchmaker can discover it, may be the source of all the difference.

And believing, as I do, with Cuvier, that the possession of articulate speech is the grand distinctive character of man (whether it be
absolutely peculiar to him or not), I find it very easy to comprehend,
that some equally inconspicuous structural difference may have been
the primary cause of the immeasurable and practically infinite divergence of the Human from the Simian Stirps.

But in enunciating this important truth I must guard myself against a form of misunderstanding, which is very prevalent. I find, in fact, that those who endeavour to teach what nature so clearly shows us in this matter, are liable to have their opinions misrepresented and their phraseology garbled, until they seem to say that the structural differences between man and even the highest apes are small and insignificant. Let me take this opportunity then of distinctly asserting, on the contrary, that they are great and significant; that every bone of a Gorilla bears marks by which it might be distinguished from the corresponding bone of a Man; and that, in the present creation, at any rate, no intermediate link bridges over the gap between *Homo* and *Troglodytes*.

It would be no less wrong than absurd to deny the existence of this chasm; but it is at least equally wrong and absurd to exaggerate its magnitude, and, resting on the admitted fact of its existence, to refuse to inquire whether it is wide or narrow. Remember, if you will, that there is no existing link between Man and the Gorilla, but do not forget that there is a no less sharp line of demarcation, a no less complete absence of any transitional form, between the Gorilla and the Orang, or the Orang and the Gibbon. I say, not less sharp, though it is somewhat narrower. The structural differences between Man and the Man-like apes certainly justify our regarding him as constituting a family apart from them; though, inasmuch as he differs less from them than they do from other families of the same order, there can be no justification for placing him in a distinct order.

And thus the sagacious foresight of the great lawgiver of systematic zoology, Linnæus, becomes justified, and a century of anatomical research brings us back to his conclusion, that man is a member of the same order (for which the Linnæan term PRIMATES ought to be retained) as the Apes and Lemurs. This order is now divisible into seven families, of about equal systematic value: the first, the ANTHROPINI, contains Man alone; the second, the CATARHINI, embraces the old world apes; the third, the PLATYRHINI, all new world apes, except the Marmosets; the fourth, the ARCTOPITHECINI, contains the

Marmosets; the fifth, the LEMURINI, the Lemurs—from
which *Cheiromys* should probably be excluded to form a
sixth distinct family, the CHEIROMYINI; while the seventh,
the GALEOPITHECINI, contains only the flying Lemur *Galeo-
pithecus*,—a strange form which almost touches on the
Bats, as the *Cheiromys* puts on a rodent clothing, and the
Lemurs simulate Insectivora.

Perhaps no order of mammals presents us with so
extraordinary a series of gradations as this—leading us
insensibly from the crown and summit of the animal
creation down to creatures, from which there is but a
step, as it seems, to the lowest, smallest, and least intelligent of the placental Mammalia. It is as if nature
herself had foreseen the arrogance of man, and with
Roman severity had provided that his intellect, by its
very triumphs, should call into prominence the slaves,
admonishing the conqueror that he is but dust.

These are the chief facts, this the immediate conclusion
from them to which I adverted in the commencement
of this Essay. The facts, I believe, cannot be disputed;
and if so, the conclusion appears to me to be inevitable.

But if Man be separated by no greater structural barrier
from the brutes than they are from one another—then it
seems to follow that if any process of physical causation
can be discovered by which the genera and families of
ordinary animals have been produced, that process of
causation is amply sufficient to account for the origin
of Man. In other words, if it could be shown that the
Marmosets, for example, have arisen by gradual modification of the ordinary Platyrhini, or that both Marmosets
and Platyrhini are modified ramifications of a primitive
stock—then, there would be no rational ground for doubting that man might have originated, in the one case, by
the gradual modification of a man-like ape; or, in the
other case, as a ramification of the same primitive stock
as those apes.

At the present moment, but one such process of
physical causation has any evidence in its favour; or,
in other words, there is but one hypothesis regarding
the origin of species of animals in general which has any

scientific existence—that propounded by Mr. Darwin. For Lamarck, sagacious as many of his views were, mingled them with so much that was crude and even absurd, as to neutralize the benefit which his originality might have effected, had he been a more sober and cautious thinker; and though I have heard of the announcement of a formula touching "the ordained continuous becoming of organic forms," it is obvious that it is the first duty of a hypothesis to be intelligible, and that a qua-quâ-versal proposition of this kind, which may be read backwards, or forwards, or sideways, with exactly the same amount of signification, does not really exist, though it may seem to do so.

At the present moment, therefore, the question of the relation of man to the lower animals resolves itself, in the end, into the larger question of the tenability or untenability of Mr. Darwin's views. But here we enter upon difficult ground, and it behoves us to define our exact position with the greatest care.

It cannot be doubted, I think, that Mr. Darwin has satisfactorily proved that what he terms selection, or selective modification, must occur, and does occur, in nature; and he has also proved to superfluity that such selection is competent to produce forms as distinct, structurally, as some genera even are. If the animated world presented us with none but structural differences, I should have no hesitation in saying that Mr. Darwin had demonstrated the existence of a true physical cause, amply competent to account for the origin of living species, and of man among the rest.

But, in addition to their structural distinctions, the species of animals and plants, or at least a great number of them, exhibit physiological characters—what are known as distinct species, structurally, being for the most part either altogether incompetent to breed one with another; or if they breed, the resulting mule, or hybrid, is unable to perpetuate its race with another hybrid of the same kind.

A true physical cause is, however, admitted to be such only on one condition—that it shall account for all the phenomena which come within the range of its operation.

If it is inconsistent with any one phenomenon, it must be rejected; if it fails to explain any one phenomenon, it is so far weak, so far to be suspected; though it may have a perfect right to claim provisional acceptance.

Now, Mr. Darwin's hypothesis is not, so far as I am aware, inconsistent with any known biological fact; on the contrary, if admitted, the facts of Development, of Comparative Anatomy, of Geographical Distribution, and of Palæontology, become connected together, and exhibit a meaning such as they never possessed before; and I, for one, am fully convinced, that if not precisely true, that hypothesis is as near an approximation to the truth as, for example, the Copernican hypothesis was to the true theory of the planetary motions.

But, for all this, our acceptance of the Darwinian hypothesis must be provisional so long as one link in the chain of evidence is wanting; and so long as all the animals and plants certainly produced by selective breeding from a common stock are fertile, and their progeny are fertile with one another, that link will be wanting. For, so long, selective breeding will not be proved to be competent to do all that is required of it to produce natural species.

I have put this conclusion as strongly as possible before the reader, because the last position in which I wish to find myself is that of an advocate for Mr. Darwin's, or any other views—if by an advocate is meant one whose business it is to smooth over real difficulties, and to persuade where he cannot convince.

In justice to Mr. Darwin, however, it must be admitted that the conditions of fertility and sterility are very ill understood, and that every day's advance in knowledge leads us to regard the hiatus in his evidence as of less and less importance, when set against the multitude of facts which harmonize with, or receive an explanation from, his doctrines.

I adopt Mr. Darwin's hypothesis, therefore, subject to the production of proof that physiological species may be produced by selective breeding; just as a physical philosopher may accept the undulatory theory of light, subject to the proof of the existence of the hypothetical ether; or as the chemist adopts the atomic theory, subject to the proof of the existence of atoms; and for exactly the same reasons, namely, that it has an immense amount of primâ facie probability; that it is the only means at present within reach of reducing the chaos of observed facts to order; and lastly, that it is the most powerful instrument of investigation which has been presented to naturalists since the invention of the natural system of classification, and the commencement of the systematic study of embryology.

But even leaving Mr. Darwin's views aside, the whole analogy of natural operations furnishes so complete and crushing an argument against the intervention of any but what are termed secondary causes, in the production of all the phenomena of the universe; that, in view of the intimate relations between Man and the rest of the living world; and between the forces exerted by the latter and all other forces, I can see no excuse for doubting that all are co-ordinated terms of Nature's great progression, from the formless to the formed—from the inorganic to the organic—from blind force to conscious intellect and will.

Science has fulfilled her function when she has ascertained and enunciated truth; and were these pages addressed to men of science only, I should now close this essay, knowing that my colleagues have learned to respect nothing but evidence, and to believe that their highest duty lies in submitting to it, however it may jar against their inclinations.

But desiring, as I do, to reach the wider circle of the intelligent public, it would be unworthy cowardice were I to ignore the repugnance with which the majority of my readers are likely to meet the conclusions to which the most careful and conscientious study I have been able to give to this matter, has led me.

On all sides I shall hear the cry—"We are men and women, not a mere better sort of apes, a little longer in the leg, more compact in the foot, and bigger in brain than your brutal Chimpanzees and Gorillas. The power of knowledge—the conscience of good and evil—the pitiful tenderness of human affections, raise us out of all real fellowship with the brutes, however closely they may seem to approximate us."

To this I can only reply that the exclamation would be most just and would have my own entire sympathy, if it were only relevant. But, it is not I who seek to base Man's dignity upon his great toe, or insinuate that we are lost if an Ape has a hippocampus minor. On the contrary, I have done my best to sweep away this vanity. I have endeavoured to show that no absolute structural line of demarcation, wider than that between the animals which immediately succeed us in the scale, can be drawn between the animal world and ourselves; and I may add the expression of my belief that the attempt to draw a psychical distinction is equally futile, and that even the highest faculties of feeling and of intellect begin to germinate in lower forms of life.[1] At the same time, no one is more strongly convinced than I am of the vastness of the gulf between civilized man and the brutes; or is more certain that whether *from* them or not, he is assuredly not *of* them. No one is less disposed to think lightly of the present dignity, or despairingly of the future hopes, of the only consciously intelligent denizen of this world.

We are indeed told by those who assume authority in these matters, that the two sets of opinions are incompatible, and that the belief in the unity of origin of man and

---

[1] It is so rare a pleasure for me to find Professor Owen's opinions in entire accordance with my own, that I cannot forbear from quoting a paragraph which appeared in his Essay "On the Characters, &c., of the Class Mammalia," in the 'Journal of the Proceedings of the Linnean Society of London' for 1857, but is unaccountably omitted in the "Reade Lecture" delivered before the University of Cambridge two years later, which is otherwise nearly a reprint of the paper in question. Prof. Owen writes:

"Not being able to appreciate or conceive of the distinction between the psychical phenomena of a Chimpanzee and of a Boschisman or of an Aztec, with arrested brain growth, as being of a nature so essential as to preclude a comparison between them, or as being other than a difference of degree, I cannot shut my eyes to the significance of that all-pervading similitude of structure—every tooth, every bone, strictly homologous—which makes the determination of the difference between *Homo* and *Pithecus* the anatomist's difficulty."

Surely it is a little singular that the 'anatomist,' who finds it 'difficult' to 'determine the difference' between *Homo* and *Pithecus*, should yet range them on anatomical grounds, in distinct sub-classes !

brutes involves the brutalization and degradation of the former. But is this really so? Could not a sensible child confute, by obvious arguments, the shallow rhetoricians who would force this conclusion upon us? Is it, indeed, true, that the Poet, or the Philosopher, or the Artist whose genius is the glory of his age, is degraded from his high estate by the undoubted historical probability, not to say certainty, that he is the direct descendant of some naked and bestial savage, whose intelligence was just sufficient to make him a little more cunning than the Fox, and by so much more dangerous than the Tiger? Or is he bound to howl and grovel on all fours because of the wholly unquestionable fact, that he was once an egg, which no ordinary power of discrimination could distinguish from that of a Dog? Or is the philanthropist or the saint to give up his endeavours to lead a noble life, because the simplest study of man's nature reveals, at its foundations, all the selfish passions and fierce appetites of the merest quadruped? Is mother-love vile because a hen shows it, or fidelity base because dogs possess it?

The common sense of the mass of mankind will answer these questions without a moment's hesitation. Healthy humanity, finding itself hard pressed to escape from real sin and degradation, will leave the brooding over speculative pollution to the cynics and the 'righteous overmuch' who, disagreeing in everything else, unite in blind insensibility to the nobleness of the visible world, and in inability to appreciate the grandeur of the place Man occupies therein.

Nay more, thoughtful men, once escaped from the blinding influences of traditional prejudice, will find in the lowly stock whence man has sprung, the best evidence of the splendour of his capacities; and will discern in his long progress through the Past, a reasonable ground of faith in his attainment of a nobler Future.

They will remember that in comparing civilized man with the animal world, one is as the Alpine traveller, who sees the mountains soaring into the sky and can hardly discern where the deep shadowed crags and roseate peaks end, and where the clouds of heaven begin. Surely the

awe-struck voyager may be excused if, at first, he refuses
to believe the geologist, who tells him that these glorious
masses are, after all, the hardened mud of primeval seas,
or the cooled slag of subterranean furnaces—of one substance with the dullest clay, but raised by inward forces
to that place of proud and seemingly inaccessible glory.

But the geologist is right ; and due reflection on his
teachings, instead of diminishing our reverence and our
wonder, adds all the force of intellectual sublimity to the
mere æsthetic intuition of the uninstructed beholder.

And after passion and prejudice have died away, the
same result will attend the teachings of the naturalist
respecting that great Alps and Andes of the living world—
Man. Our reverence for the nobility of manhood will
not be lessened by the knowledge, that Man is, in substance and in structure, one with the brutes ; for, he alone
possesses the marvellous endowment of intelligible and
rational speech, whereby, in the secular period of his
existence, he has slowly accumulated and organized the
experience which is almost wholly lost with the cessation
of every individual life in other animals ; so that now he
stands raised upon it as on a mountain top, far above the
level of his humble fellows, and transfigured from his
grosser nature by reflecting, here and there, a ray from
the infinite source of truth.

A succinct History of the Controversy respecting the Cerebral Structure of Man and the Apes

UP to the year 1857 all anatomists of authority, who had occupied themselves with the cerebral structure of the Apes —Cuvier, Tiedemann, Sandifort, Vrolik, Isidore G. St. Hilaire, Schroeder van der Kolk, Gratiolet—were agreed that the brain of the Apes possesses a POSTERIOR LOBE.

Tiedemann, in 1825, figured and acknowledged in the text of his 'Icones,' the existence of the POSTERIOR CORNU of the lateral ventricle in the Apes, not only under the title of 'Scrobiculus parvus loco cornu posterioris'—a fact which has been paraded—but as 'cornu posterius' (Icones, p. 54), a circumstance which has been, as sedulously, kept in the back ground.

Cuvier (Lecons, T. iii. p. 103) says, "the anterior or lateral ventricles possess a digital cavity [posterior cornu] only in Man and the Apes . . . Its presence depends on that of the posterior lobes."

Schroeder van der Kolk and Vrolik, and Gratiolet, had also figured and described the posterior cornu in various Apes. As to the HIPPOCAMPUS MINOR Tiedemann had erroneously asserted its absence in the Apes ; but Schroeder van der Kolk and Vrolik had pointed out the existence of what they considered a rudimentary one in the Chimpanzee, and Gratiolet had expressly affirmed its existence in these animals. Such was the state of our information on these subjects in the year 1856.

In the year 1857, however, Professor Owen, either in ignorance of these well-known facts or else unjustifiably suppressing them, submitted to the Linnæan Society a paper "On the Characters, Principles of Division, and Primary Groups of the Class Mammalia," which was printed in the Society's Journal, and contains the following passage :—"In Man, the brain presents an ascensive step in development, higher and more strongly marked than that by which the preceding subclass was distinguished from the one below it. Not only do the cerebral hemispheres overlap the olfactory lobes and cerebellum, but they extend in advance of the one and further back than the other. The posterior development is so marked, that anatomists have assigned to that part the character of a third lobe ; *it is peculiar to the genus Homo, and equally peculiar is the posterior horn of the lateral ventricle and the 'hippocampus minor,' which characterise the hind lobe of each hemisphere.*"—*Journal of the Proceedings of the Linnæan Society*, Vol. ii. p. 19.

As the essay in which this passage stands had no less ambitious an aim than the remodelling of the classification of the Mammalia, its author might be supposed to have written under a sense of peculiar responsibility, and to have tested, with especial care, the statements he ventured to promulgate. And even if this be expecting too much, hastiness, or want of opportunity for due deliberation, cannot now be pleaded in extenuation of any shortcomings ; for the propositions cited were repeated two years afterwards in the Reade Lecture, delivered before so grave a body as the University of Cambridge, in 1859.

When the assertions, which I have italicised in the above extract, first came under my notice, I was not a little astonished at so flat a contradiction of the doctrines current among well-informed anatomists ; but, not unnaturally imagining that the deliberate statements of a responsible person must have some foundation in fact, I deemed it my duty to investigate the subject anew before the time at which it would be my business to lecture thereupon came round. The result of my inquiries was to prove that Mr. Owen's three assertions, that "the third lobe, the posterior horn of the lateral ventricle, and the hippocampus minor," are "peculiar to the genus *Homo,*" are contrary to the plainest facts. I communicated this conclusion to the students of my class ; and then, having no desire to embark in a controversy which could not redound to the honour of British science, whatever its issue, I turned to more congenial occupations.

The time speedily arrived, however, when a persistence in this reticence would have involved me in an unworthy paltering with truth.

At the meeting of the British Association at Oxford, in 1860, Professor Owen repeated these assertions in my presence, and, of course, I immediately gave them a direct and unqualified contradiction, pledging myself to justify that unusual procedure elsewhere. I redeemed that pledge by publishing, in the January number of the *Natural History Review* for 1861, an article wherein the truth of the three following propositions was fully demonstrated (*l. c.* p. 71) :—

" 1. That the third lobe is neither peculiar to, nor characteristic of, man seeing that it exists in all the higher quadrumana."

" 2. That the posterior cornu of the lateral ventricle is neither peculiar to, nor characteristic of, man, inasmuch as it also exists in the higher quadrumana."

" 3. That the *hippocampus minor* is neither peculiar to, nor characteristic of, man, as it is found in certain of the higher quadrumana."

Furthermore, this paper contains the following paragraph (p. 76):

"And lastly, Schroeder van der Kolk and Vrolik (op. cit. p. 271), though they particularly note that 'the lateral ventricle is distinguished from that of Man by the very defective proportions of the posterior cornu, wherein only a stripe is visible as an indication of the hippocampus minor;' yet the Figure 4, in their second Plate, shows that this posterior cornu is a perfectly distinct and unmistakeable structure, quite as large as it often is in Man.   It is the more remarkable that Professor Owen should have overlooked the explicit statement and figure of these authors, as it is quite obvious, on comparison of the figures, that his woodcut of the brain of a Chimpanzee (l. c. p. 19) is a reduced copy of the second figure of Messrs. Schroeder van der Kolk and Vrolik's first Plate.

"As M. Gratiolet (l. c. p. 18), however, is careful to remark, 'unfortunately the brain which they have taken as a model was greatly altered (profondément affaissé), whence the general form of the brain is given in these plates in a manner which is altogether incorrect.'   Indeed, it is perfectly obvious, from a comparison of a section of the skull of the Chimpanzee with these figures, that such is the case; and it is greatly to be regretted that so inadequate a figure should have been taken as a typical representation of the Chimpanzee's brain."

From this time forth, the untenability of his position might have been as apparent to Professor Owen as it was to every one else; but, so far from retracting the grave errors into which he had fallen, Professor Owen has persisted in and reiterated them; first, in a lecture delivered before the Royal Institution on the 19th of March, 1861, which is admitted to have been accurately reproduced in the 'Athenæum' for the 23rd of the same month, in a letter addressed by Professor Owen to that journal on the 30th of March. The 'Athenæum' report was accompanied by a diagram purporting to represent a Gorilla's brain, but in reality so extraordinary a misrepresentation, that Professor Owen substantially, though not explicitly, withdraws it in the letter in question.   In amending this error, however, Professor Owen fell into another of much graver import, as his communication concludes with the following paragraph: "For the true proportion in which the cerebrum covers the cerebellum in the highest Apes, reference should be made to the figure of the undissected brain of the Chimpanzee in my 'Reade's

Lecture on the Classification, &c. of the Mammalia,' p. 25, fig. 7, 8vo. 1859."

It would not be credible, if it were not unfortunately true, that this figure, to which the trusting public is referred, without a word of qualification, "for the true proportion in which the cerebrum covers the cerebellum in the highest Apes," is exactly that unacknowledged copy of Schroeder van der Kolk and Vrolik's figure whose utter inaccuracy had been pointed out years before by Gratiolet, and had been brought to Professor Owen's knowledge by myself in the passage of my article in the 'Natural History Review' above quoted.

I drew public attention to this circumstance again in my reply to Professor Owen, published in the 'Athenæum' for April 13th, 1861 ; but the exploded figure was reproduced once more by Professor Owen, without the slightest allusion to its inaccuracy, in the 'Annals of Natural History' for June 1861 !

This proved too much for the patience of the original authors of the figure, Messrs. Schroeder van der Kolk and Vrolik, who, in a note addressed to the Academy of Amsterdam, of which they were members, declared themselves to be, though decided opponents of all forms of the doctrine of progressive development, above all things, lovers of truth : and that, therefore, at whatever risk of seeming to lend support to views which they disliked, they felt it their duty to take the first opportunity of publicly repudiating Professor Owen's misuse of their authority.

In this note they frankly admitted the justice of the criticisms of M. Gratiolet, quoted above, and they illustrated, by new and careful figures, the posterior lobe, the posterior cornu, and the hippocampus minor of the Orang. Furthermore, having demonstrated the parts, at one of the sittings of the Academy, they add, "la présence des parties contestées y a été universellement reconnue par les anatomistes présents à la séance. Le seul doute qui soit resté se rapporte au pes Hippocampi minor. . . . A l'état frais l'indice du petit pied d'Hippocampe était plus prononcé que maintenant."

Professor Owen repeated his erroneous assertions at the meeting of the British Association in 1861, and again, without any obvious necessity, and without adducing a single new fact or new argument, or being able in any way to meet the crushing evidence from original dissections of numerous Apes' brains, which had in the meanwhile been brought forward by Prof. Rolleston,[1] F.R.S., Mr. Marshall,[2] F.R.S.,

[1] On the Affinities of the Brain of the Orang. Nat. Hist. Review, April, 1861.
[2] On the Brain of a young Chimpanzee. Ibid., July, 1861.

Mr. Flower,[1] Mr. Turner,[2] and myself,[3] revived the subject at the Cambridge meeting of the same body in 1862. Not content with the tolerably vigorous repudiation which these unprecedented proceedings met with in Section D, Professor Owen sanctioned the publication of a version of his own statements, accompanied by a strange misrepresentation of mine (as may be seen by comparison of the 'Times' report of the discussion), in the 'Medical Times' for October 11th, 1862. I subjoin the conclusion of my reply in the same journal for October 25th.

" If this were a question of opinion, or a question of interpretation of parts or of terms,—were it even a question of observation in which the testimony of my own senses alone was pitted against that of another person, I should adopt a very different tone in discussing this matter. I should, in all humility, admit the likelihood of having myself erred in judgment, failed in knowledge, or been blinded by prejudice.

" But no one pretends now, that the controversy is one of terms or of opinions. Novel and devoid of authority as some of Professor Owen's proposed definitions may have been, they might be accepted without changing the great features of the case. Hence, though special investigations into these matters have been undertaken during the last two years by Dr. Allen Thomson, by Dr. Rolleston, by Mr. Marshall, and by Mr. Flower, all, as you are aware, anatomists of repute in this country, and by Professors Schroeder Van der Kolk, and Vrolik (whom Professor Owen incautiously tried to press into his own service) on the Continent, all these able and conscientious observers have with one accord testified to the accuracy of my statements, and to the utter baselessness of the assertions of Professor Owen. Even the venerable Rudolph Wagner, whom no man will accuse of progressionist proclivities, has raised his voice on the same side; while not a single anatomist, great or small, has supported Professor Owen.

" Now, I do not mean to suggest that scientific differences should be settled by universal suffrage, but I do conceive that solid proofs must be met by something more than empty and unsupported assertions. Yet during the two years through which this preposterous controversy has dragged its weary

[1] On the Posterior lobes of the Cerebrum of the Quadrumana. Philosophical Transactions, 1862.
[2] On the anatomical Relations of the Surfaces of the Tentorium to the Cerebrum and Cerebellum in Man and the lower Mammals. Proceedings of the Royal Society of Edinburgh, March, 1862.
[3] On the Brain of Ateles. Proceedings of Zoological Society, 1861.

length, Professor Owen has not ventured to bring forward a single preparation in support of his often-repeated assertions.

".The case stands thus, therefore :—Not only are the statements made by me in consonance with the doctrines of the best older authorities, and with those of all recent investigators, but I am quite ready to demonstrate them on the first monkey that comes to hand ; while Professor Owen's assertions are not only in diametrical opposition to both old and new authorities, but he has not produced, and, I will add, cannot produce, a single preparation which justifies them."

I now leave this subject, for the present.—For the credit of my calling I should be glad to be, hereafter, for ever silent upon it.   But, unfortunately, this is a matter upon which, after all that has occurred, no mistake or confusion of terms is possible—and in affirming that the posterior lobe, the posterior cornu, and the hippocampus minor exist in certain Apes, I am stating either that which is true, or that which I must know to be false.   The question has thus become one of personal veracity.   For myself, I will accept no other issue than this, grave as it is, to the present controversy.

III

ON SOME FOSSIL REMAINS OF MAN

I HAVE endeavoured to show, in the preceding Essay, that the ANTHROPINI, or Man Family, form a very well defined group of the Primates, between which and the immediately following Family, the CATARHINI, there is, in the existing world, the same entire absence of any transitional form or connecting link, as between the CATARHINI and PLATYRHINI.

It is a commonly received doctrine, however, that the structural intervals between the various existing modifications of organic beings may be diminished, or even obliterated, if we take into account the long and varied succession of animals and plants which have preceded these now living and which are known to us only by their fossilized remains. How far this doctrine is well based, how far, on the other hand, as our knowledge at present stands, it is an overstatement of the real facts of the case, and an exaggeration of the conclusions fairly deducible from them, are points of grave importance, but into the discussion of which I do not, at present, propose to enter. It is enough that such a view of the relations of extinct to living beings has been propounded, to lead us to inquire, with anxiety, how far the recent discoveries of human remains in a fossil state bear out, or oppose, that view.

I shall confine myself, in discussing this question, to those fragmentary Human skulls from the caves of Engis in the valley of the Meuse, in Belgium, and of the Neanderthal near Düsseldorf, the geological relations of which have been examined with so much care by Sir Charles

Lyell; upon whose high authority I shall take it for granted, that the Engis skull belonged to a contemporary of the Mammoth (*Elephas primigenius*) and of the woolly Rhinoceros (*Rhinocerus tichorhinus*), with the bones of which it was found associated; and that the Neanderthal skull is of great, though uncertain, antiquity. Whatever be the geological age of the latter skull, I conceive it is quite safe (on the ordinary principles of paleontological reasoning) to assume that the former takes us to, at least, the further side of the vague biological limit, which separates the present geological epoch from that which immediately preceded it. And there can be no doubt that the physical geography of Europe has changed wonderfully, since the bones of Men and Mammoths, Hyænas and Rhinoceroses were washed pell-mell into the cave of Engis.

The skull from the cave of Engis was originally discovered by Professor Schmerling, and was described by him, together with other human remains disinterred at the same time, in his valuable work, "Recherches sur les ossemens fossiles découverts dans les cavernes de la Province de Liege," published in 1833 (p. 59, *et seq.*), from which the following paragraphs are extracted, the precise expressions of the author being, as far as possible, preserved.

"In the first place, I must remark that these human remains, which are in my possession, are characterized, like the thousands of bones which I have lately been disinterring, by the extent of the decomposition which they have undergone, which is precisely the same as that of the extinct species: all, with a few exceptions, are broken; some few are rounded, as is frequently found to be the case in fossil remains of other species. The fractures are vertical or oblique; none of them are eroded; their colour does not differ from that of other fossil bones, and varies from whitish yellow to blackish. All are lighter than recent bones, with the exception of those which have a calcareous incrustation, and the cavities of which are filled with such matter.

The cranium which I have caused to be figured, Plate I., figs. 1, 2, is that of an old person. The sutures are beginning to be effaced : all the facial bones are wanting, and of the temporal bones only a fragment of that of the right side is preserved.

The face and the base of the cranium had been detached before the skull was deposited in the cave, for we were unable to find those parts, though the whole cavern

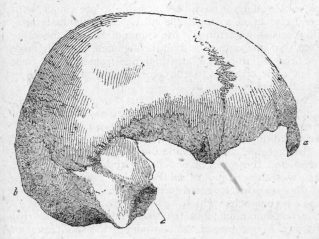

FIG. 22.—The skull from the cave of Engis—viewed from the right side.
a glabella, *b* occipital protuberance, (*a* to *b* glabello-occipital line),
c auditory foramen.

was regularly searched. The cranium was met with at a depth of a metre and a half [five feet nearly] hidden under an osseous breccia, composed of the remains of small animals, and containing one rhinoceros tusk, with several teeth of horses and of ruminants. This breccia, which has been spoken of above (p. 30), was a metre [3¼ feet about] wide, and rose to the height of a metre and a half above the floor of the cavern, to the walls of which it adhered strongly.

The earth which contained this human skull exhibited no trace of disturbance : teeth of rhinoceros, horse, hyæna, and bear, surrounded it on all sides.

The famous Blumenbach[1] has directed attention to the differences presented by the form and the dimensions of human crania of different races. This important work would have assisted us greatly, if the face, a part essential for the determination of race, with more or less accuracy, had not been wanting in our fossil cranium.

We are convinced that even if the skull had been complete, it would not have been possible to pronounce, with certainty, upon a single specimen; for individual variations are so numerous in the crania of one and the same race, that one cannot, without laying oneself open to large chances of error, draw any inference from a single fragment of a cranium to the general form of the head to which it belonged.

Nevertheless, in order to neglect no point respecting the form of this fossil skull, we may observe that, from the first, the elongated and narrow form of the forehead attracted our attention.

In fact, the slight elevation of the frontal, its narrowness, and the form of the orbit, approximate it more nearly to the cranium of an Ethiopian than to that of an European: the elongated form and the produced occiput are also characters which we believe to be observable in our fossil cranium; but to remove all doubt upon that subject I have caused the contours of the cranium of an European and of an Ethiopian to be drawn and the foreheads represented. Plate II., Figs. 1 and 2, and, in the same plate, Figs. 3 and 4, will render the differences easily distinguishable; and a single glance at the figures, will be more instructive than a long and wearisome description.

At whatever conclusion we may arrive as to the origin of the man from whence this fossil skull proceeded, we may express an opinion without exposing ourselves to a fruitless controversy. Each may adopt the hypothesis which seems to him most probable : for my own part, I hold it to be demonstrated that this cranium has belonged to a person of limited intellectual faculties, and we con-

---

[1] Decas Collectionis suæ craniorum diversarum gentium illustrata. Gottingæ, 1790–1820.

clude thence that it belonged to a man of a low degree of civilization : a deduction which is borne out by contrasting the capacity of the frontal with that of the occipital region.

Another cranium of a young individual was discovered in the floor of the cavern beside the tooth of an elephant ; the skull was entire when found, but the moment it was lifted it fell into pieces, which I have not, as yet, been able to put together again. But I have represented the bones of the upper jaw, Plate I., Fig. 5. The state of the alveoli and the teeth, shows that the molars had not yet pierced the gum. Detached milk molars and some fragments of a human skull, proceed from this same place. The Figure 3, represents a human superior incisor tooth, the size of which is truly remarkable.[1]

Figure 4 is a fragment of a superior maxillary bone, the molar teeth of which are worn down to the roots.

I possess two vertebræ, a first and last dorsal.

A clavicle of the left side (see Plate III., Fig. 1); although it belonged to a young individual, this bone shows that he must have been of great stature.[2]

Two fragments of the radius, badly preserved, do not indicate that the height of the man, to whom they belonged, exceeded five feet and a half.

As to the remains of the upper extremities, those which are in my possession, consist merely of a fragment of an ulna and of a radius (Plate III., Fig. 5 and 6).

Figure 2, Plate IV., represents a metacarpal bone, contained in the breccia, of which we have spoken ; it was found in the lower part above the cranium : add to this some metacarpal bones, found at very different distances, half-a-dozen metatarsals, three phalanges of the hand, and one of the foot.

---

[1] In a subsequent passage, Schmerling remarks upon the occurrence of an incisor tooth ' of enormous size' from the caverns of Engihoul. The tooth figured is somewhat long, but its dimensions do not appear to me to be otherwise remarkable.

[2] The figure of this clavicle measures 5 inches from end to end in a straight line—so that the bone is rather a small than a large one.

This is a brief enumeration of the remains of human bones collected in the cavern of Engis, which has preserved for us the remains of three individuals, surrounded by those of the Elephant, of the Rhinoceros, and of Carnivora of species unknown in the present creation."

From the cave of Engihoul, opposite that of Engis, on the right bank of the Meuse, Schmerling obtained the remains of three other individuals of Man, among which were only two fragments of parietal bones, but many bones of the extremities. In one case, a broken fragment of an ulna was soldered to a like fragment of a radius by stalagmite, a condition frequently observed among the bones of the Cave Bear (*Ursus spelæus*), found in the Belgian caverns.

It was in the cavern of Engis that Professor Schmerling found, incrusted with stalagmite and joined to a stone, the pointed bone implement, which he has figured in Fig. 7 of his Plate XXXVI., and worked flints were found by him in all those Belgian caves, which contained an abundance of fossil bones.

A short letter from M. Geoffroy St. Hilaire, published in the Comptes Rendus of the Academy of Sciences of Paris, for July 2nd, 1838, speaks of a visit (and apparently a very hasty one) paid to the collection of Professor 'Schermidt' (which is presumably a misprint for Schmerling) at Liège. The writer briefly criticises the drawings which illustrate Schmerling's work, and affirms that the "human cranium is a little longer than it is represented" in Schmerling's figure. The only other remark worth quoting is this :—" The aspect of the human bones differs little from that of the cave bones, with which we are familiar, and of which there is a considerable collection in the same place. With respect to their special forms, compared with those of the varieties of recent human crania, few *certain* conclusions can be put forward ; for much greater differences exist between the different specimens of well-characterized varieties, than between the fossil cranium of Liège and that of one of those varieties selected as a term of comparison."

Geoffroy St. Hilaire's remarks are, it will be observed,

little but an echo of the philosophic doubts of the describer and discoverer of the remains. As to the critique upon Schmerling's figures, I find that the side view given by the latter is really about $\frac{3}{10}$ths of an inch shorter than the original, and that the front view is diminished to about the same extent. Otherwise the representation is not, in any way, inaccurate, but corresponds very well with the cast which is in my possession.

A piece of the occipital bone, which Schmerling seems to have missed, has since been fitted on to the rest of the cranium by an accomplished anatomist, Dr. Spring of Liège, under whose direction an excellent plaster cast was made for Sir Charles Lyell. It is upon and from a duplicate of that cast that my own observations and the accompanying figures, the outlines of which are copied from very accurate Camera lucida drawings, by my friend Mr. Busk, reduced to one-half of the natural size, are made.

As Professor Schmerling observes, the base of the skull is destroyed, and the facial bones are entirely absent; but the roof of the cranium, consisting of the frontal, parietal, and the greater part of the occipital bones, as far as the middle of the occipital foramen, is entire or nearly so. The left temporal bone is wanting. Of the right temporal, the parts in the immediate neighbourhood of the auditory foramen, the mastoid process, and a considerable portion of the squamous element of the temporal are well preserved (Fig. 22).

The lines of fracture which remain between the coadjusted pieces of the skull, and are faithfully displayed in Schmerling's figure, are readily traceable in the cast. The sutures are also discernible, but the complex disposition of their serrations, shown in the figure, is not obvious in the cast. Though the ridges which give attachment to muscles are not excessively prominent, they are well marked, and taken together with the apparently well developed frontal sinuses, and the condition of the sutures, leave no doubt on my mind that the skull is that of an adult, if not middle-aged man.

The extreme length of the skull is 7.7 inches. Its

extreme breadth, which corresponds very nearly with the interval between the parietal protuberances, is not more than 5.4 inches. The proportion of the length to the breadth is therefore very nearly as 100 to 70. If a line be drawn from the point at which the brow curves in towards the root of the nose, and which is called the 'glabella' (*a*), (Fig. 22), to the occipital protuberance (*b*), and the distance to the highest point of the arch of the skull be measured perpendicularly from this line, it will be found to be 4.75 inches. Viewed from above, Fig. 23, A, the forehead presents an evenly rounded curve, and passes into the contour of the sides and back of the skull, which describes a tolerably regular elliptical curve.

The front view (Fig. 23, B) shows that the roof of the skull was very regularly and elegantly arched in the transverse direction, and that the transverse diameter was a little less below the parietal protuberances, than above them. The forehead cannot be called narrow in relation to the rest of the skull, nor can it be called a retreating forehead; on the contrary, the antero-posterior contour of the skull is well arched, so that the distance along that contour, from the nasal depression to the occipital protuberance, measures about 13.75 inches. The transverse arc of the skull, measured from one auditory foramen to the other, across the middle of the sagittal suture, is about 13 inches. The sagittal suture itself is 5.5 inches long.

The supraciliary prominences or brow-ridges (on each side of *a*, Fig. 22) are well, but not excessively, developed, and are separated by a median depression. Their principal elevation is disposed so obliquely that I judge them to be due to large frontal sinuses.

If a line joining the glabella and the occipital protuberance (*a, b,* Fig. 22) be made horizontal, no part of the occipital region projects more than $\frac{1}{10}$th of an inch behind the posterior extremity of that line, and the upper edge of the auditory foramen (*c*) is almost in contact with a line drawn parallel with this upon the outer surface of the skull.

A transverse line drawn from one auditory foramen to the other traverses, as usual, the forepart of the occipital

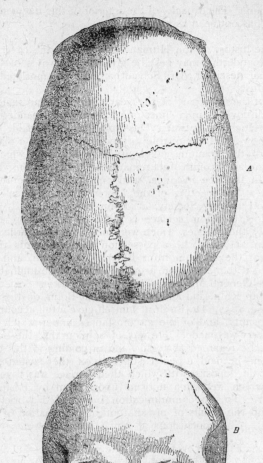

FIG. 23.—The Engis skull viewed from above (*A*) and in front (*B*).

foramen. The capacity of the interior of this fragmentary skull has not been ascertained.

The history of the Human remains from the cavern in the Neanderthal may best be given in the words of their original describer, Dr. Schaaffhausen,[1] as translated by Mr. Busk.

"In the early part of the year 1857, a human skeleton was discovered in a limestone cave in the Neanderthal, near Hochdal, between Düsseldorf and Elberfeld. Of this, however, I was unable to procure more than a plaster cast of the cranium, taken at Elberfeld, from which I drew up an account of its remarkable conformation, which was, in the first instance, read on the 4th of February, 1857, at the meeting of the Lower Rhine Medical and Natural History Society, at Bonn.[2] Subsequently Dr. Fuhlrott, to whom science is indebted for the preservation of these bones, which were not at first regarded as human, and into whose possession they afterwards came, brought the cranium from Elberfeld to Bonn, and entrusted it to me for more accurate anatomical examination. At the General Meeting of the Natural History Society of Prussian Rhineland and Westphalia, at Bonn, on the 2nd of June, 1857,[3] Dr. Fuhlrott himself gave a full account of the locality, and of the circumstances under which the discovery was made. He was of opinion that the bones might be regarded as fossil; and in coming to this conclusion, he laid especial stress upon the existence of dendritic deposits, with which their surface was covered, and which were first noticed upon them by Professor Mayer. To this communication I appended a brief report on the results of my anatomical examination of the bones. The conclusions at which I arrived were :—1st.

[1] ON THE CRANIA OF THE MOST ANCIENT RACES OF MAN. By Professor D. Schaaffhausen, of Bonn. (From Müller's Archiv., 1858, pp. 453.) With Remarks, and original Figures, taken from a Cast of the Neanderthal Cranium. By George Busk, F.R.S., &c. Natural History Review, April, 1861.

[2] Verhandl. d. Naturhist. Vereins der preuss. Rheinlande und Westphalens., xiv. Bonn, 1857.

[3] Ib. Correspondenzblatt. No. 2.

That the extraordinary form of the skull was due to a natural conformation hitherto not known to exist, even in the most barbarous races. 2nd. That these remarkable human remains belonged to a period antecedent to the time of the Celts and Germans, and were in all probability derived from one of the wild races of North-western Europe, spoken of by Latin writers; and which were encountered as autochthones by the German immigrants. And 3rdly. That it was beyond doubt that these human relics were traceable to a period at which the latest animals of the diluvium still existed; but that no proof of this assumption, nor consequently of their so-termed *fossil* condition, was afforded by the circumstances under which the bones were discovered.

As Dr. Fuhlrott has not yet published his description of these circumstances, I borrow the following account of them from one of his letters. "A small cave or grotto, high enough to admit a man, and about 15 feet deep from the entrance, which is 7 or 8 feet wide, exists in the southern wall of the gorge of the Neanderthal, as it is termed, at a distance of about 100 feet from the Düssel, and about 60 feet above the bottom of the valley. In its earlier and uninjured condition, this cavern opened upon a narrow plateau lying in front of it, and from which the rocky wall descended almost perpendicularly into the river. It could be reached, though with difficulty, from above. The uneven floor was covered to a thickness of 4 or 5 feet with a deposit of mud, sparingly intermixed with rounded fragments of chert. In the removing of this deposit, the bones were discovered. The skull was first noticed, placed nearest to the entrance of the cavern; and further in, the other bones, lying in the same horizontal plane. Of this I was assured, in the most positive terms, by two labourers who were employed to clear out the grotto, and who were questioned by me on the spot. At first no idea was entertained of the bones being human; and it was not till several weeks after their discovery that they were recognised as such by me, and placed in security. But, as the importance of the discovery was not at the time perceived, the labourers were very careless in the collecting, and secured chiefly only the larger bones ; and to this circumstance it may be attributed that fragments merely of the probably perfect skeleton came into my possession."

"My anatomical examination of these bones afforded the following results :—

The cranium is of unusual size, and of a long elliptical form. A most remarkable peculiarity is at once obvious in the extraordinary development of the frontal sinuses, owing to which the superciliary ridges, which coalesce completely in the middle, are rendered so prominent, that the frontal bone exhibits a considerable hollow or depression above, or rather behind them, whilst a deep depression is also formed in the situation of the root of the nose. The forehead is narrow and low, though the middle and hinder portions of the cranial arch are well developed. Unfortunately, the fragment of the skull that has been preserved consists only of the portion situated above the roof of the orbits and the superior occipital ridges, which are greatly developed, and almost conjoined so as to form a horizontal eminence. It includes almost the whole of the frontal bone, both parietals, a small part of the squamous and the upper-third of the occipital. The recently fractured surfaces show that the skull was broken at the time of its disinterment. The cavity holds 16,876 grains of water, whence its cubical contents may be estimated at 57.64 inches, or 1033.24 cubic centimetres. In making this estimation, the water is supposed to stand on a level with the orbital plate of the frontal, with the deepest notch in the squamous margin of the parietal, and with the superior semicircular ridges of the occipital. Estimated in dried millet-seed, the contents equalled 31 ounces, Prussian Apothecaries' weight. The semicircular line indicating the upper boundary of the attachment of the temporal muscle, though not very strongly marked, ascends nevertheless to more than half the height of the parietal bone. On the right superciliary ridge is observable an oblique furrow or depression, indicative of an injury received during life.[1] The coronal and sagittal sutures are on the exterior nearly closed,

---

[1] This, Mr. Busk has pointed out, is probably the notch for the frontal nerve.

and on the inside so completely ossified as to have left
no traces whatever, whilst the lambdoidal remains quite
open. The depressions for the Pacchionian glands are
deep and numerous; and there is an unusually deep
vascular groove immediately behind the coronal suture,
which, as it terminates in a foramen, no doubt transmitted
a *vena emissaria*. The course of the frontal suture is
indicated externally by a slight ridge; and where it joins
the coronal, this ridge rises into a small protuberance.
The course of the sagittal suture is grooved, and above
the angle of the occipital bone the parietals are depressed.

mm.[1]

The length of the skull from the nasal process of the frontal over the vertex to the superior semicircular lines of the occipital measures	303 (300) = 12.0″.
Circumference over the orbital ridges and the superior semicircular lines of the occipital	590 (590) = 23.37″ or 23″.
Width of the frontal from the middle of the temporal line on one side to the same point on the opposite . .	104 (114) = 4.1″—4.5″.
Length of the frontal from the nasal process to the coronal suture . . .	133 (125) = 5.25″—5″.
Extreme width of the frontal sinuses .	25 (23) = 1.0″—0.9″.
Vertical height above a line joining the deepest notches in the squamous border of the parietals	70 = 2.75″.
Width of hinder part of skull from one parietal protuberance to the other . .	138 (150) = 5.4″—5.9″.
Distance from the upper angle of the occipital to the superior semicircular lines	51 (60) = 1.9″—2.4″.
Thickness of the bone at the parietal protuberance	8.
—— at the angle of the occipital . .	9.
—— at the superior semicircular line of the occipital	10 = 0.3″.

[1] The numbers in brackets are those which I should assign to the
different measures, as taken from the plaster cast.—G. B.

Besides the cranium, the following bones have been secured :—

1. Both thigh-bones, perfect. These, like the skull, and all the other bones, are characterized by their unusual thickness, and the great development of all the elevations and depressions for the attachment of muscles. In the Anatomical Museum at Bonn, under the designation of "Giant's-bones," are some recent thigh-bones, with which in thickness the foregoing pretty nearly correspond, although they are shorter.

	Giant's bones. mm.	Fossil bones. mm.
Length	542 = 21.4"	...438 = 17.4"
Diameter of head of femur .	54 = 2.14"...	53 = 2.0"
,, of lower articular end, from one condyle to the other .	89 = 3.5" ...	87 = 3.4"
Diameter of femur in the middle .	33 = 1.2" ...	30 = 1.1"

2. A perfect right humerus, whose size shows that it belongs to the thigh-bones.

	mm.
Length	312 = 12.3"
Thickness in the middle	26 = 1.0"
Diameter of head	49 = 1.9"

Also a perfect right radius of corresponding dimensions, and the upper-third of a right ulna corresponding to the humerus and radius.

3. A left humerus, of which the upper-third is wanting, and which is so much slenderer than the right as apparently to belong to a distinct individual; a left *ulna*, which, though complete, is pathologically deformed, the coronoid process being so much enlarged by bony growth, that flexure of the elbow beyond a right angle must have been impossible; the anterior fossa of the humerus for the reception of the coronoid process being also filled up with a similar bony growth. At the same time, the olecranon is curved strongly downwards. As the bone presents no sign of rachitic degeneration, it may be supposed that an injury sustained during life was the cause of the anchylosis. When the left ulna is compared with

the right radius, it might at first sight be concluded that the bones respectively belonged to different individuals, the ulna being more than half an inch too short for articulation with a corresponding radius. But it is clear that this shortening, as well as the attenuation of the left humerus, are both consequent upon the pathological condition above described.

4. A left *ilium*, almost perfect, and belonging to the femur; a fragment of the right *scapula;* the anterior extremity of a rib of the right side; and the same part of a rib of the left side; the hinder part of a rib of the right side; and, lastly, two hinder portions and one middle portion of ribs, which, from their unusually rounded shape, and abrupt curvature, more resemble the ribs of a carnivorous animal than those of a man. Dr. H. v. Meyer, however, to whose judgment I defer, will not venture to declare them to be ribs of any animal; and it only remains to suppose that this abnormal condition has arisen from an unusually powerful development of the thoracic muscles.

The bones adhere strongly to the tongue, although, as proved by the use of hydrochloric acid, the greater part of the cartilage is still retained in them, which appears, however, to have undergone that transformation into gelatine which has been observed by v. Bibra in fossil bones. The surface of all the bones is in many spots covered with minute black specks, which, more especially under a lens, are seen to be formed of very delicate *dendrites*. These deposits, which were first observed on the bones by Dr. Meyer, are most distinct on the inner surface of the cranial bones. They consist of a ferruginous compound, and, from their black colour, may be supposed to contain manganese. Similar dendritic formations also occur, not unfrequently, on laminated rocks, and are usually found in minute fissures and cracks. At the meeting of the Lower Rhine Society at Bonn, on the 1st April, 1857, Prof. Meyer stated that he had noticed in the museum of Poppelsdorf similar dendritic crystallizations on several fossil bones of animals, and particularly on those of *Ursus spelæus*, but still more abundantly and beautifully displayed on the fossil bones and teeth of *Equus adamiticus, Elephas primigenius*, &c., from the caves of Bolve and Sundwig. Faint indications of similar *dendrites* were visible in a Roman skull from Siegburg; whilst other ancient skulls, which had lain for centuries in the earth, presented no trace of them.[1] I am indebted to H. v. Meyer for the following remarks on this subject:—

"The incipient formation of dendritic deposits, which were formerly regarded as a sign of a truly fossil condition, is interesting. It has even been supposed that in diluvial deposits the presence of *dendrites* might be regarded as affording a certain mark of distinction between bones mixed with the diluvium at a somewhat later period and the true diluvial relics, to which alone it was supposed that these deposits were confined. But I have long been convinced that neither can the absence of *dendrites* be regarded as indicative of recent age, nor their presence as sufficient to establish the great antiquity of the objects upon which they occur. I have myself noticed upon paper, which could scarcely be more than a year old, dendritic deposits, which could not be distinguished from those on fossil bones. Thus I possess a dog's skull from the Roman colony of the neighbouring Heddersheim, *Castrum Hadrianum*, which is in no way distinguishable from the fossil bones from the Frankish caves; it presents the same colour, and adheres to the tongue just as they do; so that this character also, which, at a former meeting of German naturalists at Bonn, gave rise to amusing scenes between Buckland and Schmerling, is no longer of any value. In disputed cases, therefore, the condition of the bone can scarcely afford the means for determining with certainty whether it be fossil, that is to say, whether it belong to geological antiquity or to the historical period."

As we cannot now look upon the primitive world as representing a wholly different condition of things, from which no transition exists to the organic life of the present time, the designation of *fossil*, as applied to *a bone*, has no longer the sense it conveyed in the time of Cuvier. Sufficient grounds exist for the assumption that man

[1] Verh. des Naturhist. Vereins in Bonn, xiv. 1857.

coexisted with the animals found in the *diluvium;* and many a barbarous race may, before all historical time, have disappeared, together with the animals of the ancient world, whilst the races whose organization is improved have continued the genus. The bones which form the subject of this paper present characters which, although not decisive as regards a geological epoch, are, nevertheless, such as indicate a very high antiquity. It may also be remarked that, common as is the occurrence of diluvial animal bones in the muddy deposits of caverns, such remains have not hitherto been met with in the caves of the Neanderthal; and that the bones, which were covered by a deposit of mud not more than four or five feet thick, and without any protective covering of stalagmite, have retained the greatest part of their organic substance.

These circumstances might be adduced against the probability of a geological antiquity. Nor should we be justified in regarding the cranial conformation as perhaps representing the most savage primitive type of the human race, since crania exist among living savages, which, though not exhibiting such a remarkable conformation of the forehead, which gives the skull somewhat the aspect of that of the large apes, still in other respects, as for instance in the greater depth of the temporal fossæ, the crest-like, prominent temporal ridges, and a generally less capacious cranial cavity, exhibit an equally low stage of development. There is no reason for supposing that the deep frontal hollow is due to any artificial flattening, such as is practised in various modes by barbarous nations in the Old and New World. The skull is quite symmetrical, and shows no indication of counter-pressure at the occiput, whilst, according to Morton, in the Flat-heads of the Columbia, the frontal and parietal bones are always unsymmetrical. Its conformation exhibits the sparing development of the anterior part of the head which has been so often observed in very ancient crania, and affords one of the most striking proofs of the influence of culture and civilization on the form of the human skull."

In a subsequent passage, Dr. Schaaffhausen remarks:

"There is no reason whatever for regarding the unusual

development of the frontal sinuses in the remarkable skull from the Neanderthal as an individual or pathological deformity; it is unquestionably a typical race-character, and is physiologically connected with the uncommon thickness of the other bones of the skeleton, which exceeds by about one-half the usual proportions. This expansion of the frontal sinuses, which are appendages of the air-passages, also indicates an unusual force and power of endurance in the movements of the body, as may be concluded from the size of all the ridges and processes for the attachment of the muscles or bones. That this conclusion may be drawn from the existence of large frontal sinuses, and a prominence of the lower frontal region, is confirmed in many ways by other observations. By the same characters, according to Pallas, the wild horse is distinguished from the domesticated, and, according to Cuvier, the fossil cave-bear from every recent species of bear, whilst, according to Roulin, the pig, which has become wild in America, and regained a resemblance to the wild boar, is thus distinguished from the same animal in the domesticated state, as is the chamois from the goat; and, lastly, the bull-dog, which is characterised by its large bones and strongly-developed muscles from every other kind of dog. The estimation of the facial angle, the determination of which, according to Professor Owen, is also difficult in the great apes, owing to the very prominent supra-orbital ridges, in the present case is rendered still more difficult from the absence both of the auditory opening and of the nasal spine. But if the proper horizontal position of the skull be taken from the remaining portions of the orbital plates, and the ascending line made to touch the surface of the frontal bone behind the prominent supra-orbital ridges, the facial angle is not found to exceed 56°.[1] Unfortunately, no portions of the facial bones, whose conformation is so decisive as regards the form and expression of the head, have been preserved. The cranial capacity, compared with the uncommon strength of the corporeal frame, would seem to indicate a small cerebral develop-

[1] Estimating the facial angle in the way suggested, on the cast I should place it at 64° to 67°.—G. B.

ment. The skull, as it is, holds about 31 ounces of millet-seed; and as, from the proportionate size of the wanting bones, the whole cranial cavity should have about 6 ounces more added, the contents, were it perfect, may be taken at 37 ounces. Tiedemann assigns, as the cranial contents in the Negro, 40, 38, and 35 ounces. The cranium holds rather more than 36 ounces of water, which corresponds to a capacity of 1033.24 cubic centimetres. Huschke estimates the cranial contents of a Negress at 1127 cubic centimetres; of an old Negro at 1146 cubic centimetres. The capacity of the Malay skulls, estimated by water, equalled 36, 33 ounces, whilst in the diminutive Hindoos it falls to as little as 27 ounces."

After comparing the Neanderthal cranium with many others, ancient and modern, Professor Schaaffhausen concludes thus:—

"But the human bones and cranium from the Neanderthal exceed all the rest in those peculiarities of conformation which lead to the conclusion of their belonging to a barbarous and savage race. Whether the cavern in which they were found, unaccompanied with any trace of human art, were the place of their interment, or whether, like the bones of extinct animals elsewhere, they had been washed into it, they may still be regarded as the most ancient memorial of the early inhabitants of Europe."

Mr. Busk, the translator of Dr. Schaaffhausen's paper, has enabled us to form a very vivid conception of the degraded character of the Neanderthal skull, by placing side by side with its outline, that of the skull of a Chimpanzee, drawn to the same absolute size.

Some time after the publication of the translation of Professor Schaaffhausen's Memoir, I was led to study the cast of the Neanderthal cranium with more attention than I had previously bestowed upon it, in consequence of wishing to supply Sir Charles Lyell with a diagram, exhibiting the special peculiarities of this skull, as compared with other human skulls. In order to do this it was necessary to identify, with precision, those points in the skulls compared which corresponded anatomically. Of these points, the glabella was obvious enough; but when I had distinguished another, defined by the occipital protuberance and superior semicircular line, and had placed the outline of the Neanderthal skull against that of the Engis skull, in such a position that the glabella and occipital protuberance of both were intersected by the same straight line, the difference was so vast and the flattening of the Neanderthal skull so prodigious (compare Figs. 22 and 24, A), that I at first imagined I must have fallen into some error. And I was the more inclined to suspect this, as, in ordinary human skulls, the occipital protuberance and superior semicircular curved line on the exterior of the occiput correspond pretty closely with the 'lateral sinuses' and the line of attachment of the tentorium internally. But on the tentorium rests, as I have said in the preceding Essay, the posterior lobe of the brain; and hence, the occipital protuberance, and the curved line in question, indicate, approximately, the lower limits of that lobe. Was it possible for a human being to have the brain thus flattened and depressed; or, on the other hand, had the muscular ridges shifted their position? In order to solve these doubts, and to decide the question whether the great supraciliary projections did, or did not, arise from the development of the frontal sinuses, I requested Sir Charles Lyell to be so good as to obtain for me from Dr. Fuhlrott, the possessor of the skull, answers to certain queries, and if possible a cast, or at any rate drawings, or photographs, of the interior of the skull.

Dr. Fuhlrott replied, with a courtesy and readiness for which I am infinitely indebted to him, to my inquiries, and furthermore sent three excellent photographs. One of these gives a side view of the skull, and from it Fig. 24, A. has been shaded. The second (Fig. 25, A.) exhibits the wide openings of the frontal sinuses upon the inferior surface of the frontal part of the skull, into which, Dr. Fuhlrott writes, "a probe may be introduced to the depth of an inch," and demonstrates the great extension of the thickened supraciliary ridges beyond the cerebral cavity. The third, lastly (Fig. 25, B.), exhibits the edge and the

On Some Fossil Remains of Man 131

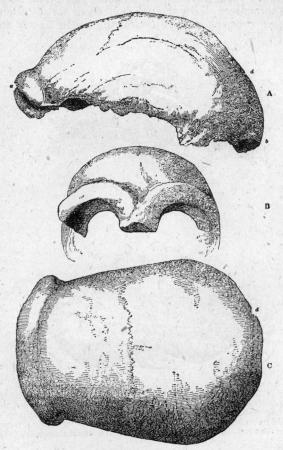

FIG. 24.—The skull from the Neanderthal cavern. A. side, B. front, and C. top view. One-third the natural size. The outlines from camera lucida drawings, one-half the natural size, by Mr. Busk: the details from the cast and from Dr. Fuhlrott's photographs. *a* glabella; *b* occipital protuberance; *d* lambdoidal suture.

interior of the posterior, or occipital, part of the skull, and shows very clearly the two depressions for the lateral sinuses, sweeping inwards towards the middle line of the

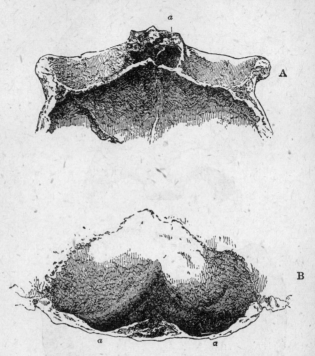

FIG. 25.—Drawings from Dr. Fuhlrott's photographs of parts of the interior of the Neanderthal cranium. A. view of the under and inner surface of the frontal region, showing the inferior apertures of the frontal sinuses (*a*). B. corresponding view of the occipital region of the skull, showing the impressions of the lateral sinuses (*a a*).

roof of the skull, to form the longitudinal sinus. It was clear, therefore, that I had not erred in my interpretation, and that the posterior lobe of the brain of the Neanderthal man must have been as much flattened as I suspected it to be.

In truth, the Neanderthal cranium has most extra-ordinary characters. It has an extreme length of 8 inches, while its breadth is only 5.75 inches, or, in other words, its length is to its breadth as 100 : 72. It is exceedingly depressed, measuring only about 3.4 inches from the glabello-occipital line to the vertex. The longitudinal arc, measured in the same way as in the Engis skull, is 12 inches; the transverse arc cannot be exactly ascertained, in consequence of the absence of the temporal bones, but was probably about the same, and certainly exceeded $10\frac{1}{4}$ inches. The horizontal circumference is 23 inches. But this great circumference arises largely from the vast development of the supraciliary ridges, though the perimeter of the brain case itself is not small. The large supraciliary ridges give the forehead a far more retreating appearance than its internal contour would bear out.

To an anatomical eye the posterior part of the skull is even more striking than the anterior. The occipital protuberance occupies the extreme posterior end of the skull, when the glabello-occipital line is made horizontal, and so far from any part of the occipital region extending beyond it, this region of the skull slopes obliquely upward and forward, so that the lambdoidal suture is situated well upon the upper surface of the cranium. At the same time, notwithstanding the great length of the skull, the sagittal suture is remarkably short ($4\frac{1}{2}$ inches), and the squamosal suture is very straight.

In reply to my questions Dr. Fuhlrott writes that the occipital bone "is in a state of perfect preservation as far as the upper semicircular line, which is a very strong ridge, linear at its extremities, but enlarging towards the middle, where it forms two ridges (bourrelets), united by a linear continuation, which is slightly depressed in the middle."

"Below the left ridge the bone exhibits an obliquely inclined surface, six lines (French) long, and twelve lines wide."

This last must be the surface, the contour of which is shown in Fig. 24, A, below *b*. It is particularly interesting, as it suggests that, notwithstanding the flattened condition of the occiput, the posterior cerebral lobes must have projected considerably beyond the cerebellum, and as it constitutes one among several points of similarity between the Neanderthal cranium and certain Australian skulls.

Such are the two best known forms of human cranium, which have been found in what may be fairly termed a fossil state. Can either be shown to fill up or diminish, to any appreciable extent, the structural interval which exists between Man and the man-like apes? Or, on the other hand, does neither depart more widely from the average structure of the human cranium, than normally formed skulls of men are known to do at the present day?

It is impossible to form any opinion on these questions, without some preliminary acquaintance with the range of variation exhibited by human structure in general— a subject which has been but imperfectly studied, while even of what is known, my limits will necessarily allow me to give only a very imperfect sketch.

The student of anatomy is perfectly well aware that there is not a single organ of the human body the structure of which does not vary, to a greater or less extent, in different individuals. The skeleton varies in the proportions, and even to a certain extent in the connexions, of its constituent bones. The muscles which move the bones vary largely in their attachments. The varieties in the mode of distribution of the arteries are carefully classified, on account of the practical importance of a knowledge of their shiftings to the surgeon. The characters of the brain vary immensely, nothing being less constant than the form and size of the cerebral hemispheres, and the richness of the convolutions upon their surface, while the most changeable structures of all in the human brain, are exactly those on which the unwise attempt has been made to base the distinctive characters of humanity, viz. the posterior cornu of the lateral ventricle, the hippocampus minor, and the degree of projection of the posterior lobe beyond the cerebellum. Finally, as all the world knows, the hair and skin of human beings may present the most extraordinary diversities in colour and in texture.

So far as our present knowledge goes, the majority of the structural varieties to which allusion is here made, are individual. The ape-like arrangement of certain muscles which is occasionally met with[1] in the white races of mankind, is not known to be more common among Negroes or Australians: nor because the brain of the Hottentot Venus was found to be smoother, to have its convolutions more symmetrically disposed, and to be, so far, more ape-like than that of ordinary Europeans, are we justified in concluding a like condition of the brain to prevail universally among the lower races of mankind, however probable that conclusion may be.

We are, in fact, sadly wanting in information respecting the disposition of the soft and destructible organs of every Race of Mankind but our own; and even of the skeleton, our Museums are lamentably deficient in every part but the cranium. Skulls enough there are, and since the time when Blumenbach and Camper first called attention to the marked and singular differences which they exhibit, skull collecting and skull measuring has been a zealously pursued branch of Natural History, and the results obtained have been arranged and classified by various writers, among whom the late active and able Retzius must always be the first named.

Human skulls have been found to differ from one another, not merely in their absolute size and in the absolute capacity of the brain case, but in the proportions which the diameters of the latter bear to one another; in the relative size of the bones of the face (and more particularly of the jaws and teeth) as compared with those of the skull; in the degree to which the upper jaw (which is of course followed by the lower) is thrown backwards and downwards under the fore-part of the brain case, or forwards and upwards in front of and beyond it. They differ further in the relations of the transverse diameter of the face, taken through the cheek bones, to the transverse diameter of the skull; in the more rounded or more gable-like form of the roof of the skull, and in the degree to which the hinder part of the skull is flattened

[1] See an excellent Essay by Mr. Church on the Myology of the Orang, in the Natural History Review, for 1861.

or projects beyond the ridge, into and below which, the muscles of the neck are inserted.

In some skulls the brain case may be said to be '*round*,' the extreme length not exceeding the extreme breadth by a greater proportion than 100 to 80, while the difference may be much less.[1] Men possessing such skulls were termed by Retzius '*brachycephalic*,' and the skull of a Calmuck, of which a front and side view (reduced outline copies of which are given in Figure 26) are depicted by Von Baer in his excellent "Crania selecta," affords a very admirable example of that kind of skull. Other skulls, such as that of a Negro copied in Fig. 27 from Mr. Busk's 'Crania typica,' have a very different, greatly elongated form, and may be termed '*oblong*.' In this skull the extreme length is to the extreme breadth as 100 to not more than 67, and the transverse diameter of the human skull may fall below even this proportion. People having such skulls were called by Retzius '*dolichocephalic*.'

The most cursory glance at the side views of these two skulls will suffice to prove that they differ, in another respect, to a very striking extent. The profile of the face of the Calmuck is almost vertical, the facial bones being thrown downwards and under the fore part of the skull. The profile of the face of the Negro, on the other hand, is singularly inclined, the front part of the jaws projecting far forward beyond the level of the fore part of the skull. In the former case the skull is said to be '*orthognathous*' or straight-jawed ; in the latter, it is called '*prognathous*,' a term which has been rendered, with more force than elegance, by the Saxon equivalent,—'snouty.'

Various methods have been devised in order to express with some accuracy the degree of prognathism or orthognathism of any given skull ; most of these methods being essentially modifications of that devised by Peter Camper, in order to attain what he called the 'facial angle.'

But a little consideration will show that any 'facial angle' that has been devised, can be competent to express the structural modifications involved in prognathism and

[1] In no normal human skull does the breadth of the brain-case exceed its length.

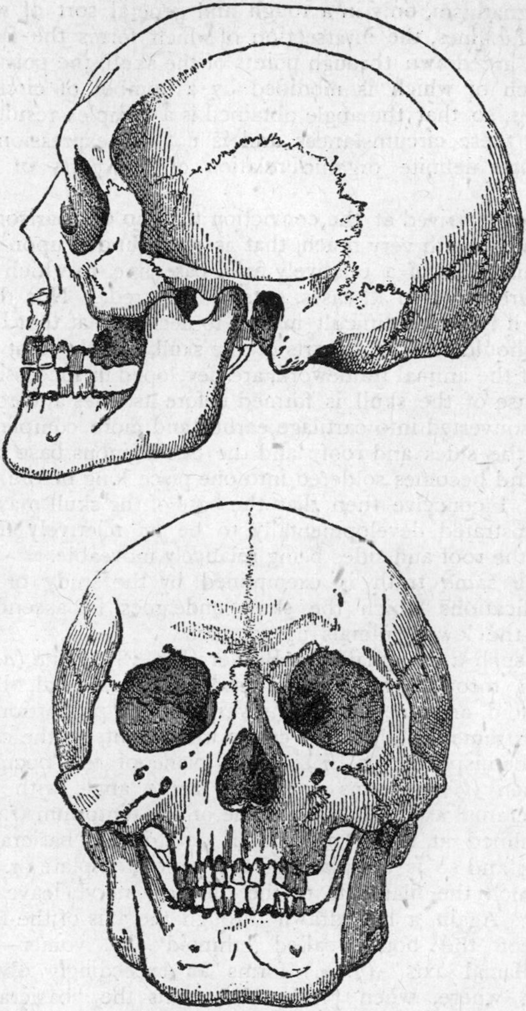

FIG. 26.—Side and front views of the round and orthognathous skull of a Calmuck after Von Baer.   One-third the natural size.

orthognathism, only in a rough and general sort of way.
For the lines, the intersection of which forms the facial
angle, are drawn through points of the skull, the position
of each of which is modified by a number of circumstances, so that the angle obtained is a complex resultant
of all these circumstances, and is not the expression of
any one definite organic relation of the parts of the
skull.

I have arrived at the conviction that no comparison of
crania is worth very much, that is not founded upon the
establishment of a relatively fixed base line, to which the
measurements, in all cases, must be referred.   Nor do I
think it is a very difficult matter to decide what that base
line should be.   The parts of the skull, like those of the
rest of the animal framework, are developed in succession:
the base of the skull is formed before its sides and roof;
it is converted into cartilage earlier and more completely
than the sides and roof: and the cartilaginous base ossi-
fies, and becomes soldered into one piece long before the
roof.   I conceive then that the base of the skull may be
demonstrated developmentally to be its relatively fixed
part, the roof and sides being relatively moveable.

The same truth is exemplified by the study of the
modifications which the skull undergoes in ascending
from the lower animals up to man.

In such a mammal as a Beaver (Fig. 28), a line (*a. b.*)
drawn through the bones, termed basioccipital, basi-
sphenoid, and presphenoid, is very long in proportion to
the extreme length of the cavity which contains the cerebral hemispheres (*g. h.*).   The plane of the occipital
foramen (*b. c.*) forms a slightly acute angle with this
'basicranial axis,' while the plane of the tentorium (*i. T.*)
is inclined at rather more than 90° to the 'basicranial
axis'; and so is the plane of the perforated plate (*a. d.*),
by which the filaments of the olfactory nerve leave the
skull.   Again, a line drawn through the axis of the face,
between the bones called ethmoid and vomer—the
"basifacial axis" (*f. e.*) forms an exceedingly obtuse
angle, where, when produced, it cuts the 'basicranial
axis.'

If the angle made by the line *b. c.* with *a. b.*, be called

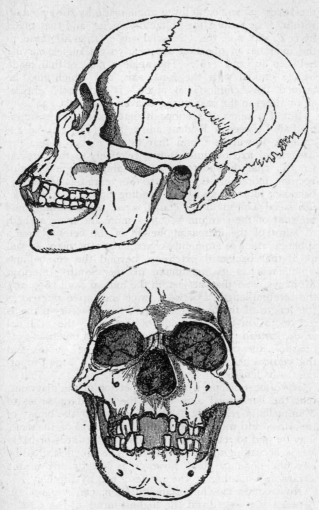

FIG. 27.—Oblong and prognathous skull of a Negro; side and front
views. One-third of the natural size.

the 'occipital angle,' and the angle made by the line *a. d.* with *a. b.* be termed the 'olfactory angle,' and that made by *i. T.* with *a. b.* the 'tentorial angle,' then all these, in the mammal in question, are nearly right angles, varying between 80° and 110°. The angle *e. f. b.*, or that made by the cranial with the facial axis, and which may be termed the 'cranio-facial angle,' is extremely obtuse, amounting, in the case of the Beaver, to at least 150°.

But if a series of sections of mammalian skulls, inter-mediate between a Rodent and a Man (Fig. 28), be ex-amined, it will be found that in the higher crania the basicranial axis becomes shorter relatively to the cerebral length ; that the 'olfactory angle' and 'occipital angle' become more obtuse; and that the 'cranio-facial angle' becomes more acute by the bending down, as it were, of the facial axis upon the cranial axis. At the same time, the roof of the cranium becomes more and more arched, to allow of the increasing height of the cerebral hemi-spheres, which is eminently characteristic of man, as well as of that backward extension, beyond the cerebellum, which reaches its maximum in the South American Monkeys. So that, at last, in the human skull (Fig. 29), the cerebral length is between twice and thrice as great as the length of the basicranial axis ; the olfactory plane is 20° or 30° on the *under* side of that axis ; the occipital angle, instead of being less than 90°, is as much as 150° or 160° ; the cranio-facial angle may be 90° or less, and the vertical height of the skull may have a large propor-tion to its length.

It will be obvious, from an inspection of the diagrams, that the basicranial axis is, in the ascending series of Mammalia, a relatively fixed line, on which the bones of the sides and roof of the cranial cavity, and of the face, may be said to revolve downwards and forwards or back-wards, according to their position. The arc described by any one bone or plane, however, is not by any means always in proportion to the arc described by another.

Now comes the important question, can we discern, between the lowest and the highest forms of the human cranium anything answering, in however slight a degree, to this revolution of the side and roof bones of the skull

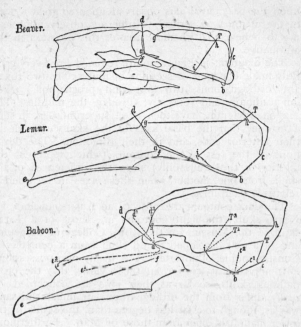

FIG. 28.—Longitudinal and vertical sections of the skulls of a Beaver (*Castor Canadensis*), a Lemur (*L. Catta*), and a Baboon (*Cynocephalus Papio*), $a\,b$, the basicranial axis; $b\,c$, the occipital plane; $i\,T$, the tentorial plane; $a\,d$, the olfactory plane; $f\,e$, the basifacial axis; $c\,b\,a$, occipital angle; $T\,i\,a$, tentorial angle; $d\,a\,b$, olfactory angle; $e\,f\,b$, cranio-facial angle; $g\,h$, extreme length of the cavity which lodges the cerebral hemispheres or 'cerebral length.' The length of the basicranial axis as to this length, or, in other words, the proportional length of the line $g\,h$ to that of $a\,b$ taken as 100, in the three skulls, is as follows:—Beaver 70 to 100; Lemur 119 to 100; Baboon 144 to 100. In an adult male Gorilla the cerebral length is as 170 to the basicranial axis taken as 100, in the Negro (Fig. 29) as 236 to 100. In the Constantinople skull (Fig. 29) as 266 to 100. The cranial difference between the highest Ape's skull and the lowest Man's is therefore very strikingly brought out by these measurements.

In the diagram of the Baboon's skull the dotted lines $d^1 d^2$, &c., give the angles of the Lemur's and Beaver's skull, as laid down upon the basicranial axis of the Baboon. The line $a\,b$ has the same length in each diagram.

upon the basicranial axis observed upon so great a scale
in the mammalian series? Numerous observations lead
me to believe that we must answer this question in the
affirmative.

The diagrams in Figure 29 are reduced from very carefully made diagrams of sections of four skulls, two round
and orthognathous, two long and prognathous, taken
longitudinally and vertically, through the middle. The
sectional diagrams have then been superimposed, in such
a manner, that the basal axes of the skulls coincide by
their anterior ends, and in their direction. The deviations of the rest of the contours (which represent the
interior of the skulls only) show the differences of the
skulls from one another, when these axes are regarded as
relatively fixed lines.

The dark contours are those of an Australian and of a
Negro skull: the light contours are those of a Tartar
skull, in the Museum of the Royal College of Surgeons;
and of a well developed round skull from a cemetery in
Constantinople, of uncertain race, in my own possession.

It appears, at once, from these views, that the prognathous skulls, so far as their jaws are concerned, do
really differ from the orthognathous in much the same
way as, though to a far less degree than, the skulls of the
lower mammals differ from those of Man. Furthermore,
the plane of the occipital foramen ($b\ c$) forms a somewhat
smaller angle with the axis in these particular prognathous
skulls than in the orthognathous; and the like may be
slightly true of the perforated plate of the ethmoid—
though this point is not so clear. But it is singular to
remark that, in another respect, the prognathous skulls
are less ape-like than the orthognathous, the cerebral
cavity projecting decidedly more beyond the anterior end
of the axis in the prognathous, than in the orthognathous,
skulls.

It will be observed that these diagrams reveal an
immense range of variation in the capacity and relative
proportion to the cranial axis, of the different regions of
the cavity which contains the brain, in the different skulls.
Nor is the difference in the extent to which the cerebral
overlaps the cerebellar cavity less singular. A round

skull (Fig. 29, *Const.*) may have a greater posterior cerebral projection than a long one (Fig. 29, *Negro*).

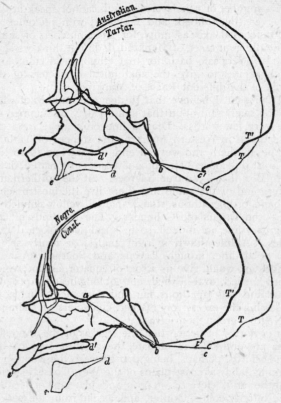

FIG. 29.—Sections of orthognathous (light contour) and prognathous (dark contour) skulls, one-third of the natural size. *a b*, Basicranial axis; *b c*, *b′ c′*, plane of the occipital foramen; *d d′*, hinder end of the palatine bone; *e e′*, front end of the upper jaw; *TT′*, insertion of the tentorium.

Until human crania have been largely worked out in a manner similar to that here suggested—until it shall be an opprobrium to an ethnological collection to possess a single skull which is not bisected longitudinally—until the angles and measurements here mentioned, together with a number of others of which I cannot speak in this place, are determined, and tabulated with reference to the basicranial axis as unity, for large numbers of skulls of the different races of Mankind, I do not think we shall have any very safe basis for that ethnological craniology which aspires to give the anatomical characters of the crania of the different Races of Mankind.

At present, I believe that the general outlines of what may be safely said upon that subject may be summed up in a very few words. Draw a line on a globe from the Gold Coast in Western Africa to the steppes of Tartary. At the southern and western end of that line there live the most dolichocephalic, prognathous, curly-haired, dark-skinned of men—the true Negroes. At the northern and eastern end of the same line there live the most brachy-cephalic, orthognathous, straight-haired, yellow-skinned of men—the Tartars and Calmucks. The two ends of this imaginary line are indeed, so to speak, ethnological anti-podes. A line drawn at right angles, or nearly so, to this polar line through Europe and Southern Asia to Hindostan, would give us a sort of equator, around which round-headed, oval-headed, and oblong-headed, progna-thous and orthognathous, fair and dark races—but none possessing the excessively marked characters of Calmuck or Negro—group themselves.

It is worthy of notice that the regions of the antipodal races are antipodal in climate, the greatest contrast the world affords, perhaps, being that between the damp, hot, steaming, alluvial coast plains of the West Coast of Africa and the arid, elevated steppes and plateaux of Central Asia, bitterly cold in winter, and as far from the sea as any part of the world can be.

From Central Asia eastward to the Pacific Islands and subcontinents on the one hand, and to America on the other, brachycephaly and orthognathism gradually diminish, and are replaced by dolichocephaly and prognathism, less, however, on the American Continent (throughout the whole length of which a rounded type of skull prevails largely, but not exclusively)[1] than in the Pacific region, where, at length, on the Australian Continent and in the adjacent islands, the oblong skull, the projecting jaws, and the dark skin reappear; with so much departure, in other respects, from the Negro type, that ethnologists assign to these people the special title of 'Negritoes.'

The Australian skull is remarkable for its narrowness and for the thickness of its walls, especially in the region of the supraciliary ridge, which is frequently, though not by any means invariably, solid throughout, the frontal sinuses remaining undeveloped. The nasal depression, again, is extremely sudden, so that the brows overhang and give the countenance a particularly lowering, threatening expression. The occipital region of the skull, also, not unfrequently becomes less prominent; so that it not only fails to project beyond a line drawn perpendicular to the hinder extremity of the glabello-occipital line, but even, in some cases, begins to shelve away from it, forwards, almost immediately. In consequence of this circumstance, the parts of the occipital bone which lie above and below the tuberosity make a much more acute angle with one another than is usual, whereby the hinder part of the base of the skull appears obliquely truncated. Many Australian skulls have a considerable height, quite equal to that of the average of any other race, but there are others in which the cranial roof becomes remarkably depressed, the skull, at the same time, elongating so much that, probably, its capacity is not diminished. The majority of skulls possessing these characters, which I have seen, are from the neighbourhood of Port Adelaide in South Australia, and have been used by the natives as water vessels; to which end the face has been knocked away, and a string passed through the vacuity and the occipital foramen, so that the skull was suspended by the greater part of its basis.

Figure 30 represents the contour of a skull of this kind from Western Port, with the jaw attached, and of the Neanderthal skull, both reduced to one-third of the size

[1] See Dr. D. Wilson's valuable paper "On the supposed prevalence of one Cranial Type throughout the American aborigines."— Canadian Journal, vol. ii., 1857.

of nature. A small additional amount of flattening and lengthening, with a corresponding increase of the supra-ciliary ridge, would convert the Australian brain case into a form identical with that of the aberrant fossil.

And now, to return to the fossil skulls, and to the rank which they occupy among, or beyond, these existing varieties of cranial conformation. In the first place, I must remark, that, as Professor Schmerling well observed

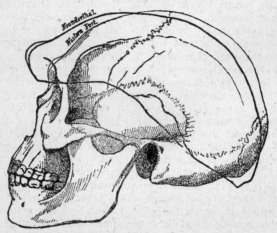

FIG. 30.—An Australian skull from Western Port, in the Museum of the Royal College of Surgeons, with the contour of the Neanderthal skull. Both reduced to one-third the natural size.

(*supra*, p. 114) in commenting upon the Engis skull, the formation of a safe judgment upon the question is greatly hindered by the absence of the jaws from both the crania, so that there is no means of deciding, with certainty, whether they were more or less prognathous than the lower existing races of mankind. And yet, as we have seen, it is more in this respect than any other, that human skulls vary, towards and from, the brutal type—the brain case of an average dolichocephalic European differing far less from that of a Negro, for example, than his jaws do.

In the absence of the jaws, then, any judgment on the relations of the fossil skulls to recent Races must be accepted with a certain reservation.

But taking the evidence as it stands, and turning first to the Engis skull, I confess I can find no character in the remains of that cranium which, if it were a recent skull, would give any trustworthy clue as to the Race to which it might appertain.   Its contours and measurements agree very well with those of some Australian skulls which I have examined—and especially has it a tendency towards that occipital flattening, to the great extent of which, in some Australian skulls, I have alluded.   But all Australian skulls do not present this flattening, and the supraciliary ridge of the Engis skull is quite unlike that of the typical Australians.

On the other hand, its measurements agree equally well with those of some European skulls.   And assuredly, there is no mark of degradation about any part of its structure.   It is, in fact, a fair average human skull, which might have belonged to a philosopher, or might have contained the thoughtless brains of a savage.

The case of the Neanderthal skull is very different. Under whatever aspect we view this cranium, whether we regard its vertical depression, the enormous thickness of its supraciliary ridges, its sloping occiput, or its long and straight squamosal suture, we meet with ape-like characters, stamping it as the most pithecoid of human crania yet discovered.   But Professor Schaaffhausen states (*supra*, p. 122), that the cranium, in its present condition, holds 1033.24 cubic centimetres of water, or about 63 cubic inches, and as the entire skull could hardly have held less than an additional 12 cubic inches, its capacity may be estimated at about 75 cubic inches, which is the average capacity given by Morton for Polynesian and Hottentot skulls.

So large a mass of brain as this, would alone suggest that the pithecoid tendencies, indicated by this skull, did not extend deep into the organization ; and this conclusion is borne out by the dimensions of the other bones of the skeleton given by Professor Schaaffhausen, which show that the absolute height and relative proportions of the limbs, were quite those of an European of middle stature. The bones are indeed stouter, but this and the

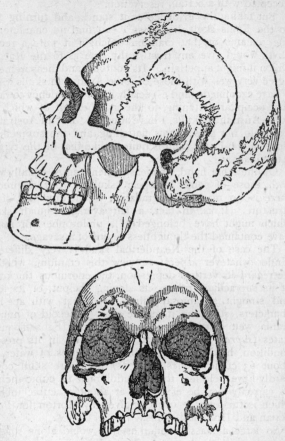

FIG. 31.—Ancient Danish skull from a tumulus at Borreby; one-third of the natural size. From a camera lucida drawing by Mr. Busk.

great development of the muscular ridges noted by Dr. Schaaffhausen, are characters to be expected in savages.

The Patagonians, exposed without shelter or protection to a climate possibly not very dissimilar from that of Europe at the time during which the Neanderthal man lived, are remarkable for the stoutness of their limb bones.

In no sense, then, can the Neanderthal bones be regarded as the remains of a human being intermediate between Men and Apes. At most, they demonstrate the existence of a man whose skull may be said to revert somewhat towards the pithecoid type—just as a Carrier, or a Pouter, or a Tumbler, may sometimes put on the plumage of its primitive stock, the *Columba livia*. And indeed, though truly the most pithecoid of known human skulls, the Neanderthal cranium is by no means so isolated as it appears to be at first, but forms, in reality, the extreme term of a series leading gradually from it to the highest and best developed of human crania. On the one hand, it is closely approached by the flattened Australian skulls, of which I have spoken, from which other Australian forms lead us gradually up to skulls having very much the type of the Engis cranium. And, on the other hand, it is even more closely affined to the skulls of certain ancient people who inhabited Denmark during the 'stone period,' and were probably either contemporaneous with, or later than, the makers of the 'refuse heaps,' or 'Kjokkenmöddings' of that country.

The correspondence between the longitudinal contour of the Neanderthal skull and that of some of those skulls from the tumuli at Borreby, very accurate drawings of which have been made by Mr. Busk, is very close. The occiput is quite as retreating, the supraciliary ridges are nearly as prominent, and the skull is as low. Furthermore, the Borreby skull resembles the Neanderthal form more closely than any of the Australian skulls do, by the much more rapid retrocession of the forehead. On the other hand, the Borreby skulls are all somewhat broader, in proportion to their length, than the Neanderthal skull, while some attain that proportion of breadth to length (80 : 100) which constitutes brachycephaly.

In conclusion, I may say, that the fossil remains of Man hitherto discovered do not seem to me to take us appreciably nearer to that lower pithecoid form, by the modification of which he has, probably, become what he is. And considering what is now known of the most ancient races of men ; seeing that they fashioned flint axes and flint knives and bone-skewers, of much the same pattern as those fabricated by the lowest savages at the present day, and that we have every reason to believe the habits and modes of living of such people to have remained the same from the time of the Mammoth and the tichorhine Rhinoceros till now, I do not know that this result is other than might be expected.

Where, then, must we look for primæval Man ? Was the oldest *Homo sapiens* pliocene or miocene, or yet more ancient ? In still older strata do the fossilized bones of an Ape more anthropoid, or a Man more pithecoid, than any yet known await the researches of some unborn paleontologist ?

Time will show. But, in the meanwhile, if any form of the doctrine of progressive development is correct, we must extend by long epochs the most liberal estimate that has yet been made of the antiquity of Man.

IV

THE PRESENT CONDITION OF ORGANIC NATURE

WHEN it was my duty to consider what subject I would select for the six lectures which I shall now have the pleasure of delivering to you, it occurred to me that I could not do better than endeavour to put before you in a true light, or in what I might perhaps with more modesty call, that which I conceive myself to be the true light, the position of a book which has been more praised and more abused, perhaps, than any book which has appeared for some years;—I mean Mr. Darwin's work on the "Origin of Species." That work, I doubt not, many of you have read; for I know the inquiring spirit which is rife among you. At any rate, all of you will have heard of it,—some by one kind of report and some by another kind of report; the attention of all and the curiosity of all have been probably more or less excited on the subject of that work. All I can do, and all I shall attempt to do, is to put before you that kind of judgment which has been formed by a man, who, of course, is liable to judge erroneously; but at any rate, of one whose business and profession it is to form judgments upon questions of this nature.

And here, as it will always happen when dealing with an extensive subject, the greater part of my course—if, indeed, so small a number of lectures can be properly called a course—must be devoted to preliminary matters, or rather to a statement of those facts and of those principles which the work itself dwells upon, and brings more or less directly before us. I have no right to suppose that all or any of you are naturalists; and even if you were, the misconceptions and misunderstandings prevalent even among naturalists on these matters would make it desirable that I should take the course I now propose to take, —that I should start from the beginning,—that I should endeavour to point out what is the existing state of the organic world—that I should point out its past condition, —that I should state what is the precise nature of the undertaking which Mr. Darwin has taken in hand; that I should endeavour to show you what are the only methods by which that undertaking can be brought to an issue, and to point out to you how far the author of the work in question has satisfied those conditions, how far he has not satisfied them, how far they are satisfiable by man, and how far they are not satisfiable by man.

To-night, in taking up the first part of the question, I shall endeavour to put before you a sort of broad notion of our knowledge of the condition of the living world. There are many ways of doing this. I might deal with it pictorially and graphically. Following the example of Humboldt in his "Aspects of Nature," I might endeavour to point out the infinite variety of organic life in every mode of its existence, with reference to the variations of climate and the like; and such an attempt would be fraught with interest to us all; but considering the subject before us, such a course would not be that best calculated to assist us. In an argument of this kind we must go further and dig deeper into the matter; we must endeavour to look into the foundations of living Nature, if I may so say, and discover the principles involved in some of her most secret operations. I propose, therefore, in the first place, to take some ordinary animal with which you are all familiar, and, by easily comprehensible and obvious examples drawn from it, to show what are the kind of problems which living beings in general lay before us; and I shall then show you that the same problems are laid open to us by all kinds of living beings. But, first, let me say in what sense I have used the words "organic nature." In speaking of the causes which lead to our present knowledge of organic nature, I have used it almost as an equivalent of the word "living," and for this reason,—that in almost all living beings you can distinguish several distinct portions set apart to do particular things and work in a particular way. These are termed "organs," and the whole together is called "organic." And as it is universally characteristic of them, the term "organic" has been very conveniently employed to denote the whole of living nature,—the whole of the plant world, and the whole of the animal world.

Few animals can be more familiar to you than that whose skeleton is shown on our diagram. You need not bother yourselves with this "*Equus caballus*" written under it; that is only the Latin name of it, and does not make it any better. It simply means the common Horse. Suppose we wish to understand all about the Horse. Our first object must be to study the structure of the animal. The whole of his body is inclosed within a hide, a skin covered with hair; and if that hide or skin be taken off, we find a great mass of flesh, or what is technically called muscle, being the substance which by its power of contraction enables the animal to move. These muscles move the hard parts one upon the other, and so give that strength and power of motion which renders the Horse so useful to us in the performance of those services in which we employ him.

And then, on separating and removing the whole of this skin and flesh, you have a great series of bones, hard structures, bound together with ligaments, and forming the skeleton which is represented here.

In that skeleton there are a number of parts to be recognized. The long series of bones, beginning from the skull and ending in the tail, is called the spine, and those in front are the ribs; and then there are two pairs of limbs, one before and one behind; and there are what we all know as the fore-legs and the hind-legs. If we pursue our researches into the interior of this animal, we find within the framework of the skeleton a great cavity, or rather, I should say, two great cavities,—one cavity beginning in the skull and running through the neck-bones, along the spine, and ending in the tail, containing the brain and the spinal marrow, which are extremely important organs. The second great cavity, commencing with the mouth, contains the gullet, the stomach, the long intestine, and all the rest of those internal apparatus which are essential for digestion; and then in the same great cavity, there are lodged the heart and all the great vessels going from it; and, besides that, the organs of respiration — the lungs; and then the kidneys, and the organs of reproduction, and so on. Let us now endeavour to reduce this notion of a horse that we now have, to some such kind of simple expression as can be at once, and without difficulty, retained

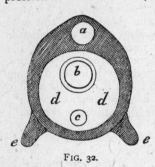

FIG. 32.

in the mind, apart from all minor details. If I make a transverse section, that is, if I were to saw a dead horse across, I should find that, if I left out the details, and supposing I took my section through the anterior region, and through the fore-limbs, I should have here this kind of section of the body (Fig. 32). Here would be the upper part of the animal — that great mass of bones that we spoke of as the spine (a, Fig. 32). Here I should have the alimentary canal (b, Fig. 32). Here I should have the heart (c, Fig. 32); and then you see, there would be a kind of double tube, the whole being inclosed within the hide; the spinal marrow would be placed in the upper tube (a, Fig. 32), and in the lower tube (d d, Fig. 32), there would be the alimentary canal (b), and the heart (c); and here I shall have the legs proceeding from each side. For simplicity's sake, I represent them merely as stumps (e e, Fig. 32). Now that is a horse—as mathematicians would say—reduced to its most simple expression. Carry that in your minds, if you please, as a simplified idea of the structure of the Horse. The considerations which I have now put before you belong to what we technically call the 'Anatomy' of the Horse. Now, suppose we go to work upon these several parts,—

flesh and hair, and skin and bone, and lay open these
various organs with our scalpels, and examine them by
means of our magnifying-glasses, and see what we can
make of them. We shall find that the flesh is made
up of bundles of strong fibres. The brain and nerves,
too, we shall find, are made up of fibres, and these queer-
looking things that are called ganglionic corpuscles. If
we take a slice of the bone and examine it, we shall find
that it is very like this diagram of a section of the bone
of an ostrich, though differing, of course, in some details;
and if we take any part whatsoever of the tissue, and
examine it, we shall find it all has a minute structure,
visible only under the microscope. All these parts constitute microscopic anatomy or 'Histo-
logy.' These parts are constantly being
changed; every part is constantly growing, decaying, and being replaced during
the life of the animal. The tissue is constantly replaced by new material; and if
you go back to the young state of the
tissue in the case of muscle, or in the
case of skin, or any of the organs I have

FIG. 33.

mentioned, you will find that they all come under the
same condition. Every one of these microscopic filaments
and fibres (I now speak merely of the general character
of the whole process)—every one of these parts—could
be traced down to some modification of a tissue which
can be readily divided into little particles of fleshy matter,
of that substance which is composed of the chemical
elements, carbon, hydrogen, oxygen, and nitrogen, having
such a shape as this (Fig. 33). These particles, into which
all primitive tissues break up, are called cells. If I were
to make a section of a piece of the skin of my hand, I
should find that it was made up of these cells. If I
examine the fibres which form the various organs of all
living animals, I should find that all of them, at one time
or other, had been formed out of a substance consisting
of similar elements; so that you see, just as we reduced
the whole body in the gross to that sort of simple expression given in Fig. 32, so we may reduce the whole of the
microscopic structural elements to a form of even greater

simplicity; just as the plan of the whole body may be so represented in a sense (Fig. 32), so the primary structure of every tissue may be represented by a mass of cells (Fig. 33).

Having thus, in this sort of general way, sketched to you what I may call, perhaps, the architecture of the body of the Horse, (what we term technically its Morphology,) I must now turn to another aspect. A horse is not a mere dead structure: it is an active, living, working machine. Hitherto we have, as it were, been looking at a steam-engine with the fires out, and nothing in the boiler; but the body of the living animal is a beautifully-formed active machine, and every part has its different work to do in the working of that machine, which is what we call its life. The Horse, if you see him after his day's work is done, is cropping the grass in the fields, as it may be, or munching the oats in his stable. What is he doing? His jaws are working as a mill—and a very complex mill too—grinding the corn, or crushing the grass to a pulp. As soon as that operation has taken place, the food is passed down to the stomach, and there it is mixed with the chemical fluid called the gastric juice, a substance which has the peculiar property of making soluble and dissolving out the nutritious matter in the grass, and leaving behind those parts which are not nutritious; so that you have, first, the mill, then a sort of chemical digester; and then the food, thus partially dissolved, is carried back by the muscular contractions of the intestines into the hinder parts of the body, while the soluble portions are taken up into the blood. The blood is contained in a vast system of pipes, spreading through the whole body, connected with a force-pump,—the heart,—which, by its position and by the contractions of its valves, keeps the blood constantly circulating in one direction, never allowing it to rest; and then, by means of this circulation of the blood, laden as it is with the products of digestion, the skin, the flesh, the hair, and every other part of the body, draws from it that which it wants, and every one of these organs derives those materials which are necessary to enable it to do its work.

The action of each of these organs, the performance of each of these various duties, involve in their operation a continual absorption of the matters necessary for their support, from the blood, and a constant formation of waste products, which are returned to the blood, and conveyed by it to the lungs and the kidneys, which are organs that have allotted to them the office of extracting, separating, and getting rid of these waste products; and thus the general nourishment, labour, and repair of the whole machine is kept up with order and regularity. But not only is it a machine which feeds and appropriates to its own support the nourishment necessary to its existence— it is an engine for locomotive purposes. The Horse desires to go from one place to another; and to enable it to do this, it has those strong contractile bundles of muscles attached to the bones of its limbs, which are put in motion by means of a sort of telegraphic apparatus formed by the brain and the great spinal cord running through the spine or backbone; and to this spinal cord are attached a number of fibres termed nerves, which proceed to all parts of the structure. By means of these the eyes, nose, tongue, and skin—all the organs of perception—transmit impressions or sensations to the brain, which acts as a sort of great central telegraph-office, receiving impressions and sending messages to all parts of the body, and putting in motion the muscles necessary to accomplish any movement that may be desired. So that you have here an extremely complex and beautifully-proportioned machine, with all its parts working harmoniously together towards one common object — the preservation of the life of the animal.

Now, note this: the Horse makes up its waste by feeding, and its food is grass or oats, or perhaps other vegetable products; therefore, in the long run, the source of all this complex machinery lies in the vegetable kingdom. But where does the grass, or the oat, or any other plant, obtain this nourishing food-producing material? At first it is a little seed, which soon begins to draw into itself from the earth and the surrounding air matters which in themselves contain no vital properties whatever; it absorbs into its own substance water, an inorganic body; it draws into its substance carbonic acid, an inorganic matter; and ammonia, another inorganic matter, found in the air; and then, by some wonderful chemical process, the details of which chemists do not yet understand, though they are near foreshadowing them, it combines them into one substance, which is known to us as 'Protein,' a complex compound of carbon, hydrogen, oxygen, and nitrogen, which alone possesses the property of manifesting vitality and of permanently supporting animal life. So that, you see, the waste products of the animal economy, the effete materials which are continually being thrown off by all living beings, in the form of organic matters, are constantly replaced by supplies of the necessary repairing and rebuilding materials drawn from the plants, which in their turn manufacture them, so to speak, by a mysterious combination of those same inorganic materials.

Let us trace out the history of the Horse in another direction. After a certain time, as the result of sickness or disease, the effect of accident, or the consequence of old age, sooner or later, the animal dies. The multitudinous operations of this beautiful mechanism flag in their performance, the Horse loses its vigour, and after passing through the curious series of changes comprised in its formation and preservation, it finally decays, and ends its life by going back into that inorganic world from which all but an inappreciable fraction of its substance was derived. Its bones become mere carbonate and phosphate of lime; the matter of its flesh, and of its other parts, becomes, in the long run, converted into carbonic acid, into water, and into ammonia. You will now, perhaps, understand the curious relation of the animal with the plant, of the organic with the inorganic world, which is shown in this diagram.

The plant gathers these inorganic materials together and makes them up into its own substance. The animal eats the plant and appropriates the nutritious portions to its own sustenance, rejects and gets rid of the useless matters; and, finally, the animal itself dies, and its whole body is decomposed and returned into the inorganic world. There is thus a constant circulation from one to the other, a continual formation of organic life from inorganic matters, and as constant a return of the matter of living bodies to the inorganic world; so that the materials of which our bodies are composed are largely, in all probability, the substances which constituted the matter of long extinct creations, but which have in the interval constituted a part of the inorganic world.

Thus we come to the conclusion, strange at first sight, that the MATTER constituting the living world is identical with that which forms the inorganic world. And not less true is it that, remarkable as are the powers or, in other words, as are the FORCES which are exerted by living beings, yet all these forces are either identical with

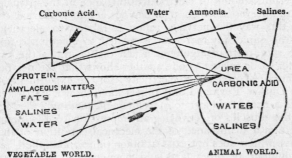

INORGANIC WORLD.

Carbonic Acid.   Water   Ammonia.   Salines.

PROTEIN
AMYLACEOUS MATTERS
FATS
SALINES
WATER

UREA
CARBONIC ACID
WATER
SALINES

VEGETABLE WORLD.   ANIMAL WORLD.

FIG. 34.

those which exist in the inorganic world, or they are convertible into them; I mean in just the same sense as the researches of physical philosophers have shown that heat is convertible into electricity, that electricity is convertible into magnetism, magnetism into mechanical force or chemical force, and any one of them with the other, each being measurable in terms of the other,—even so, I say, that great law is applicable to the living world. Consider why is the skeleton of this horse capable of supporting the masses of flesh and the various organs forming the living body, unless it is because of the action of the same forces of cohesion which combines together the particles of matter composing this piece of chalk? What is there in the muscular contractile power of the animal but the force which is expressible, and which is in a certain sense convertible, into the force of gravity which it overcomes? Or, if you go to more hidden processes, in what does the process of digestion differ from those processes which are carried on in the laboratory of the chemist? Even if we take the most recondite and most complex operations of animal life—those of the nervous system, these of late years have been shown to be—I do not say identical in any sense with the electrical processes—but this has been shown, that they are in some way or other associated with them; that is to say, that every amount of nervous action is accompanied by a certain amount of electrical disturbance in the particles of the nerves in which that nervous action is carried on. In this way the nervous action is related to electricity in the same way that heat is related to electricity; and the same sort of argument which demonstrates the two latter to be related to one another shows that the nervous forces are correlated to electricity; for the experiments of M. Dubois Reymond and others have shown that whenever a nerve is in a state of excitement, sending a message to the muscles or conveying an impression to the brain, there is a disturbance of the electrical condition of that nerve which does not exist at other times; and there are a number of other facts and phenomena of that sort; so that we come to the broad conclusion that not only as to living matter itself, but as to the forces that matter exerts, there is a close relationship between the organic and the inorganic world—the difference between them arising from the diverse combination and disposition of identical forces, and not from any primary diversity, so far as we can see.

I said just now that the Horse eventually died and became converted into the same inorganic substances from whence all but an inappreciable fraction of its substance demonstrably originated, so that the actual wanderings of matter are as remarkable as the transmigrations of the soul fabled by Indian tradition. But before death has occurred, in the one sex or the other, and in fact in both, certain products or parts of the organism have been set free, certain parts of the organisms of the two sexes have come into contact with one another, and from that conjunction, from that union which then takes place, there results the formation of a new being. At stated times the mare, from a particular part of the interior of her body, called the ovary, gets rid of a minute particle of matter comparable in all essential respects with that which we called a cell a little while since, which cell contains a kind of nucleus in its centre, surrounded by a clear space and by a viscid mass of protein substance (Fig. 33); and though it is different in appearance from the eggs which we are mostly acquainted with, it is really an egg. After a time this minute particle of matter, which may only be a small fraction of a grain in weight, undergoes a series of changes, — wonderful, complex changes. Finally, upon its surface there is fashioned a little elevation, which afterwards becomes divided and marked by a groove. The lateral boundaries of the groove extend upwards and downwards, and at length give rise to a double tube. In the upper and smaller tube the spinal marrow and brain are fashioned; in the lower, the alimentary canal and heart; and at length two pairs of buds shoot out at the sides of the body, and they are the rudiments of the limbs. In fact a true drawing of a section of the embryo in this state would in all essential respects resemble that diagram of a horse reduced to its simplest expression, which I first placed before you (Fig. 32).

Slowly and gradually these changes take place. The whole of the body, at first, can be broken up into "cells," which become in one place metamorphosed into muscle, —in another place into gristle and bone,—in another place into fibrous tissue,—and in another into hair; every part becoming gradually and slowly fashioned, as if there were an artificer at work in each of these complex structures that I have mentioned. This embryo, as it is called, then passes into other conditions. I should tell you that there is a time when the embryos of neither dog, nor horse, nor porpoise, nor monkey, nor man, can be distinguished by any essential feature one from the other; there is a time when they each and all of them resemble this one of the Dog. But as development advances, all the parts acquire their speciality, till at length you have the embryo converted into the form of the parent from which it started. So that, you see, this living animal, this horse, begins its existence as a minute particle of nitrogenous matter, which, being supplied with nutriment (derived, as I have shown, from the inorganic world), grows up according to the special type and construction of its parents, works and undergoes a constant waste, and that waste is made good by nutriment derived from the inorganic world; the waste given off in this way being directly added to the inorganic world. Eventually the animal itself dies, and, by the process of decomposition, its whole body is returned to those conditions of inorganic matter in which its substance originated.

This, then, is that which is true of every living form, from the lowest plant to the highest animal—to man himself. You might define the life of every one in exactly the same terms as those which I have now used; the difference between the highest and the lowest being simply in the complexity of the developmental changes, the variety of the structural forms, and the diversity of the physiological functions which are exerted by each.

If I were to take an oak tree, as a specimen of the plant world, I should find that it originated in an acorn, which, too, commenced in a cell; the acorn is placed in the ground, and it very speedily begins to absorb the inorganic matters I have named, adds enormously to its bulk, and we can see it, year after year, extending itself upward and downward, attracting and appropriating to itself inorganic materials, which it vivifies, and eventually, as it ripens, gives off its own proper acorns, which again run the same course. But I need not multiply examples, —from the highest to the lowest the essential features of life are the same, as I have described in each of these cases.

So much, then, for these particular features of the organic world, which you can understand and comprehend, so long as you confine yourself to one sort of living being, and study that only.

But, as you know, horses are not the only living

creatures in the world; and again, horses, like all other animals, have certain limits—are confined to a certain area on the surface of the earth on which we live,—and, as that is the simpler matter, I may take that first. In its wild state, and before the discovery of America, when the natural state of things was interfered with by the Spaniards, the Horse was only to be found in parts of the earth which are known to geographers as the Old World; that is to say, you might meet with horses in Europe, Asia, or Africa; but there were none in Australia, and there were none whatsoever in the whole continent of America, from Labrador down to Cape Horn. This is an empirical fact, and it is what is called, stated in the way I have given it you, the 'Geographical Distribution' of the Horse.

Why horses should be found in Europe, Asia, and Africa, and not in America, is not obvious; the explanation that the conditions of life in America are unfavourable to their existence, and that, therefore, they had not been created there, evidently does not apply; for when the invading Spaniards, or our own yeomen farmers, conveyed horses to these countries for their own use, they were found to thrive well and multiply very rapidly; and many are even now running wild in those countries, and in a perfectly natural condition. Now, suppose we were to do for every animal what we have here done for the Horse,—that is, to mark off and distinguish the particular district or region to which each belonged; and supposing we tabulated all these results, that would be called the Geographical Distribution of animals, while a corresponding study of plants would yield as a result the Geographical Distribution of plants.

I pass on from that now, as I merely wished to explain to you what I meant by the use of the term 'Geographical Distribution.' As I said, there is another aspect, and a much more important one, and that is, the relations of the various animals to one another. The Horse is a very well-defined matter-of-fact sort of animal, and we are all pretty familiar with its structure. I dare say it may have struck you, that it resembles very much no other member of the animal kingdom, except perhaps the Zebra or the Ass. But let me ask you to look along these diagrams.

Here is the skeleton of the Horse, and here the skeleton of the Dog. You will notice that we have in the Horse a skull, a backbone and ribs, shoulder-blades and haunch-bones. In the fore-limb, one upper arm-bone, two fore arm-bones, wrist-bones (wrongly called knee), and middle hand-bones, ending in the three bones of a finger, the last of which is sheathed in the horny hoof of the fore-foot: in the hind-limb, one thigh-bone, two leg-bones, ankle-bones, and middle foot-bones, ending in the three bones of a toe, the last of which is encased in the hoof of the hind-foot. Now turn to the Dog's skeleton. We find identically the same bones, but more of them, there being more toes in each foot, and hence more toe-bones.

Well, that is a very curious thing! The fact is that the Dog and the Horse—when one gets a look at them without the outward impediments of the skin—are found to be made in very much the same sort of fashion. And if I were to make a transverse section of the Dog, I should find the same organs that I have already shown you as forming parts of the Horse. Well, here is another skeleton—that of a kind of Lemur—you see he has just the same bones; and if I were to make a transverse section of it, it would be just the same again. In your mind's eye turn him round, so as to put his backbone in a position inclined obliquely upwards and forwards, just as in the next three diagrams, which represent the skeletons of an Orang, a Chimpanzee, and a Gorilla, and you find you have no trouble in identifying the bones throughout; and lastly turn to the end of the series, the diagram representing a man's skeleton, and still you find no great structural feature essentially altered. There are the same bones in the same relations. From the Horse we pass on and on, with gradual steps, until we arrive at last at the highest known forms. On the other hand, take the other line of diagrams, and pass from the Horse downwards in the scale to this fish; and still, though the modifications are vastly greater, the essential framework of the organiza-tion remains unchanged. Here, for instance, is a Por-poise; here is its strong backbone, with the cavity running through it, which contains the spinal cord; here are the ribs, here the shoulder-blade; here is the little short upper-arm bone, here are the two forearm bones, the wrist-bone, and the finger-bones.

Strange, is it not, that the Porpoise should have in this queer-looking affair—its flapper (as it is called), the same fundamental elements as the fore-leg of the Horse or the Dog, or the Ape or Man; and here you will notice a very curious thing,—the hinder limbs are absent. Now, let us make another jump. Let us go to the Codfish : here you see is the forearm, in this large pectoral fin—carrying your mind's eye onward from the flapper of the Porpoise. And here you have the hinder limbs restored in the shape of these ventral fins. If I were to make a transverse section of this, I should find just the same organs that we have before noticed. So that, you see, there comes out this strange conclusion as the result of our investigations, that the Horse, when examined and compared with other animals, is found by no means to stand alone in nature ; but that there are an enormous number of other creatures which have backbones, ribs, and legs, and other parts arranged in the same general manner, and in all their formation exhibiting the same broad peculiarities.

I am sure that you cannot have followed me even in this extremely elementary exposition of the structural relations of animals, without seeing what I have been driving at all through, which is, to show you that, step by step, naturalists have come to the idea of a unity of plan, or conformity of construction, among animals which appeared at first sight to be extremely dissimilar.

And here you have evidence of such a unity of plan among all the animals which have backbones, and which we technically call *Vertebrata*. But there are multitudes of other animals, such as crabs, lobsters, spiders, and so on, which we term *Annulosa*. In these I could not point out to you the parts that correspond with those of the Horse,—the backbone, for instance,—as they are constructed upon a very different principle, which is also common to all of them ; that is to say, the Lobster, the Spider, and the Centipede, have a common plan running through their whole arrangement, in just the same way that the Horse, the Dog, and the Porpoise assimilate to each other.

Yet other creatures—whelks, cuttlefishes, oysters, snails, and all their tribe (*Mollusca*)—resemble one another in the same way, but differ from both *Vertebrata* and *Annulosa*; and the like is true of the animals called *Cœlenterata* (Polypes) and *Protozoa* (animalcules and sponges).

Now, by pursuing this sort of comparison, naturalists have arrived at the conviction that there are,—some think five, and some seven,—but certainly not more than the latter number—and perhaps it is simpler to assume five—distinct plans or constructions in the whole of the animal world; and that the hundreds of thousands of species of creatures on the surface of the earth, are all reducible to those five, or, at most, seven, plans of organization.

But can we go no further than that? When one has got so far, one is tempted to go on a step and inquire whether we cannot go back yet further and bring down the whole to modifications of one primordial unit. The anatomist cannot do this; but if he call to his aid the study of development, he can do it. For we shall find that, distinct as those plans are, whether it be a porpoise or man, or lobster, or any of those other kinds I have mentioned, every one begins its existence with one and the same primitive form,—that of the egg, consisting, as we have seen, of a nitrogenous substance, having a small particle or nucleus in the centre of it. Furthermore, the earlier changes of each are substantially the same. And it is in this that lies that true "unity of organization" of the animal kindgom which has been guessed at and fancied for many years; but which it has been left to the present time to be demonstrated by the careful study of development. But is it possible to go another step further still, and to show that in the same way the whole of the organic world is reducible to one primitive condition of form? Is there among the plants the same primitive form of organization, and is that identical with that of the animal kindgom? The reply to that question, too, is not uncertain or doubtful. It is now proved that every plant begins its existence under the same form; that is to say, in that of a cell—a particle of nitrogenous matter having substantially the same conditions. So that if you trace back the oak to its first germ, or a man, or a horse, or lobster, or oyster, or any other animal you choose to name, you shall find each and all of these commencing their existence in forms essentially similar to each other: and, furthermore, that the first processes of growth, and many of the subsequent modifications, are essentially the same in principle in almost all.

In conclusion, let me, in a few words, recapitulate the positions which I have laid down. And you must understand that I have not been talking mere theory; I have been speaking of matters which are as plainly demonstrable as the commonest propositions of Euclid—of facts that must form the basis of all speculations and beliefs in Biological science. We have gradually traced down all organic forms, or, in other words, we have analyzed the present condition of animated nature, until we found that each species took its origin in a form similar to that under which all the others commenced their existence. We have found the whole of the vast array of living forms with which we are surrounded, constantly growing, increasing, decaying, and disappearing; the animal constantly attracting, modifying, and applying to its sustenance the matter of the vegetable kingdom, which derived its support from the absorption and conversion of inorganic matter. And so constant and universal is this absorption, waste, and reproduction, that it may be said with perfect certainty that there is left in no one of our bodies at the present moment a millionth part of the matter of which they were originally formed! We have seen, again, that not only is the living matter derived from the inorganic world, but that the forces of that matter are all of them correlative with and convertible into those of inorganic nature.

This, for our present purposes, is the best view of the present condition of organic nature which I can lay before you: it gives you the great outlines of a vast picture, which you must fill up by your own study.

In the next lecture I shall endeavour in the same way to go back into the past, and to sketch in the same broad manner the history of life in epochs preceding our own.

V

THE PAST CONDITION OF ORGANIC NATURE

IN the lecture which I delivered last Monday evening, I endeavoured to sketch in a very brief manner, but as well as the time at my disposal would permit, the present condition of organic nature, meaning by that large title simply an indication of the great, broad, and general principles which are to be discovered by those who look attentively at the phenomena of organic nature as at present displayed. The general result of our investigations might be summed up thus : we found that the multiplicity of the forms of animal life, great as that may be, may be reduced to a comparatively few primitive plans or types of construction ; that a further study of the development of those different forms revealed to us that they were again reducible, until we at last brought the infinite diversity of animal, and even vegetable life, down to the primordial form of a single cell.

We found that our analysis of the organic world, whether animals or plants, showed, in the long run, that they might both be reduced into, and were, in fact, composed of the same constituents. And we saw that the plant obtained the materials constituting its substance by a peculiar combination of matters belonging entirely to the inorganic world ; that, then, the animal was constantly appropriating the nitrogenous matters of the plant to its own nourishment, and returning them back to the inorganic world, in what we spoke of as its waste ; and that, finally, when the animal ceased to exist, the constituents of its body were dissolved and transmitted to that inorganic world whence they had been at first abstracted. Thus we saw in both the blade of grass and the horse but the same elements differently combined and arranged. We discovered a continual circulation going on,—the plant drawing in the elements of inorganic nature and combining them into food for the animal creation ; the animal borrowing from the plant the matter for its own support, giving off during its life products which returned immediately to the inorganic world ; and that, eventually, the constituent materials of the whole structure of both animals and plants were thus returned to their original source : there was a constant passage from one state of existence to another, and a returning back again.

Lastly, when we endeavoured to form some notion of the nature of the forces exercised by living beings, we discovered that they—if not capable of being subjected to the same minute analysis as the constituents of those beings themselves—that they were correlative with—that they were the equivalents of the forces of inorganic nature—that they were, in the sense in which the term is now used, convertible with them. That was our general result.

And now, leaving the Present, I must endeavour in the same manner to put before you the facts that are to be discovered in the Past history of the living world, in the past conditions of organic nature. We have, to-night, to deal with the facts of that history—a history involving periods of time before which our mere human records sink into utter insignificance—a history the variety and physical magnitude of whose events cannot even be foreshadowed by the history of human life and human phenomena—a history of the most varied and complex character.

We must deal with the history, then, in the first place, as we should deal with all other histories. The historical student knows that his first business should be to inquire into the validity of his evidence, and the nature of the record in which the evidence is contained, that he may be able to form a proper estimate of the correctness of the conclusions which have been drawn from that evidence. So, here, we must pass, in the first place, to the consideration of a matter which may seem foreign to the question under discussion. We must dwell upon the nature of the records, and the credibility of the evidence they contain; we must look to the completeness or incompleteness of those records themselves, before we turn to that which they contain and reveal. The question of the credibility of the history, happily for us, will not require much consideration, for, in this history, unlike those of human origin, there can be no cavilling, no differences as to the reality and truth of the facts of which it is made up; the facts state themselves, and are laid out clearly before us.

But, although one of the greatest difficulties of the historical student is cleared out of our path, there are other difficulties—difficulties in rightly interpreting the facts as they are presented to us—which may be compared with the greatest difficulties of any other kinds of historical study.

What is this record of the past history of the globe, and what are the questions which are involved in an inquiry into its completeness or incompleteness? That record is composed of mud; and the question which we have to investigate this evening resolves itself into a question of the formation of mud. You may think, perhaps, that this is a vast step—of almost from the sublime to the ridiculous—from the contemplation of the history of the past ages of the world's existence to the consideration of the history of the formation of mud! But, in nature, there is nothing mean and unworthy of attention; there is nothing ridiculous or contemptible in any of her works; and this inquiry, you will soon see, I hope, takes us to the very root and foundations of our subject.

How, then, is mud formed? Always, with some trifling exception, which I need not consider now—always, as the result of the action of water, wearing down and disintegrating the surface of the earth and rocks with which it comes in contact—pounding and grinding it down, and carrying the particles away to places where they cease to be disturbed by this mechanical action, and where they can subside and rest. For the ocean, urged by winds, washes, as we know, a long extent of coast, and every wave, loaded as it is with particles of sand and gravel as it breaks upon the shore, does something towards the disintegrating process. And thus, slowly but surely, the hardest rocks are gradually ground down to a powdery substance; and the mud thus formed, coarser or finer, as the case may be, is carried by the rush of the tides, or currents, till it reaches the comparatively deeper parts of the ocean, in which it can sink to the bottom, that is, to parts where there is a depth of about fourteen or fifteen fathoms, a depth at which the water is, usually, nearly motionless, and in which, of course, the finer particles of this detritus, or mud as we call it, sinks to the bottom.

Or, again, if you take a river, rushing down from its mountain sources, brawling over the stones and rocks that intersect its path, loosening, removing, and carrying with it in its downward course the pebbles and lighter matters from its banks, it crushes and pounds down the rocks and earths in precisely the same way as the wearing action of the sea waves. The matters forming the deposit are torn from the mountain-side and whirled impetuously into the valley, more slowly over the plain, thence into the estuary, and from the estuary they are swept into the sea. The coarser and heavier fragments are obviously deposited first, that is, as soon as the current begins to lose its force by becoming amalgamated with the stiller depths of the ocean, but the finer and lighter particles are carried further on, and eventually deposited in a deeper and stiller portion of the ocean.

It clearly follows from this that mud gives us a chronology; for it is evident that supposing this, which I now sketch, to be the sea bottom, and supposing this to be a coast-line; from the washing action of the sea upon the rock, wearing and grinding it down into a sediment of mud, the mud will be carried down and, at length, deposited in the deeper parts of this sea-bottom, where it will form a layer; and then while that first layer is hardening, other mud which is coming from the same source will, of course, be carried to the same place; and, as it is quite impossible for it to get beneath the layer already there, it deposits itself above it, and forms another layer, and in that way you gradually have layers of mud constantly forming and hardening one above the other, and conveying a record of time.

It is a necessary result of the operation of the law of gravitation that the uppermost layer shall be the youngest and the lowest the oldest, and that the different beds shall be older at any particular point or spot in exactly the ratio of their depth from the surface. So that if they were upheaved afterwards, and you had a series of these different layers of mud, converted into sandstone, or limestone, as the case might be, you might be sure that the bottom layer was deposited first, and that the upper layers were formed afterwards. Here, you see, is the first step in the history—these layers of mud give us an idea of time.

The whole surface of the earth,—I speak broadly, and leave out minor qualifications, — is made up of such layers of mud, so hard, the majority of them, that we call them rock, whether limestone or sandstone, or other varieties of rock. And, seeing that every part of the crust of the earth is made up in this way, you might think that the determination of the chronology, the fixing of the time which it has taken to form this crust is a comparatively simple matter. Take a broad average, ascertain how fast the mud is deposited upon the bottom of the sea, or in the estuary of rivers; take it to be an inch, or two, or three inches a year, or whatever you may roughly estimate it at; then take the total thickness of the whole series of stratified rocks, which geologists estimate at twelve or thirteen miles, or about seventy thousand feet, make a sum in short division, divide the total thickness by that of the quantity deposited in one year, and the result will, of course, give you the number of years which the crust has taken to form.

Truly, that looks a very simple process! It would be so except for certain difficulties, the very first of which is that of finding how rapidly sediments are deposited; but the main difficulty—a difficulty which renders any certain calculations of such a matter out of the question—is this, the sea-bottom on which the deposit takes place is continually shifting.

Instead of the surface of the earth being that stable,

fixed thing that it is popularly believed to be, being, in
common parlance, the very emblem of fixity itself, it is
incessantly moving, and is, in fact, as unstable as the
surface of the sea, except that its undulations are infinitely slower and enormously higher and deeper.

Now, what is the effect of this oscillation? Take the
case to which I have previously referred. The finer or
coarser sediments that are carried down by the current of
the river will only be carried out a certain distance, and
eventually, as we have already seen, on reaching the
stiller part of the ocean, will be deposited at the bottom.

Let C y (Fig. 35) be the sea-bottom, y D the shore, $x y$
the sea-level, then the coarser deposit will subside over

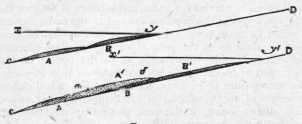

FIG. 35.

the region B, the finer over A, while beyond A there will
be no deposit at all ; and, consequently, no record will be
kept, simply because no deposit is going on. Now, suppose that the whole land, C, D, which we have regarded
as stationary, goes down, as it does so, both A and B go
further out from the shore, which will be at y^1, $x^1 y^1$,
being the new sea-level. The consequence will be that
the layer of mud (A), being now, for the most part,
further than the force of the current is strong enough to
convey even the finest *débris*, will, of course, receive no
more deposits, and having attained a certain thickness,
will now grow no thicker.

We should be misled in taking the thickness of that
layer, whenever it may be exposed to our view, as a
record of time in the manner in which we are now regarding this subject, as it would give us only an imperfect

and partial record : it would seem to represent too short a period of time.

Suppose, on the other hand, that the land (C D) had gone on rising slowly and gradually—say an inch or two inches in the course of a century,—what would be the practical effect of that movement? Why, that the sediment A and B which has been already deposited, would eventually be brought nearer to the shore-level, and again subjected to the wear and tear of the sea ; and directly the sea begins to act upon it, it would of course soon cut up and carry it away, to a greater or less extent, to be re-deposited further out.

Well, as there is, in all probability, not one single spot on the whole surface of the earth, which has not been up and down in this way a great many times, it follows that the thickness of the deposits formed at any particular spot cannot be taken (even supposing we had at first obtained correct data as to the rate at which they took place) as affording reliable information as to the period of time occupied in its deposit. So that you see it is absolutely necessary from these facts, seeing that our record entirely consists of accumulations of mud, superimposed one on the other ; seeing in the next place that any particular spots on which accumulations have occurred, have been constantly moving up and down, and sometimes out of the reach of a deposit, and at other times its own deposit broken up and carried away, it follows that our record must be in the highest degree imperfect, and we have hardly a trace left of thick deposits, or any definite knowledge of the area that they occupied in a great many cases. And mark this ! That supposing even that the whole surface of the earth had been accessible to the geologist, —that man had had access to every part of the earth, and had made sections of the whole, and put them all together, —even then his record must of necessity be imperfect.

But to how much has man really access? If you will look at this Map you will see that it represents the proportion of the sea to the earth : this coloured part indicates all the dry land, and this other portion is the water. You will notice at once that the water covers three-fifths of the whole surface of the globe, and has covered it in the same manner ever since man has kept any record of his own observations, to say nothing of the minute period during which he has cultivated geological inquiry. So that three-fifths of the surface of the earth is shut out from us because it is under the sea. Let us look at the other two-fifths, and see what are the countries in which anything that may be termed searching geological inquiry has been carried out: a good deal of France, Germany, and Great Britain and Ireland, bits of Spain, of Italy, and of Russia, have been examined, but of the whole great mass of Africa, except parts of the southern extremity, we know next to nothing; little bits of India, but of the greater part of the Asiatic continent nothing; bits of the Northern American States and of Canada, but of the greater part of the continent of North America, and in still larger proportion, of South America, nothing!

Under these circumstances, it follows that even with reference to that kind of imperfect information which we can possess, it is only of about the ten-thousandth part of the accessible parts of the earth that has been examined properly. Therefore, it is with justice that the most thoughtful of those who are concerned in these inquiries insist continually upon the imperfection of the geological record; for, I repeat, it is absolutely necessary, from the nature of things, that that record should be of the most fragmentary and imperfect character. Unfortunately this circumstance has been constantly forgotten. Men of science, like young colts in a fresh pasture, are apt to be exhilarated on being turned into a new field of inquiry, to go off at a hand-gallop, in total disregard of hedges and ditches, to lose sight of the real limitation of their inquiries, and to forget the extreme imperfection of what is really known. Geologists have imagined that they could tell us what was going on at all parts of the earth's surface during a given epoch; they have talked of this deposit being contemporaneous with that deposit, until, from our little local histories of the changes at limited spots of the earth's surface, they have constructed a universal history of the globe as full of wonders and portents as any other story of antiquity.

But what does this attempt to construct a universal

history of the globe imply? It implies that we shall not only have a precise knowledge of the events which have occurred at any particular point, but that we shall be able to say what events, at any one spot, took place at the same time with those at other spots.

Let us see how far that is in the nature of things practicable. Suppose that here I make a section of the Lake of Killarney, and here the section of another lake—that of Loch Lomond in Scotland for instance. The rivers that flow into them are constantly carrying down deposits of mud, and beds, or strata, are being as constantly formed, one above the other, at the bottom of those lakes. Now, there is not a shadow of doubt that in these two lakes the lower beds are all older than the

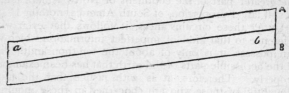

FIG. 36.

upper—there is no doubt about that; but what does *this* tell us about the age of any given bed in Loch Lomond, as compared with that of any given bed in the Lake of Killarney? It is, indeed, obvious that if any two sets of deposits are separated and discontinuous, there is absolutely no means whatever given you by the nature of the deposit of saying whether one is much younger or older than the other; but you may say, as many have said and think, that the case is very much altered if the beds which we are comparing are continuous. Suppose two beds of mud hardened into rock,—A and B are seen in section (Fig. 36.)

Well, you say, it is admitted that the lowermost bed is always the older. Very well; B, therefore, is older than A. No doubt, *as a whole*, it is so; or if any parts of the two beds which are in the same vertical line are compared, it is so. But suppose you take what seems a

very natural step further, and say that the part *a* of the
bed A is younger than the part *b* of the bed B. Is this
sound reasoning? If you find any record of changes
taking place at *b*, did they occur before any events which
took place while *a* was being deposited? It looks all
very plain sailing, indeed, to say that they did; and yet
there is no proof of anything of the kind. As the former
Director of this Institution, Sir H. De la Beche, long
ago showed, this reasoning may involve an entire fallacy.
It is extremely possible that *a* may have been deposited
ages before *b*. It is very easy to understand how that
can be. To return to Fig. 35; when A and B were
deposited, they were *substantially* contemporaneous; A
being simply the finer deposit, and B the coarser of the
same detritus or waste of land. Now suppose that that
sea-bottom goes down (as shown in Fig. 35), so that the
first deposit is carried no farther than *a*, forming the bed
A^1, and the coarse no farther than *b*, forming the bed
B^1, the result will be the formation of two continuous
beds, one of fine sediment (A A^1) over-lapping another
of coarse sediment (B B^1). Now suppose the whole
sea-bottom is raised up, and a section exposed about
the point A^1; no doubt, *at this spot*, the upper bed
is younger than the lower. But we should obviously
greatly err if we concluded that the mass of the upper
bed at A was younger than the lower bed at B; for we
have just seen that they are contemporaneous deposits.
Still more should we be in error if we supposed the
upper bed at A to be younger than the continuation of
the lower bed at B^1; for A was deposited long before B^1.
In fine, if, instead of comparing immediately adjacent
parts of two beds, one of which lies upon another, we
compare distant parts, it is quite possible that the upper
may be any number of years older than the under, and
the under any number of years younger than the upper.

Now you must not suppose that I put this before you
for the purpose of raising a paradoxical difficulty; the fact
is, that the great mass of deposits have taken place in
sea-bottoms which are gradually sinking, and have been
formed under the very conditions I am here supposing.

Do not run away with the notion that this subverts the

principle I laid down at first.   The error lies in extending a principle which is perfectly applicable to deposits in the same vertical line to deposits which are not in that relation to one another.

It is in consequence of circumstances of this kind, and of others that I might mention to you, that our conclusions on and interpretations of the record are really and strictly only valid so long as we confine ourselves to one vertical section.   I do not mean to tell you that there are no qualifying circumstances, so that, even in very considerable areas, we may safely speak of conformably superimposed beds being older or younger than others at many different points.   But we can never be quite sure in coming to that conclusion, and especially we cannot be sure if there is any break in their continuity, or any very great distance between the points to be compared.

Well now, so much for the record itself,—so much for its imperfections,—so much for the conditions to be observed in interpreting it, and its chronological indications, the moment we pass beyond the limits of a vertical linear section.

Now let us pass from the record to that which it contains,—from the book itself to the writing and the figures on its pages.   This writing and these figures consist of remains of animals and plants which, in the great majority of cases, have lived and died in the very spot in which we now find them, or at least in the immediate vicinity.   You must all of you be aware—and I referred to the fact in my last lecture—that there are vast numbers of creatures living at the bottom of the sea.   These creatures, like all others, sooner or later die, and their shells and hard parts lie at the bottom ; and then the fine mud which is being constantly brought down by rivers and the action of the wear and tear of the sea, covers them over and protects them from any further change or alteration ; and, of course, as in process of time the mud becomes hardened and solidified, the shells of these animals are preserved and firmly embedded in the limestone or sandstone which is being thus formed.   You may see in the galleries of the Museum upstairs specimens of limestones in which such fossil remains of existing animals are embedded. There are some specimens in which turtles' eggs have been embedded in calcareous sand, and before the sun had hatched the young turtles, they became covered over with calcareous mud, and thus have been preserved and fossilized.

Not only does this process of embedding and fossilization occur with marine and other aquatic animals and plants, but it affects those land animals and plants which are drifted away to sea, or become buried in bogs or morasses ; and the animals which have been trodden down by their fellows and crushed in the mud at the river's bank, as the herd have come to drink. In any of these cases, the organisms may be crushed or be mutilated, before or after putrefaction, in such a manner that perhaps only a part will be left in the form in which it reaches us. It is, indeed, a most remarkable fact, that it is quite an exceptional case to find a skeleton of any one of all the thousands of wild land animals that we know are constantly being killed, or dying in the course of nature : they are preyed on and devoured by other animals, or die in places where their bodies are not afterwards protected by mud. There are other animals existing in the sea, the shells of which form exceedingly large deposits. You are probably aware that before the attempt was made to lay the Atlantic telegraphic cable, the Government employed vessels in making a series of very careful observations and soundings of the bottom of the Atlantic ; and although, as we must all regret, that up to the present time that project has not succeeded, we have the satisfaction of knowing that it yielded some most remarkable results to science. The Atlantic Ocean had to be sounded right across, to depths of several miles in some places, and the nature of its bottom was carefully ascertained. Well, now, a space of about 1000 miles wide from east to west, and I do not exactly know how many from north to south, but at any rate 600 or 700 miles, was carefully examined, and it was found that over the whole of that immense area an excessively fine chalky mud is being deposited ; and this deposit is entirely made up of animals whose hard parts are deposited in this part of the ocean, and are doubtless gradually acquiring solidity and becoming metamorphosed into a chalky limestone. Thus, you see, it is quite possible in this way to preserve unmistakable records of animal and vegetable life. Whenever the sea-bottom, by some of those undulations of the earth's crust that I have referred to, becomes upheaved, and sections or borings are made, or pits are dug, then we become able to examine the contents and constituents of these ancient sea-bottoms, and find out what manner of animals lived at that period.

Now it is a very important consideration in its bearing on the completeness of the record, to inquire how far the remains contained in these fossiliferous limestones are able to convey anything like an accurate or complete account of the animals which were in existence at the time of its formation. Upon that point we can form a very clear judgment, and one in which there is no possible room for any mistake. There are of course a great number of animals—such as jelly-fishes, and other animals—without any hard parts, of which we cannot reasonably expect to find any traces whatever: there is nothing of them to preserve. Within a very short time, you will have noticed, after they are removed from the water, they dry up to a mere nothing; certainly they are not of a nature to leave any very visible traces of their existence on such bodies as chalk or mud. Then again, look at land animals; it is, as I have said, a very uncommon thing to find a land animal entire after death. Insects and other carnivorous animals very speedily pull them to pieces, putrefaction takes place, and so, out of the hundreds of thousands that are known to die every year, it is the rarest thing in the world to see one embedded in such a way that its remains would be preserved for a lengthened period. Not only is this the case, but even when animal remains have been safely embedded, certain natural agents may wholly destroy and remove them.

Almost all the hard parts of animals—the bones and so on—are composed chiefly of phosphate of lime and carbonate of lime. Some years ago, I had to make an inquiry into the nature of some very curious fossils sent to me from the North of Scotland. Fossils are usually hard bony structures that have become embedded in the way I have described, and have gradually acquired the nature and solidity of the body with which they are associated; but in this case I had a series of *holes* in some pieces of rock, and nothing else. Those holes, however, had a certain definite shape about them, and when I got a skilful workman to make castings of the interior of these holes, I found that they were the impressions of the joints of a backbone and of the armour of a great reptile, twelve or more feet long. This great beast had died and got buried in the sand, the sand had gradually hardened over the bones, but remained porous. Water had trickled through it, and that water being probably charged with a superfluity of carbonic acid, had dissolved all the phosphate and carbonate of lime, and the bones themselves had thus decayed and entirely disappeared; but as the sandstone happened to have consolidated by that time, the precise shape of the bones was retained. If that sandstone had remained soft a little longer, we should have known nothing whatsoever of the existence of the reptile whose bones it had encased.

How certain it is that a vast number of animals which have existed at one period on this earth have entirely perished, and left no trace whatever of their forms, may be proved to you by other considerations. There are large tracts of sandstone in various parts of the world, in which nobody has yet found anything but footsteps. Not a bone of any description, but an enormous number of traces of footsteps. There is no question about them. There is a whole valley in Connecticut covered with these footsteps, and not a single fragment of the animals which made them have yet been found. Let me mention another case while upon that matter, which is even more surprising than those to which I have yet referred. There is a limestone formation near Oxford, at a place called Stonesfield, which has yielded the remains of certain very interesting mammalian animals, and up to this time, if I recollect rightly, there have been found seven specimens of its lower jaws, and not a bit of anything else, neither limb-bones nor skull, or any part whatever; not a fragment of the whole system! Of course, it would be preposterous to imagine that the beasts had nothing else but a lower jaw! The probability is, as Dr. Buckland showed, as the result of his observations on dead dogs in the river Thames, that the lower jaw, not being secured by very firm ligaments to the bones of the head, and being a weighty affair, would easily be knocked off, or might drop away from the body as it floated in water in a state of decomposition. The jaw would thus be deposited immediately, while the rest of the body would float and drift away altogether, ultimately reaching the sea, and perhaps becoming destroyed. The jaw becomes covered up and preserved in the river silt, and thus it comes that we have such a curious circumstance as that of the lower jaws in the Stonesfield slates. So that, you see, faulty as these layers of stone in the earth's crust are, defective as they necessarily are as a record, the account of contemporaneous vital phenomena presented by them is, by the necessity of the case, infinitely more defective and fragmentary.

It was necessary that I should put all this very strongly before you, because, otherwise, you might have been led to think differently of the completeness of our knowledge by the next facts I shall state to you.

The researches of the last three-quarters of a century have, in truth, revealed a wonderful richness of organic life in those rocks. Certainly not fewer than thirty or forty thousand different species of fossils have been discovered. You have no more ground for doubting that these creatures really lived and died at or near the places in which we find them than you have for like scepticism about a shell on the sea-shore. The evidence is as good in the one case as in the other.

Our next business is to look at the general character of these fossil remains, and it is a subject which will be requisite to consider carefully; and the first point for us is to examine how much the extinct *Flora* and *Fauna* as a *whole*—disregarding altogether the *succession* of their constituents, of which I shall speak afterwards—differ from the *Flora* and *Fauna* of the present day;—how far they differ in what we *do* know about them, leaving altogether out of consideration speculations based on what we *do not* know.

I strongly imagine that if it were not for the peculiar appearance that fossilized animals have, that any of you might readily walk through a museum which contains fossil remains mixed up with those of the present forms of life, and I doubt very much whether your uninstructed eyes would lead you to see any vast or wonderful difference between the two. If you looked closely, you would notice, in the first place, a great many things very like animals with which you are acquainted now : you would see differences of shape and proportion, but on the whole a close similarity.

I explained what I meant by ORDERS the other day, when I described the animal kingdom as being divided into sub-kingdoms, classes, and orders. If you divide the animal kingdom into orders, you will find that there are above one hundred and twenty. The number may vary on one side or the other, but this is a fair estimate. That is the sum total of the orders of all the animals which we know now, and which have been known in past times, and left remains behind.

Now, how many of those are absolutely extinct ? That is to say, how many of these orders of animals have lived at a former period of the world's history, but have at present no representatives ? That is the sense in which I meant to use the word "extinct." I mean that those animals did live on this earth at one time, but have left no one of their kind with us at the present moment. So that estimating the number of extinct animals is a sort of way of comparing the past creation as a whole with the present as a whole. Among the mammalia and birds there are none extinct ; but when we come to the reptiles there is a most wonderful thing : out of the eight orders, or thereabouts, which you can make among reptiles, one-half are extinct. These diagrams of the plesiosaurus, the ichthyosaurus, the pterodactyle, give you a notion of some of these extinct reptiles. And here is a cast of the pterodactyle and bones of the ichthyosaurus and the plesiosaurus, just as fresh as if it had been recently dug up in a churchyard. Thus, in the reptile class, there are no less than half of the orders which are absolutely extinct. If we turn to the *Amphibia*, there was one extinct order, the Labyrinthodonts, typified by the large salamander-like beast shown in this diagram.

No order of fishes is known to be extinct. Every fish that we find in the strata—to which I have been referring —can be identified and placed in one of the orders which exist at the present day. There is not known to be a single ordinal form of insect extinct. There are only two orders extinct among the *Crustacea*. There is not known to be an extinct order of these creatures, the parasitic and other worms; but there are two, not to say three, absolutely extinct orders of this class, the *Echinodermata*; out of all the orders of the *Cœlenterata* and *Protozoa* only one, the Rugose Corals.

So that, you see, out of somewhere about 120 orders of animals, taking them altogether, you will not, at the outside estimate, find above ten or a dozen extinct. Summing up all the order of animals which have left remains behind them, you will not find above ten or a dozen which cannot be arranged with those of the present day; that is to say, that the difference does not amount to much more than ten per cent.: and the proportion of extinct orders of plants is still smaller. I think that that is a very astounding, a most astonishing fact: seeing the enormous epochs of time which have elapsed during the constitution of the surface of the earth as it at present exists; it is, indeed, a most astounding thing that the proportion of extinct ordinal types should be so exceedingly small.

But now, there is another point of view in which we must look at this past creation. Suppose that we were to sink a vertical pit through the floor beneath us, and that I could succeed in making a section right through in the direction of New Zealand, I should find in each of the different beds through which I passed the remains of animals which I should find in that stratum and not in the others. First, I should come upon beds of gravel or drift containing the bones of large animals, such as the elephant, rhinoceros, and cave tiger. Rather curious things to fall across in Piccadilly! If I should dig lower still, I should come upon a bed of what we call the London clay, and in this, as you will see in our galleries upstairs, are found remains of strange cattle, remains of turtles, palms, and large tropical fruits; with shell-fish such as you see the like of now only in tropical regions. If I went below that, I should come upon the chalk, and there I should find something altogether different, the remains of ichthyosauri and pterodactyles, and ammonites, and so forth.

I do not know what Mr. Godwin Austin would say comes next, but probably rocks containing more ammonites, and more ichthyosauri and plesiosauri, with a vast number of other things; and under that I should meet with yet older rocks, containing numbers of strange shells and fishes; and in thus passing from the surface to the lowest depths of the earth's crust, the forms of animal life and vegetable life which I should meet with in the successive beds would, looking at them broadly, be the more different the further that I went down. Or, in other words, inasmuch as we started with the clear principle, that in a series of naturally-disposed mud beds the lowest are the oldest, we should come to this result, that the farther we go back in time the more difference exists between the animal and vegetable life of an epoch and that which now exists. That was the conclusion to which I wished to bring you at the end of this Lecture.

VI

THE METHOD BY WHICH THE CAUSES OF THE PRESENT AND PAST CONDITIONS OF ORGANIC NATURE ARE TO BE DISCOVERED.—THE ORIGINATION OF LIVING BEINGS.

In the two preceding lectures I have endeavoured to indicate to you the extent of the subject-matter of the inquiry upon which we are engaged; and having thus acquired some conception of the Past and Present phenomena of Organic Nature, I must now turn to that which constitutes the great problem which we have set before ourselves;—I mean, the question of what knowledge we have of the causes of these phenomena of organic nature, and how such knowledge is obtainable.

Here, on the threshold of the inquiry, an objection meets us. There are in the world a number of extremely worthy, well-meaning persons, whose judgments and opinions are entitled to the utmost respect on account of their sincerity, who are of opinion that Vital Phenomena, and especially all questions relating to the origin of vital phenomena, are questions quite apart from the ordinary run of inquiry, and are, by their very nature, placed out of our reach. They say that all these phenomena originated miraculously, or in some way totally different from the ordinary course of nature, and that therefore they conceive it to be futile, not to say presumptuous, to attempt to inquire into them.

To such sincere and earnest persons, I would only say, that a question of this kind is not to be shelved upon theoretical or speculative grounds. You may remember the story of the Sophist who demonstrated to Diogenes in the most complete and satisfactory manner that he could not walk; that, in fact, all motion was an impossibility; and that Diogenes refuted him by simply getting up and walking round his tub. So, in the same way, the man of science replies to objections of this kind, by simply getting up and walking onward, and showing what science has done and is doing,—by pointing to that immense mass of facts which have been ascertained and systematized under the forms of the great doctrines of Morphology, of Development, of Distribution, and the like. He sees an enormous mass of facts and laws relating to organic beings, which stand on the same good sound foundation as every other natural law. With this mass of facts and laws before us, therefore, seeing that, as far as organic matters have hitherto been accessible and studied, they have shown themselves capable of yielding to scientific investigation, we may accept this as proof that order and law reign there as well as in the rest of nature. The man of science says nothing to objectors of this sort, but supposes that we can and shall walk to a knowledge of the origin of organic nature, in the same way that we have walked to a knowledge of the laws and principles of the inorganic world.

But there are objectors who say the same from ignorance and ill-will. To such I would reply that the objection comes ill from them, and that the real presumption, I may almost say the real blasphemy, in this matter, is in the attempt to limit that inquiry into the causes of phenomena, which is the source of all human blessings, and from which has sprung all human prosperity and progress; for, after all, we can accomplish comparatively little; the limited range of our own faculties bounds us on every side,—the field of our powers of observation is small enough, and he who endeavours to narrow the sphere of our inquiries is only pursuing a course that is likely to produce the greatest harm to his fellow-men.

But now, assuming, as we all do, I hope, that these phenomena are properly accessible to inquiry, and setting out upon our search into the causes of the phenomena of organic nature, or, at any rate, setting out to discover how much we at present know upon these abstruse matters, the question arises as to what is to be our course of proceeding, and what method we must lay down for our guidance. I reply to that question, that our method must be exactly the same as that which is pursued in any other scientific inquiry, the method of scientific investigation being the same for all orders of facts and phenomena whatsoever.

I must dwell a little on this point, for I wish you to leave this room with a very clear conviction that scientific investigation is not, as many people seem to suppose, some kind of modern black art. I say that you might easily gather this impression from the manner in which many persons speak of scientific inquiry, or talk about inductive and deductive philosophy, or the principles of the "Baconian philosophy." I do protest that, of the vast number of cants in this world, there are none, to my mind, so contemptible as the pseudo-scientific cant which is talked about the "Baconian philosophy."

To hear people talk about the great Chancellor,—and a very great man he certainly was,—you would think that it was he who had invented science, and that there was no such thing as sound reasoning before the time of Queen Elizabeth! Of course you say, that cannot possibly be true; you perceive, on a moment's reflection, that such an idea is absurdly wrong; and yet, so firmly rooted is this sort of impression,—I cannot call it an idea, or conception,—the thing is too absurd to be entertained, —but so completely does it exist at the bottom of most men's minds, that this has been a matter of observation with me for many years past. There are many men who, though knowing absolutely nothing of the subject with which they may be dealing, wish, nevertheless, to damage the author of some view with which they think fit to disagree. What they do, then, is not to go and learn something about the subject, which one would naturally think the best way of fairly dealing with it; but they abuse the originator of the view they question, in a general manner, and wind up by saying that, "After all, you know, the principles and method of this author are totally opposed to the canons of the Baconian philosophy." Then everybody applauds, as a matter of course, and agrees that it must be so. But if you were to stop them all in the middle of their applause, you would probably find that neither the speaker nor his applauders could tell you how or in what way it was so; neither the one nor the other having the slightest idea of what they mean when they speak of the "Baconian philosophy."

You will understand, I hope, that I have not the slightest desire to join in the outcry against either the morals, the intellect, or the great genius of Lord Chancellor Bacon. He was undoubtedly a very great man, let people say what they will of him; but notwithstanding all that he did for philosophy, it would be entirely wrong to suppose that the methods of modern scientific inquiry originated with him, or with his age; they originated with the first man, whoever he was; and indeed existed long before him, for many of the essential processes of reasoning are exerted by the higher order of brutes as completely and effectively as by ourselves. We see in many of the brute creation the exercise of one, at least, of the same powers of reasoning as that which we ourselves employ.

The method of scientific investigation is nothing but the expression of the necessary mode of working of the human mind. It is simply the mode at which all phenomena are reasoned about, rendered precise and exact. There is no more difference, but there is just the same kind of difference, between the mental operations of a man of science and those of an ordinary person, as there is between the operations and methods of a baker or of a butcher weighing out his goods in common scales, and the operations of a chemist in performing a difficult and complex analysis by means of his balance and finely-graduated weights. It is not that the action of the scales in the one case, and the balance in the other, differ in the principles of their construction or manner of working; but the beam of one is set on an infinitely finer axis than the other, and of course turns by the addition of a much smaller weight.

You will understand this better, perhaps, if I give you some familiar example. You have all heard it repeated, I dare say, that men of science work by means of Induc-

tion and Deduction, and that by the help of these operations, they, in a sort of sense, wring from Nature certain
other things, which are called Natural Laws, and Causes,
and that out of these, by some cunning skill of their
own, they build up Hypotheses and Theories. And it is
imagined by many, that the operations of the common
mind can be by no means compared with these processes,
and that they have to be acquired by a sort of special
apprenticeship to the craft. To hear all these large words,
you would think that the mind of a man of science must
be constituted differently from that of his fellow-men;
but if you will not be frightened by terms, you will discover that you are quite wrong, and that all these terrible
apparatus are being used by yourselves every day and
every hour of your lives.

There is a well-known incident in one of Molière's
plays, where the author makes the hero express unbounded
delight on being told that he had been talking prose during
the whole of his life. In the same way, I trust, that you
will take comfort, and be delighted with yourselves, on
the discovery that you have been acting on the principles of inductive and deductive philosophy during the
same period. Probably there is not one here who has not
in the course of the day had occasion to set in motion
a complex train of reasoning, of the very same kind,
though differing of course in degree, as that which a
scientific man goes through in tracing the causes of
natural phenomena.

A very trivial circumstance will serve to exemplify this.
Suppose you go into a fruiterer's shop, wanting an apple,—
you take up one, and, on biting it, you find it is sour; you
look at it, and see that it is hard and green. You take
up another one, and that too is hard, green, and sour.
The shopman offers you a third; but, before biting it,
you examine it, and find that it is hard and green, and
you immediately say that you will not have it, as it must
be sour, like those that you have already tried.

Nothing can be more simple than that, you think; but
if you will take the trouble to analyze and trace out into
its logical elements what has been done by the mind,
you will be greatly surprised. In the first place, you have

performed the operation of Induction. You found that, in two experiences, hardness and greenness in apples went together with sourness. It was so in the first case, and it was confirmed by the second. True, it is a very small basis, but still it is enough to make an induction from; you generalize the facts, and you expect to find sourness in apples where you get hardness and greenness. You found upon that a general law, that all hard and green apples are sour; and that, so far as it goes, is a perfect induction. Well, having got your natural law in this way, when you are offered another apple which you find is hard and green, you say, "All hard and green apples are sour; this apple is hard and green, therefore this apple is sour." That train of reasoning is what logicians call a syllogism, and has all its various parts and terms,—its major premiss, its minor premiss, and its conclusion. And, by the help of further reasoning, which, if drawn out, would have to be exhibited in two or three other syllogisms, you arrive at your final determination, "I will not have that apple." So that, you see, you have, in the first place, established a law by Induction, and upon that you have founded a Deduction, and reasoned out the special conclusion of the particular case. Well now, suppose, having got your law, that at some time afterwards, you are discussing the qualities of apples with a friend: you will say to him, "It is a very curious thing, —but I find that all hard and green apples are sour!" Your friend says to you, "But how do you know that?" You at once reply, "Oh, because I have tried them over and over again, and have always found them to be so." Well, if we were talking science instead of common sense, we should call that an Experimental Verification. And, if still opposed, you go further, and say, "I have heard from the people in Somersetshire and Devonshire, where a large number of apples are grown, that they have observed the same thing. It is also found to be the case in Normandy, and in North America. In short, I find it to be the universal experience of mankind wherever attention has been directed to the subject." Whereupon, your friend, unless he is a very unreasonable man, agrees with you, and is convinced that you are quite right in the conclusion you have drawn. He believes, although perhaps he does not know he believes it, that the more extensive Verifications are, — that the more frequently experiments have been made, and results of the same kind arrived at,—that the more varied the conditions under which the same results are attained, the more certain is the ultimate conclusion, and he disputes the question no further. He sees that the experiment has been tried under all sorts of conditions, as to time, place, and people, with the same result; and he says with you, therefore, that the law you have laid down must be a good one, and he must believe it.

In science we do the same thing;—the philosopher exercises precisely the same faculties, though in a much more delicate manner. In scientific inquiry it becomes a matter of duty to expose a supposed law to every possible kind of verification, and to take care, moreover, that this is done intentionally, and not left to a mere accident, as in the case of the apples. And in science, as in common life, our confidence in a law is in exact proportion to the absence of variation in the result of our experimental verifications. For instance, if you let go your grasp of an article you may have in your hand, it will immediately fall to the ground. That is a very common verification of one of the best established laws of nature—that of gravitation. The method by which men of science establish the existence of that law is exactly the same as that by which we have established the trivial proposition about the sourness of hard and green apples. But we believe it in such an extensive, thorough, and unhesitating manner because the universal experience of mankind verifies it, and we can verify it ourselves at any time; and that is the strongest possible foundation on which any natural law can rest.

So much, then, by way of proof that the method of establishing laws in science is exactly the same as that pursued in common life. Let us now turn to another matter, (though really it is but another phase of the same question,) and that is, the method by which, from the relations of certain phenomena, we prove that some stand in the position of causes towards the others.

I want to put the case clearly before you, and I will therefore show you what I mean by another familiar example. I will suppose that one of you, on coming down in the morning to the parlour of your house, finds that a tea-pot and some spoons which had been left in the room on the previous evening are gone,—the window is open, and you observe the mark of a dirty hand on the window-frame, and perhaps, in addition to that, you notice the impress of a hob-nailed shoe on the gravel outside. All these phenomena have struck your attention instantly, and before two seconds have passed you say, "Oh, somebody has broken open the window, entered the room, and run off with the spoons and the tea-pot!" That speech is out of your mouth in a moment. And you will probably add, "I know there has; I am quite sure of it!" You mean to say exactly what you know; but in reality you are giving expression to what is, in all essential particulars, an Hypothesis. You do not *know* it at all; it is nothing but an hypothesis rapidly framed in your own mind! And, it is an hypothesis founded on a long train of inductions and deductions.

What are those inductions and deductions, and how have you got at this hypothesis? You have observed, in the first place, that the window is open; but by a train of reasoning involving many Inductions and Deductions, you have probably arrived long before at the General Law—and a very good one it is—that windows do not open of themselves; and you therefore conclude that something has opened the window. A second general law that you have arrived at in the same way is, that tea-pots and spoons do not go out of a window spontaneously, and you are satisfied that, as they are not now where you left them, they have been removed. In the third place, you look at the marks on the window-sill, and the shoe-marks outside, and you say that in all previous experience the former kind of mark has never been produced by anything else but the hand of a human being; and the same experience shows that no other animal but man at present wears shoes with hob-nails in them such as would produce the marks in the gravel. I do not know, even if we could discover any of those "missing links" that are talked about, that they would help us to any other conclusion! At any rate the law which states our present experience is strong enough for my present purpose. You next reach the conclusion, that as these kinds of marks have not been left by any other animals than men, or are liable to be formed in any other way than by a man's hand and shoe, the marks in question have been formed by a man in that way. You have, further, a general law, founded on observation and experience, and that, too, is, I am sorry to say, a very universal and unimpeachable one,—that some men are thieves; and you assume at once from all these premises—and that is what constitutes your hypothesis —that the man who made the marks outside and on the window-sill, opened the window, got into the room, and stole your tea-pot and spoons. You have now arrived at a *Vera Causa ;*—you have assumed a Cause which it is plain is competent to produce all the phenomena you have observed. You can explain all these phenomena only by the hypothesis of a thief. But that is a hypothetical conclusion, of the justice of which you have no absolute proof at all ; it is only rendered highly probable by a series of inductive and deductive reasonings.

I suppose your first action, assuming that you are a man of ordinary common sense, and that you have established this hypothesis to your own satisfaction, will very likely be to go off for the police, and set them on the track of the burglar, with the view to the recovery of your property. But just as you are starting with this object, some person comes in, and on learning what you are about, says, " My good friend, you are going on a great deal too fast. How do you know that the man who really made the marks took the spoons ? It might have been a monkey that took them, and the man may have merely looked in afterwards." You would probably reply, " Well, that is all very well, but you see it is contrary to all experience of the way tea-pots and spoons are abstracted ; so that, at any rate, your hypothesis is less probable than mine." While you are talking the thing over in this way, another friend arrives, one of that good kind of people that I was talking of a little while ago. And he might say, "Oh, my dear sir, you are certainly going on a great deal too fast. You are most presumptuous. You admit that all these occurrences took place when you were fast asleep, at a time when you could not possibly have known anything about what was taking place. How do you know that the laws of Nature are not suspended during the night? It may be that there has been some kind of supernatural interference in this case." In point of fact, he declares that your hypothesis is one of which you cannot at all demonstrate the truth, and that you are by no means sure that the laws of Nature are the same when you are asleep as when you are awake.

Well, now, you cannot at the moment answer that kind of reasoning. You feel that your worthy friend has you somewhat at a disadvantage. You will feel perfectly convinced in your own mind, however, that you are quite right, and you say to him, "My good friend, I can only be guided by the natural probabilities of the case, and if you will be kind enough to stand aside and permit me to pass, I will go and fetch the police." Well, we will suppose that your journey is successful, and that by good luck you meet with a policeman; that eventually the burglar is found with your property on his person, and the marks correspond to his hand and to his boots. Probably any jury would consider those facts a very good experimental verification of your hypothesis, touching the cause of the abnormal phenomena observed in your parlour, and would act accordingly.

Now, in this supposititious case, I have taken phenomena of a very common kind, in order that you might see what are the different steps in an ordinary process of reasoning, if you will only take the trouble to analyze it carefully. All the operations I have described, you will see, are involved in the mind of any man of sense in leading him to a conclusion as to the course he should take in order to make good a robbery and punish the offender. I say that you are led, in that case, to your conclusion by exactly the same train of reasoning as that which a man of science pursues when he is endeavouring to discover the origin and laws of the most occult phenomena. The

process is, and always must be, the same; and precisely
the same mode of reasoning was employed by Newton
and Laplace in their endeavours to discover and define
the causes of the movements of the heavenly bodies,
as you, with your own common sense, would employ to
detect a burglar. The only difference is, that the nature
of the inquiry being more abstruse, every step has to be
most carefully watched, so that there may not be a single
crack or flaw in your hypothesis. A flaw or crack in
many of the hypotheses of daily life may be of little or no
moment as affecting the general correctness of the conclusions at which we may arrive; but in a scientific inquiry a fallacy, great or small, is always of importance,
and is sure to be in the long run constantly productive
of mischievous, if not fatal results.

Do not allow yourselves to be misled by the common
notion that an hypothesis is untrustworthy simply because
it is an hypothesis. It is often urged, in respect to some
scientific conclusion, that, after all, it is only an hypothesis. But what more have we to guide us in nine-tenths
of the most important affairs of daily life than hypotheses,
and often very ill-based ones? So that in science, where
the evidence of an hypothesis is subjected to the most
rigid examination, we may rightly pursue the same course.
You may have hypotheses and hypotheses. A man may
say, if he likes, that the moon is made of green cheese:
that is an hypothesis. But another man, who has devoted a great deal of time and attention to the subject,
and availed himself of the most powerful telescopes and
the results of the observations of others, declares that in
his opinion it is probably composed of materials very
similar to those of which our own earth is made up : and
that is also only an hypothesis. But I need not tell you
that there is an enormous difference in the value of the
two hypotheses. That one which is based on sound
scientific knowledge is sure to have a corresponding
value; and that which is a mere hasty random guess
is likely to have but little value. Every great step in
our progress in discovering causes has been made in
exactly the same way as that which I have detailed to
you. A person observing the occurrence of certain facts

and phenomena asks, naturally enough, what process, what kind of operation known to occur in nature applied to the particular case, will unravel and explain the mystery? Hence you have the scientific hypothesis; and its value will be proportionate to the care and completeness with which its basis had been tested and verified. It is in these matters as in the commonest affairs of practical life: the guess of the fool will be folly, while the guess of the wise man will contain wisdom. In all cases, you see that the value of the result depends on the patience and faithfulness with which the investigator applies to his hypothesis every possible kind of verification.

I dare say I may have to return to this point by-and-by; but having dealt thus far with our logical methods, I must now turn to something which, perhaps, you may consider more interesting, or, at any rate, more tangible. But in reality there are but few things that can be more important for you to understand than the mental processes and the means by which we obtain scientific conclusions and theories.[1] Having granted that the inquiry is a proper one, and having determined on the nature of the methods we are to pursue and which only can lead to success, I must now turn to the consideration of our knowledge of the nature of the processes which have resulted in the present condition of organic nature.

Here, let me say at once, lest some of you misunderstand me, that I have extremely little to report. The question of how the present condition of organic nature came about, resolves itself into two questions. The first is: How has organic or living matter commenced its existence? And the second is: How has it been perpetuated? On the second question I shall have more to say hereafter. But on the first one, what I now have to say will be for the most part of a negative character.

If you consider what kind of evidence we can have upon this matter, it will resolve itself into two kinds. We may have historical evidence and we may have experimental evidence. It is, for example, conceivable, that

[1] Those who wish to study fully the doctrines of which I have endeavoured to give some rough and ready illustrations, must read Mr. John Stuart Mill's "System of Logic."

inasmuch as the hardened mud which forms a considerable portion of the thickness of the earth's crust contains faithful records of the past forms of life, and inasmuch as these differ more and more as we go further down,—it is possible and conceivable that we might come to some particular bed or stratum which should contain the remains of those creatures with which organic life began upon the earth. And if we did so, and if such forms of organic life were preservable, we should have what I would call historical evidence of the mode in which organic life began upon this planet. Many persons will tell you, and indeed you will find it stated in many works on geology, that this has been done, and that we really possess such a record ; there are some who imagine that the earliest forms of life of which we have as yet discovered any record, are in truth the forms in which animal life began upon the globe. The grounds on which they base that supposition are these :—That if you go through the enormous thickness of the earth's crust and get down to the older rocks, the higher vertebrate animals—the quadrupeds, birds, and fishes—cease to be found ; beneath them you find only the invertebrate animals ; and in the deepest and lowest rocks those remains become scantier and scantier, not in any very gradual progression, however, until, at length, in what are supposed to be the oldest rocks, the animal remains which are found are almost always confined to four forms,—*Oldhamia*, whose precise nature is not known, whether plant or animal; *Lingula*, a kind of mollusc ; *Trilobites*, a crustacean animal, having the same essential plan of construction, though differing in many details from a lobster or crab ; and *Hymenocaris*, which is also a crustacean. So that you have all the *Fauna* reduced, at this period, to four forms : one a kind of animal or plant that we know nothing about, and three undoubted animals—two crustaceans and one mollusc.

I think, considering the organization of these mollusca and crustacea, and looking at their very complex nature, that it does indeed require a very strong imagination to conceive that these were the first created of all living things. And you must take into consideration the fact that we have not the slightest proof that these which we call the oldest beds are really so : I repeat, we have not the slightest proof of it. When you find in some places that in an enormous thickness of rocks there are but very scanty traces of life, or absolutely none at all ; and that in other parts of the world rocks of the very same formation are crowded with the records of living forms, I think it is impossible to place any reliance on the supposition, or to feel oneself justified in supposing that these are the forms in which life first commenced. I have not time here to enter upon the technical grounds upon which I am led to this conclusion,—that could hardly be done properly in half a dozen lectures on that part alone ;—I must content myself with saying that I do not at all believe that these are the oldest forms of life.

I turn to the experimental side to see what evidence we have there. To enable us to say that we know anything about the experimental origination of organization and life, the investigator ought to be able to take inorganic matters, such as carbonic acid, ammonia, water, and salines, in any sort of inorganic combination, and be able to build them up into Protein matter, and then that Protein matter ought to begin to live in an organic form. That, nobody has done as yet, and I suspect it will be a long while before anybody does do it. But the thing is by no means so impossible as it looks ; for the researches of modern chemistry have shown us—I won't say the road towards it, but, if I may so say, they have shown the finger-post pointing to the road that may lead to it.

It is not many years ago—and you must recollect that Organic Chemistry is a young science, not above a couple of generations old, you must not expect too much of it,— it is not many years ago since it was said to be perfectly impossible to fabricate any organic compound ; that is to say, any non-mineral compound which is to be found in an organized being. It remained so for a very long period ; but it is now a considerable number of years since a distinguished foreign chemist contrived to fabri- cate Urea, a substance of a very complex character, which forms one of the waste products of animal structures. And of late years a number of other compounds, such as

Butyric Acid, and others, have been added to the list. I need not tell you that chemistry is an enormous distance from the goal I indicate; all I wish to point out to you is, that it is by no means safe to say that that goal may not be reached one day. It may be that it is impossible for us to produce the conditions requisite to the origination of life; but we must speak modestly about the matter, and recollect that Science has put her foot upon the bottom round of the ladder. Truly he would be a bold man who would venture to predict where she will be fifty years hence.

There is another inquiry which bears indirectly upon this question, and upon which I must say a few words. You are all of you aware of the phenomena of what is called spontaneous generation. Our forefathers, down to the seventeenth century, or thereabouts, all imagined, in perfectly good faith, that certain vegetable and animal forms gave birth, in the process of their decomposition, to insect life. Thus, if you put a piece of meat in the sun, and allowed it to putrefy, they conceived that the grubs which soon began to appear were the result of the action of a power of spontaneous generation which the meat contained. And they could give you receipts for making various animal and vegetable preparations which would produce particular kinds of animals. A very distinguished Italian naturalist, named Redi, took up the question, at a time when everybody believed in it; among others our own great Harvey, the discoverer of the circulation of the blood. You will constantly find his name quoted, however, as an opponent of the doctrine of spontaneous generation; but the fact is, and you will see it if you take the trouble to look into his works, Harvey believed it as profoundly as any man of his time; but he happened to enunciate a very curious proposition—that every living thing came from an *egg;* he did not mean to use the word in the sense in which we now employ it, he only meant to say that every living thing originated in a little rounded particle of organized substance; and it is from this circumstance, probably, that the notion of Harvey having opposed the doctrine originated. Then came Redi, and he proceeded to upset the doctrine in a very simple manner.   He merely covered the piece of meat with some very fine gauze, and then he exposed it to the same conditions.   The result of this was that no grubs or insects were produced ; he proved that the grubs originated from the insects who came and deposited their eggs in the meat, and that they were hatched by the heat of the sun. By this kind of inquiry he thoroughly upset the doctrine of spontaneous generation, for his time at least.

Then came the discovery and application of the microscope to scientific inquiries, which showed to naturalists that besides the organisms which they already knew as living beings and plants, there were an immense number of minute things which could be obtained apparently almost at will from decaying vegetable and animal forms. Thus, if you took some ordinary black pepper or some hay, and steeped it in water, you would find in the course of a few days that the water had become impregnated with an immense number of animalcules swimming about in all directions.   From facts of this kind naturalists were led to revive the theory of spontaneous generation.   They were headed here by an English naturalist,—Needham,—and afterwards in France by the learned Buffon.   They said that these things were absolutely begotten in the water of the decaying substances out of which the infusion was made.   It did not matter whether you took animal or vegetable matter, you had only to steep it in water and expose it, and you would soon have plenty of animalcules.   They made an hypothesis about this which was a very fair one.   They said, this matter of the animal world, or of the higher plants, appears to be dead, but in reality it has a sort of dim life about it, which, if it is placed under fair conditions, will cause it to break up into the forms of these little animalcules, and they will go through their lives in the same way as the animal or plant of which they once formed a part.

The question now became very hotly debated.   Spallanzani, an Italian naturalist, took up opposite views to those of Needham and Buffon, and by means of certain experiments he showed that it was quite possible to stop the process by boiling the water, and closing the vessel in

which it was contained. "Oh!" said his opponents;
"but what do you know you may be doing when you heat
the air over the water in this way? You may be destroy-
ing some property of the air requisite for the spontaneous
generation of the animalcules."

However, Spallanzani's views were supposed to be upon
the right side, and those of the others fell into discredit;
although the fact was that Spallanzani had not made good
his views. Well, then, the subject continued to be revived
from time to time, and experiments were made by several
persons; but these experiments were not altogether satisfactory. It was found that if you put an infusion in
which animalcules would appear if it were exposed to the
air into a vessel and boiled it, and then sealed up the
mouth of the vessel, so that no air, save such as had been
heated to 212°, could reach its contents, that then no
animalcules would be found; but if you took the same
vessel and exposed the infusion to the air, then you would
get animalcules. Furthermore, it was found that if you
connected the mouth of the vessel with a red-hot tube in
such a way that the air would have to pass through the
tube before reaching the infusion, that then you would
get no animalcules. Yet another thing was noticed: if
you took two flasks containing the same kind of infusion,
and left one entirely exposed to the air, and in the mouth
of the other placed a ball of cotton wool, so that the air
would have to filter itself through it before reaching the
infusion, that then, although you might have plenty of
animalcules in the first flask, you would certainly obtain
none from the second.

These experiments, you see, all tended towards one
conclusion—that the infusoria were developed from little
minute spores or eggs which were constantly floating in
the atmosphere, and which lose their power of germination
if subjected to heat. But one observer now made another
experiment, which seemed to go entirely the other way,
and puzzled him altogether. He took some of this boiled
infusion that I have been speaking of, and by the use of
a mercurial bath—a kind of trough used in laboratories—
he deftly inverted a vessel containing the infusion into
the mercury, so that the latter reached a little beyond the

level of the mouth of the *inverted* vessel. You see that he thus had a quantity of the infusion shut off from any possible communication with the outer air by being inverted upon a bed of mercury.

He then prepared some pure oxygen and nitrogen gases, and passed them by means of a tube going from the outside of the vessel, up through the mercury into the infusion; so that he thus had it exposed to a perfectly pure atmosphere of the same constituents as the external air. Of course, he expected he would get no infusorial animalcules at all in that infusion; but, to his great dismay and discomfiture, he found he almost always did get them.

Furthermore, it has been found that experiments made in the manner described above answer well with most infusions; but that if you fill the vessel with boiled milk, and then stop the neck with cotton-wool, you *will* have infusoria. So that you see there were two experiments that brought you to one kind of conclusion, and three to another; which was a most unsatisfactory state of things to arrive at in a scientific inquiry.

Some few years after this, the question began to be very hotly discussed in France. There was M. Pouchet, a professor at Rouen, a very learned man, but certainly not a very rigid experimentalist. He published a number of experiments of his own, some of which were very ingenious, to show that if you went to work in a proper way, there was a truth in the doctrine of spontaneous generation. Well, it was one of the most fortunate things in the world that M. Pouchet took up this question, because it induced a distinguished French chemist, M. Pasteur, to take up the question on the other side; and he has certainly worked it out in the most perfect manner. I am glad to say, too, that he has published his researches in time to enable me to give you an account of them. He verified all the experiments which I have just mentioned to you— and then finding those extraordinary anomalies, as in the case of the mercury bath and the milk, he set himself to work to discover their nature. In the case of milk he found it to be a question of temperature. Milk in a fresh state is slightly alkaline; and it is a very curious circumstance, but this very slight degree of alkalinity seems to have the effect of preserving the organisms which fall into it from the air from being destroyed at a temperature of 212°, which is the boiling point. But if you raise the temperature 10° when you boil it, the milk behaves like everything else ; and if the air with which it comes in contact, after being boiled at this temperature, is passed through a red-hot tube, you will not get a trace of organisms.

He then turned his attention to the mercury bath, and found on examination that the surface of the mercury was almost always covered with a very fine dust. He found that even the mercury itself was positively full of organic matters ; that from being constantly exposed to the air, it had collected an immense number of these infusorial organisms from the air. Well, under these circumstances he felt that the case was quite clear, and that the mercury was not what it had appeared to M. Schwann to be,—a bar to the admission of these organisms ; but that, in reality, it acted as a reservoir from which the infusion was immediately supplied with the large quantity that had so puzzled him.

But not content with explaining the experiments of others, M. Pasteur went to work to satisfy himself completely. He said to himself : " If my view is right, and if, in point of fact, all these appearances of spontaneous generation are altogether due to the falling of minute germs suspended in the atmosphere,—why, I ought not only to be able to show the germs, but I ought to be able to catch and sow them, and produce the resulting organisms." He, accordingly, constructed a very ingenious apparatus to enable him to accomplish the trapping of the "*germ dust*" in the air. He fixed in the window of his room a glass tube, in the centre of which he had placed a ball of gun-cotton, which, as you all know, is ordinary cotton-wool, which, from having been steeped in strong acid, is converted into a substance of great explosive power. It is also soluble in alcohol and ether. One end of the glass tube was, of course, open to the external air ; and at the other end of it he placed an aspirator, a contrivance for causing a current of the external air to pass through the tube. He kept this apparatus going for four-and-twenty hours, and then removed the *dusted* gun-cotton, and dissolved it in alcohol and ether. He then allowed this to stand for a few hours, and the result was, that a very fine dust was gradually deposited at the bottom of it. That dust, on being transferred to the stage of a microscope, was found to contain an enormous number of starch grains. You know that the materials of our food and the greater portion of plants are composed of starch, and we are constantly making use of it in a variety of ways, so that there is always a quantity of it suspended in the air. It is these starch grains which form many of those bright specks that we see dancing in a ray of light sometimes. But besides these, M. Pasteur found also an immense number of other organic substances such as spores of fungi, which had been floating about in the air and had got caged in this way.

He went farther, and said to himself, "If these really are the things that give rise to the appearance of spontaneous generation, I ought to be able to take a ball of this *dusted* gun-cotton and put it into one of my vessels, containing that boiled infusion which has been kept away from the air, and in which no infusoria are at present developed, and then, if I am right, the introduction of this gun-cotton will give rise to organisms."

Accordingly, he took one of these vessels of infusion, which had been kept eighteen months, without the least appearance of life in it, and by a most ingenious contrivance, he managed to break it open and introduce such a ball of gun-cotton, without allowing the infusion or the cotton ball to come into contact with any air but that which had been subjected to a red heat, and in twenty-four hours he had the satisfaction of finding all the indications of what had been hitherto called spontaneous generation. He had succeeded in catching the germs and developing organisms in the way he had anticipated.

It now struck him that the truth of his conclusions might be demonstrated without all the apparatus he had employed. To do this, he took some decaying animal or vegetable substance, such as urine, which is an extremely decomposable substance, or the juice of yeast, or perhaps some other artificial preparation, and filled a vessel having a long tubular neck, with it. He then boiled the liquid and bent that long neck into an S shape or zig-zag, leaving it open at the end. The infusion then gave no trace of any appearance of spontaneous generation, however long it might be left, as all the germs in the air were deposited in the beginning of the bent neck. He then cut the tube close to the vessel, and allowed the ordinary air to have free and direct access; and the result of that was the appearance of organisms in it, as soon as the infusion had been allowed to stand long enough to allow of the growth of those it received from the air, which was about forty-eight hours. The result of M. Pasteur's experiments proved, therefore, in the most conclusive manner, that all the appearances of spontaneous generation arose from nothing more than the deposition of the germs of organisms which were constantly floating in the air.

To this conclusion, however, the objection was made, that if that were the cause, then the air would contain such an enormous number of these germs, that it would be a continual fog. But M. Pasteur replied that they are not there in anything like the number we might suppose, and that an exaggerated view has been held on that subject; he showed that the chances of animal or vegetable life appearing in infusions, depend entirely on the conditions under which they are exposed. If they are exposed to the ordinary atmosphere around us, why, of course, you may have organisms appearing early. But, on the other hand, if they are exposed to air at a great height, or in some very quiet cellar, you will often not find a single trace of life.

So that M. Pasteur arrived at last at the clear and definite result, that all these appearances are like the case of the worms in the piece of meat, which was refuted by Redi, simply germs carried by the air and deposited in the liquids in which they afterwards appear. For my own part, I conceive that, with the particulars of M. Pasteur's experiments before us, we cannot fail to arrive at his conclusions ; and that the doctrine of spontaneous generation has received a final *coup de grâce*.

You, of course, understand that all this in no way interferes with the *possibility* of the fabrication of organic matters by the direct method to which I have referred. remote as that possibility may be.

VII

THE PERPETUATION OF LIVING BEINGS, HEREDITARY TRANSMISSION AND VARIATION.

THE inquiry which we undertook, at our last meeting, into the state of our knowledge of the causes of the phenomena of organic nature,—of the past and of the present,—resolved itself into two subsidiary inquiries: the first was, whether we know anything, either historically or experimentally, of the mode of origin of living beings; the second subsidiary inquiry was, whether, granting the origin, we know anything about the perpetuation and modifications of the forms of organic beings. The reply which I had to give to the first question was altogether negative, and the chief result of my last lecture was, that, neither historically nor experimentally, do we at present know anything whatsoever about the origin of living forms. We saw that, historically, we are not likely to know anything about it, although we may perhaps learn something experimentally; but that at present we are an enormous distance from the goal I indicated.

I now, then, take up the next question, What do we know of the reproduction, the perpetuation, and the modifications of the forms of living beings, supposing that we have put the question as to their origination on one side, and have assumed that at present the causes of their origination are beyond us, and that we know nothing about them? Upon this question the state of our knowledge is extremely different; it is exceedingly large: and, if not complete, our experience is certainly most extensive. It would be impossible to lay it all before you, and the most I can do, or need do to-night, is to take up the principal points and put them before you with such prominence as may subserve the purposes of our present argument.

The method of the perpetuation of organic beings is of two kinds,—the asexual and the sexual. In the first the perpetuation takes place from and by a particular act of an individual organism, which sometimes may not be classed as belonging to any sex at all. In the second case, it is in consequence of the mutual action and interaction of certain portions of the organisms of usually two distinct individuals—the male and the female. The cases of asexual perpetuation are by no means so common as the cases of sexual perpetuation ; and they are by no means so common in the animal as in the vegetable world. You are all probably familiar with the fact, as a matter of experience, that you can propagate plants by means of what are called " cuttings "; for example, that by taking a cutting from a geranium plant, and rearing it properly, by supplying it with light and warmth and nourishment from the earth, it grows up and takes the form of its parent, having all the properties and peculiarities of the original plant.

Sometimes this process, which the gardener performs artificially, takes place naturally ; that is to say, a little bulb, or portion of the plant, detaches itself, drops off, and becomes capable of growing as a separate thing. That is the case with many bulbous plants, which throw off in this way secondary bulbs, which are lodged in the ground and become developed into plants. This is an asexual process, and from it results the repetition or reproduction of the form of the original being from which the bulb proceeds.

Among animals the same thing takes place. Among the lower forms of animal life, the infusorial animalculæ we have already spoken of throw off certain portions, or break themselves up in various directions, sometimes transversely or sometimes longitudinally ; or they may give off buds, which detach themselves and develop into their proper forms. There is the common fresh-water Polype, for instance, which multiplies itself in this way. Just in the same way as the gardener is able to multiply and reproduce the peculiarities and characters of particular plants by means of cuttings, so can the physiological experimentalist,—as was shown by the Abbé Trembley many years ago,—so can he do the same thing with many of the lower forms of animal life. M. de Trembley showed that you could take a polype and cut it into two, or four, or many pieces, mutilating it in all directions, and the pieces would still grow up and reproduce completely the original form of the animal. These are all cases of asexual multiplication, and there are other instances, and still more extraordinary ones, in which this process takes place naturally, in a more hidden, a more recondite kind of way. You are all of you familiar with that little green insect, the *Aphis* or blight, as it is called. These little animals, during a very considerable part of their existence, multiply themselves by means of a kind of internal budding, the buds being developed into essentially asexual animals, which are neither male nor female ; they become converted into young *Aphides*, which repeat the process, and their offspring after them, and so on again ; you may go on for nine or ten, or even twenty or more successions ; and there is no very good reason to say how soon it might terminate, or how long it might not go on if the proper conditions of warmth and nourishment were kept up.

Sexual reproduction is quite a distinct matter. Here, in all these cases, what is required is the detachment of two portions of the parental organisms, which portions we know as the egg or the spermatozoon. In plants it is the ovule and the pollen-grain, as in the flowering plants, or the ovule and the antherozooid, as in the flowerless. Among all forms of animal life, the spermatozoa proceed from the male sex, and the egg is the product of the female. Now, what is remarkable about this mode of reproduction is this, that the egg by itself, or the spermatozoa by themselves, are unable to assume the parental form ; but if they be brought into contact with one another, the effect of the mixture of organic substances proceeding from two sources appears to confer an altogether new vigour to the mixed product. This process is brought about, as we all know, by the sexual intercourse of the two sexes, and is called the act of impregnation. The result of this act on the part of the male and female is, that the formation of a new being is set up in the ovule or egg; this ovule or egg soon begins to be divided and subdivided, and to be fashioned into various complex organisms, and eventually to develop into the form of one of its parents, as I explained in the first lecture. These are the processes by which the perpetuation of organic beings is secured. Why there should be the two modes—why this reinvigoration should be required on the part of the female element we do not know; but it is most assuredly the fact, and it is presumable, that, however long the process of asexual multiplication could be continued,—I say there is good reason to believe that it would come to an end if a new commencement were not obtained by a conjunction of the two sexual elements.

That character which is common to these two distinct processes is this, that, whether we consider the reproduction, or perpetuation, or modification of organic beings as they take place asexually, or as they may take place sexually,—in either case, I say, the offspring has a constant tendency to assume, speaking generally, the character of the parent. As I said just now, if you take a slip of a plant, and tend it with care, it will eventually grow up and develop into a plant like that from which it had sprung; and this tendency is so strong that, as gardeners know, this mode of multiplying by means of cuttings is the only secure mode of propagating very many varieties of plants; the peculiarity of the primitive stock seems to be better preserved if you propagate it by means of a slip than if you resort to the sexual mode.

Again, in experiments upon the lower animals, such as the polype, to which I have referred, it is most extraordinary that, although cut up into various pieces, each particular piece will grow up into the form of the primitive stock; the head, if separated, will reproduce the body and the tail; and if you cut off the tail, you will find that that will reproduce the body and all the rest of the members, without in any way deviating from the plan of the organism from which these portions have been detached. And so far does this go, that some experimentalists have carefully examined the lower orders of animals,—among them the Abbé Spallanzani, who made a number of experiments upon snails and salamanders,— and have found that they might mutilate them to an incredible extent; that you might cut off the jaw or the greater part of the head, or the leg or the tail, and repeat the experiment several times, perhaps, cutting off the same member again and again; and yet each of those types would be reproduced according to the primitive type: nature making no mistake, never putting on a fresh kind of leg, or head, or tail, but always tending to repeat and to return to the primitive type.

It is the same in sexual reproduction: it is a matter of perfectly common experience, that the tendency on the part of the offspring always is, speaking broadly, to reproduce the form of the parents. The proverb has it that the thistle does not bring forth grapes; so, among ourselves, there is always a likeness, more or less marked and distinct, between children and their parents. That is a matter of familiar and ordinary observation. We notice the same thing occurring in the cases of the domestic animals—dogs, for instance, and their offspring. In all these cases of propagation and perpetuation, there seems to be a tendency in the offspring to take the characters of the parental organisms. To that tendency a special name is given—and as I may very often use it, I will write it up here on this black-board that you may remember it—it is called *Atavism;* it expresses this tendency to revert to the ancestral type, and comes from the Latin word *atavus,* ancestor.

Well, this *Atavism* which I shall speak of, is, as I said before, one of the most marked and striking tendencies of organic beings; but, side by side with this hereditary tendency there is an equally distinct and remarkable tendency to variation. The tendency to reproduce the original stock has, as it were, its limits, and side by side with it there is a tendency to vary in certain directions, as if there were two opposing powers working upon the organic being, one tending to take it in a straight line, and the other tending to make it diverge from that straight line, first to one side and then to the other.

So that you see these two tendencies need not precisely contradict one another, as the ultimate result may not always be very remote from what would have been the case if the line had been quite straight.

This tendency to variation is less marked in that mode of propagation which takes place asexually; it is in that mode that the minor characters of animal and vegetable structures are most completely preserved. Still, it will happen sometimes, that the gardener, when he has planted a cutting of some favourite plant, will find, contrary to his expectation, that the slip grows up a little different from the primitive stock — that it produces flowers of a different colour or make, or some deviation in one way or another. This is what is called the 'sporting' of plants.

In animals the phenomena of asexual propagation are so obscure, that at present we cannot be said to know much about them; but if we turn to that mode of perpetuation which results from the sexual process, then we find variation a perfectly constant occurrence, to a certain extent; and, indeed, I think that a certain amount of variation from the primitive stock is the necessary result of the method of sexual propagation itself; for, inasmuch as the thing propagated proceeds from two organisms of different sexes and different makes and temperaments, and as the offspring is to be either of one sex or the other, it is quite clear that it cannot be an exact diagonal of the two, or it would be of no sex at all; it cannot be an exact intermediate form between that of each of its parents—it must deviate to one side or the other. You do not find that the male follows the precise type of the male parent, nor does the female always inherit the precise characteristics of the mother,—there is always a proportion of the female character in the male offspring, and of the male character in the female offspring. That must be quite plain to all of you who have looked at all attentively on your own children or those of your neighbours; you will have noticed how very often it may happen that the son shall exhibit the maternal type of character, or the daughter possess the characteristics of the father's family. There are all sorts of intermixtures

and intermediate conditions between the two, where com-
plexion, or beauty, or fifty other different peculiarities
belonging to either side of the house, are reproduced in
other members of the same family.   Indeed, it is sometimes to be remarked in this kind of variation, that the
variety belongs, strictly speaking, to neither of the immediate parents; you will see a child in a family who is
not like either its father or its mother; but some old
person who knew its grandfather or grandmother, or, it
may be, an uncle, or, perhaps, even a more distant
relative, will see a great similarity between the child and
one of these.   In this way it constantly happens that the
characteristic of some previous member of the family
comes out and is reproduced and recognized in the most
unexpected manner.

But apart from that matter of general experience, there
are some cases which put that curious mixture in a very
clear light.   You are aware that the offspring of the Ass
and the Horse, or rather of the he-Ass and the Mare, is
what is called a Mule; and, on the other hand, the offspring of the Stallion and the she-Ass is what is called a
Hinny.   It is a very rare thing in this country to see a
Hinny.   I never saw one myself; but they have been
very carefully studied.   Now, the curious thing is this,
that although you have the same elements in the experiment in each case, the offspring is entirely different in
character, according as the male influence comes from
the Ass or the Horse.   Where the Ass is the male, as in
the case of the Mule, you find that the head is like that
of the Ass, that the ears are long, the tail is tufted at the
end, the feet are small, and the voice is an unmistakable
bray; these are all points of similarity to the Ass; but,
on the other hand, the barrel of the body and the cut of
the neck are much more like those of the Mare.   Then,
if you look at the Hinny,—the result of the union of the
Stallion and the she-Ass, then you find it is the Horse
that has the predominance; that the head is more like
that of the Horse, the ears are shorter, the legs coarser,
and the type is altogether altered; while the voice, instead
of being a bray, is the ordinary neigh of the Horse.   Here,
you see, is a most curious thing: you take exactly the

same elements, Ass and Horse, but you combine the sexes in a different manner, and the result is modified accordingly. You have in this case, however, a result which is not general and universal—there is usually an important preponderance, but not always on the same side.

Here, then, is one intelligible, and, perhaps, necessary cause of variation : the fact, that there are two sexes sharing in the production of the offspring, and that the share taken by each is different and variable, not only for each combination, but also for different members of the same family.

Secondly, there is a variation, to a certain extent,—though in all probability the influence of this cause has been very much exaggerated—but there is no doubt that variation is produced, to a certain extent, by what are commonly known as external conditions,—such as temperature, food, warmth, and moisture. In the long run, every variation depends, in some sense, upon external conditions, seeing that everything has a cause of its own. I use the term "external conditions" now in the sense in which it is ordinarily employed : certain it is, that external conditions have a definite effect. You may take a plant which has single flowers, and by dealing with the soil, and nourishment, and so on, you may by-and-by convert single flowers into double flowers, and make thorns shoot out into branches. You may thicken or make various modifications in the shape of the fruit. In animals, too, you may produce analogous changes in this way, as in the case of that deep bronze colour which persons rarely lose after having passed any length of time in tropical countries. You may also alter the development of the muscles very much, by dint of training ; all the world knows that exercise has a great effect in this way ; we always expect to find the arm of a blacksmith hard and wiry, and possessing a large development of the brachial muscles. No doubt, training, which is one of the forms of external conditions, converts what are originally only instructions, teachings, into habits, or, in other words, into organizations, to a great extent ; but this second cause of variation cannot be considered to be

by any means a large one. The third cause that I have
to mention, however, is a very extensive one. It is
one that, for want of a better name, has been called
"spontaneous variation"; which means that when we
do not know anything about the cause of phenomena,
we call it spontaneous. In the orderly chain of causes
and effects in this world, there are very few things of
which it can be said with truth that they are spontaneous.
Certainly not in these physical matters,—in these there
is nothing of the kind,—everything depends on previous
conditions. But when we cannot trace the cause of
phenomena, we call them spontaneous.

Of these variations, multitudinous as they are, but
little is known with perfect accuracy. I will mention to
you some two or three cases, because they are very remarkable in themselves, and also because I shall want
to use them afterwards. Réaumur, a famous French
naturalist, a great many years ago, in an essay which he
wrote upon the art of hatching chickens,—which was
indeed a very curious essay,—had occasion to speak of
variations and monstrosities. One very remarkable case
had come under his notice of a variation in the form of
a human member, in the person of a Maltese, of the
name of Gratio Kelleia, who was born with six fingers
upon each hand, and the like number of toes to each
of his feet. That was a case of spontaneous variation.
Nobody knows why he was born with that number of
fingers and toes, and as we don't know, we call it a case
of "spontaneous" variation. There is another remarkable case also. I select these, because they happen to
have been observed and noted very carefully at the time.
It frequently happens that a variation occurs, but the
persons who notice it do not take any care in noting
down the particulars, until at length, when inquiries come
to be made, the exact circumstances are forgotten; and
hence, multitudinous as may be such "spontaneous"
variations, it is exceedingly difficult to get at the origin
of them.

The second case is one of which you may find the
whole details in the "Philosophical Transactions" for
the year 1813, in a paper communicated by Colonel

Humphreys to the President of the Royal Society,—"On a new Variety in the Breed of Sheep," giving an account of a very remarkable breed of sheep, which at one time was well known in the northern states of America, and which went by the name of the Ancon or the Otter breed of sheep. In the year 1791, there was a farmer of the name of Seth Wright in Massachusetts, who had a flock of sheep, consisting of a ram and, I think, of some twelve or thirteen ewes. Of this flock of ewes, one at the breeding-time bore a lamb which was very singularly formed; it had a very long body, very short legs, and those legs were bowed! I will tell you by-and-by how this singular variation in the breed of sheep came to be noted, and to have the prominence that it now has. For the present, I mention only these two cases; but the extent of variation in the breed of animals is perfectly obvious to any one who has studied natural history with ordinary attention, or to any person who compares animals with others of the same kind. It is strictly true that there are never any two specimens which are exactly alike; however similar, they will always differ in some certain particular.

Now let us go back to Atavism,—to the hereditary tendency I spoke of. What will come of a variation when you breed from it, when Atavism comes, if I may say so, to intersect variation? The two cases of which I have mentioned the history, give a most excellent illustration of what occurs. Gratio Kelleia, the Maltese, married when he was twenty-two years of age, and, as I suppose there were no six-fingered ladies in Malta, he married an ordinary five-fingered person. The result of that marriage was four children; the first, who was christened Salvator, had six fingers and six toes, like his father; the second was George, who had five fingers and toes, but one of them was deformed, showing a tendency to variation; the third was Andrè; he had five fingers and five toes, quite perfect; the fourth was a girl, Marie; she had five fingers and five toes, but her thumbs were deformed, showing a tendency toward the sixth.

These children grew up, and when they came to adult years, they all married, and of course it happened that they all married five-fingered and five-toed persons. Now let us see what were the results. Salvator had four children; they were two boys, a girl, and another boy: the first two boys and the girl were six-fingered and six-toed like their grandfather; the fourth boy had only five fingers and five toes. George had only four children: there were two girls with six fingers and six toes; there was one girl with six fingers and five toes on the right side, and five fingers and five toes on the left side, so that she was half and half. The last, a boy, had five fingers and five toes. The third, Andrè, you will recollect, was perfectly well-formed, and he had many children whose hands and feet were all regularly developed. Marie, the last, who, of course, married a man who had only five fingers, had four children: the first, a boy, was born with six toes, but the other three were normal.

Now observe what very extraordinary phenomena are presented here. You have an accidental variation arising from what you may call a monstrosity; you have that monstrosity tendency or variation diluted in the first instance by an admixture with a female of normal construction, and you would naturally expect that, in the results of such an union, the monstrosity, if repeated, would be in equal proportion with the normal type; that is to say, that the children would be half and half, some taking the peculiarity of the father, and the others being of the purely normal type of the mother; but you see we have a great preponderance of the abnormal type. Well, this comes to be mixed once more with the pure, the normal type, and the abnormal is again produced in large proportion, notwithstanding the second dilution. Now what would have happened if these abnormal types had intermarried with each other; that is to say, suppose the two boys of Salvator had taken it into their heads to marry their first cousins, the two first girls of George, their uncle? You will remember that these are all of the abnormal type of their grandfather. The result would probably have been, that their offspring would have been in every case a further development of that abnormal type. You see it is only in the fourth, in the person of Marie, that the tendency, when it appears but slightly in the second generation, is washed out in the third, while the progeny of Andrè, who escaped in the first instance, escape altogether.

We have in this case a good example of nature's tendency to the perpetuation of a variation. Here it is certainly a variation which carried with it no use or benefit; and yet you see the tendency to perpetuation may be so strong, that, notwithstanding a great admixture of pure blood, the variety continues itself up to the third generation, which is largely marked with it. In this case, as I have said, there was no means of the second generation intermarrying with any but five-fingered persons, and the question naturally suggests itself, What would have been the result of such marriage? Réaumur narrates this case only as far as the third generation. Certainly it would have been an exceedingly curious thing if we could have traced this matter any further; had the cousins intermarried, a six-fingered variety of the human race might have been set up.

To show you that this supposition is by no means an unreasonable one, let me now point out what took place in the case of Seth Wright's sheep, where it happened to be a matter of moment to him to obtain a breed or raise a flock of sheep like that accidental variety that I have described—and I will tell you why. In that part of Massachusetts where Seth Wright was living, the fields were separated by fences, and the sheep, which were very active and robust, would roam abroad, and without much difficulty jump over these fences into other people's farms. As a matter of course, this exuberant activity on the part of the sheep constantly gave rise to all sorts of quarrels, bickerings, and contentions among the farmers of the neighbourhood; so it occurred to Seth Wright, who was, like his successors, more or less 'cute, that if he could get a stock of sheep like those with the bandy legs, they would not be able to jump over the fences so readily; and he acted upon that idea. He killed his old ram, and as soon as the young one arrived at maturity, he bred altogether from it. The result was even more striking than in the human experiment which I mentioned just now. Colonel Humphreys testifies that it

always happened that the offspring were either pure
Ancons or pure ordinary sheep; that in no case was
there any mixing of the Ancons with the others. In
consequence of this, in the course of a very few years,
the farmer was able to get a very considerable flock of
this variety, and a large number of them were spread
throughout Massachusetts. Most unfortunately, however
—I suppose it was because they were so common—
nobody took enough notice of them to preserve their
skeletons; and although Colonel Humphreys states that
he sent a skeleton to the President of the Royal Society
at the same time that he forwarded his paper, I am
afraid that the variety has entirely disappeared; for a
short time after these sheep had become prevalent in
that district, the Merino sheep were introduced; and as
their wool was much more valuable, and as they were a
quiet race of sheep, and showed no tendency to trespass
or jump over fences, the Otter breed of sheep, the wool
of which was inferior to that of the Merino, was gradually
allowed to die out.

You see that these facts illustrate perfectly well what
may be done if you take care to breed from stocks that
are similar to each other. After having got a variation,
if, by crossing a variation with the original stock, you
multiply that variation, and then take care to keep that
variation distinct from the original stock, and make them
breed together,—then you may almost certainly produce
a race whose tendency to continue the variation is exceedingly strong.

This is what is called "selection"; and it is by exactly
the same process as that by which Seth Wright bred his
Ancon sheep, that our breeds of cattle, dogs, and fowls,
are obtained. There are some possibilities of exception,
but still, speaking broadly, I may say that this is the way
in which all our varied races of domestic animals have
arisen; and you must understand that it is not one
peculiarity or one characteristic alone in which animals
may vary. There is not a single peculiarity or characteristic of any kind, bodily or mental, in which offspring may
not vary to a certain extent from the parent and other
animals.

Among ourselves this is well known. The simplest physical peculiarity is mostly reproduced. I know a case of a woman who has the lobe of one of her ears a little flattened. An ordinary observer might scarcely notice it, and yet every one of her children has an approximation to the same peculiarity to some extent. If you look at the other extreme, too, the gravest diseases, such as gout, scrofula, and consumption, may be handed down with just the same certainty and persistence as we noticed in the perpetuation of the bandy legs of the Ancon sheep.

However, these facts are best illustrated in animals, and the extent of the variation, as is well known, is very remarkable in dogs. For example, there are some dogs very much smaller than others; indeed, the variation is so enormous that probably the smallest dog would be about the size of the head of the largest; there are very great variations in the structural forms not only of the skeleton but also in the shape of the skull, and in the proportions of the face and the disposition of the teeth.

The Pointer, the Retriever, Bulldog, and the Terrier, differ very greatly, and yet there is every reason to believe that every one of these races has arisen from the same source,—that all the most important races have arisen by this selective breeding from accidental variation.

A still more striking case of what may be done by selective breeding, and it is a better case, because there is no chance of that partial infusion of error to which I alluded, has been studied very carefully by Mr. Darwin,—the case of the domestic pigeons. I dare say there may be some among you who may be pigeon *fanciers*, and I wish you to understand that in approaching the subject, I would speak with all humility and hesitation, as I regret to say that I am not a pigeon fancier. I know it is a great art and mystery, and a thing upon which a man must not speak lightly; but I shall endeavour, as far as my understanding goes, to give you a summary of the published and unpublished information which I have gained from Mr. Darwin.

Among the enormous variety,—I believe there are somewhere about a hundred and fifty kinds of pigeons,—

varies from eleven to fourteen, and that without any diminution in the number of the vertebræ of the back or of the tail. Then the number and position of the tail-feathers may vary enormously, and so may the number of the primary and secondary feathers of the wings. Again, the length of the feet and of the beak,—although they have no relation to each other, yet appear to go together,—that is, you have a long beak wherever you have long feet. There are differences also in the periods of the acquirement of the perfect plumage,—the size and shape of the eggs,—the nature of flight, and the powers of flight,—so-called "*homing*" birds having enormous flying powers ; [1] while, on the other hand, the little Tumbler is so called because of its extraordinary faculty of turning head over heels in the air, instead of pursuing a distinct course. And, lastly, the dispositions and voices of the birds may vary. Thus the case of the pigeons shows you that there is hardly a single particular,—whether of instinct, or habit, or bony structure, or of plumage,—of either the internal economy or the external shape, in which some variation or change may not take place, which, by selective breeding, may become perpetuated, and form the foundation of, and give rise to, a new race.

If you carry in your mind's eye these four varieties of pigeons, you will bear with you as good a notion as you can have, perhaps, of the enormous extent to which a deviation from a primitive type may be carried by means of this process of selective breeding.

[1] The "*Carrier*," I learn from Mr. Tegetmeier, does not *carry* ; a high-bred bird of this breed being but a poor flier. The birds which fly long distances, and come home,—"homing" birds,—and are consequently used as carriers, are not "carriers" in the fancy sense.

VIII

THE CONDITIONS OF EXISTENCE AS AFFECTING THE PERPETUATION OF LIVING BEINGS.

IN the last Lecture I endeavoured to prove to you that, while, as a general rule, organic beings tend to reproduce their kind, there is in them, also, a constantly recurring tendency to vary—to vary to a greater or to a less extent. Such a variety, I pointed out to you, might arise from causes which we do not understand; we therefore called it spontaneous; and it might come into existence as a definite and marked thing, without any gradations between itself and the form which preceded it. I further pointed out, that such a variety having once arisen, might be perpetuated to some extent, and indeed to a very marked extent, without any direct interference, or without any exercise of that process which we called selection. And then I stated further, that by such selection, when exercised artificially—if you took care to breed only from those forms which presented the same peculiarities of any variety which had arisen in this manner—the variation might be perpetuated, as far as we can see, indefinitely.

The next question, and it is an important one for us, is this: Is there any limit to the amount of variation from the primitive stock which can be produced by this process of selective breeding? In considering this question, it will be useful to class the characteristics, in respect of which organic beings vary, under two heads: we may consider structural characteristics, and we may consider physiological characteristics.

In the first place, as regards structural characteristics, I endeavoured to show you, by the skeletons which I had upon the table, and by reference to a great many well-ascertained facts, that the different breeds of Pigeons, the Carriers, Pouters, and Tumblers, might vary in any of their internal and important structural characters to a very great degree; not only might there be changes in the proportions of the skull, and the characters of the feet and beaks, and so on; but that there might be an absolute difference in the number of the vertebræ of the back, as in the sacral vertebræ of the Pouter; and so great is the extent of the variation in these and similar characters that I pointed out to you, by reference to the skeletons and the diagrams, that these extreme varieties may absolutely differ more from one another in their structural characters than do what naturalists call distinct Species of pigeons; that is to say, that they differ so much in structure that there is a greater difference between the Pouter and the Tumbler than there is between such wild and distinct forms as the Rock Pigeon or the Ring Pigeon, or the Ring Pigeon and the Stock Dove; and indeed the differences are of greater value than this, for the structural differences between these domesticated pigeons are such as would be admitted by a naturalist, supposing he knew nothing at all about their origin, to entitle them to constitute even distinct genera.

As I have used this term Species, and shall probably use it a good deal, I had better perhaps devote a word or two to explaining what I mean by it.

Animals and plants are divided into groups, which become gradually smaller, beginning with a Kingdom, which is divided into Sub-Kingdoms; then come the smaller divisions called Provinces; and so on from a Province to a Class, from a Class to an Order, from Orders to Families, and from these to Genera, until we come at length to the smallest groups of animals which can be defined one from the other by constant characters, which are not sexual; and these are what naturalists call Species in practice, whatever they may do in theory.

If in a state of nature you find any two groups of living beings, which are separated one from the other by some constantly-recurring characteristic, I don't care how slight and trivial, so long as it is defined and constant, and does not depend on sexual peculiarities, then all naturalists agree in calling them two species ; that is what is meant by the use of the word species—that is to say, it is, for the practical naturalist, a mere question of structural differences.[1]

We have seen now—to repeat this point once more, and it is very essential that we should rightly understand it—we have seen that breeds, known to have been derived from a common stock by selection, may be as different in their structure from the original stock as species may be distinct from each other.

But is the like true of the physiological characteristics of animals? Do the physiological differences of varieties amount in degree to those observed between forms which naturalists call distinct species? This is a most important point for us to consider.

As regards the great majority of physiological characteristics, there is no doubt that they are capable of being developed, increased, and modified by selection.

There is no doubt that breeds may be made as different as species in many physiological characters. I have already pointed out to you very briefly the different habits of the breeds of Pigeons, all of which depend upon their physiological peculiarities,—as the peculiar habit of tumbling, in the Tumbler,—the peculiarities of flight, in the "homing" birds,—the strange habit of spreading out the tail, and walking in a peculiar fashion, in the Fantail, —and, lastly, the habit of blowing out the gullet, so characteristic of the Pouter. These are all due to physiological modifications, and in all these respects these birds differ as much from each other as any two ordinary species do.

So with Dogs in their habits and instincts. It is a physiological peculiarity which leads the Greyhound to chase its prey by sight,—that enables the Beagle to track it by the scent,—that impels the Terrier to its rat-hunting

---

[1] I lay stress here on the *practical* signification of " Species." Whether a physiological test between species exist or not, it is hardly ever applicable by the practical naturalist.

propensity,—and that leads the Retriever to its habits of retrieving. These habits and instincts are all the results of physiological differences and peculiarities, which have been developed from a common stock, at least there is every reason to believe so. But it is a most singular circumstance, that while you may run through almost the whole series of physiological processes, without finding a check to your argument, you come at last to a point where you do find a check, and that is in the reproductive processes. For there is a most singular circumstance in respect to natural species—at least about some of them— and it would be sufficient for the purposes of this argument, if it were true of only one of them, but there is, in fact, a great number of such cases—and that is, that similar as they may appear to be to mere races or breeds, they present a marked peculiarity in the reproductive process. If you breed from the male and female of the same race, you of course have offspring of the like kind, and if you make the offspring breed together, you obtain the same result, and if you breed from these again, you will still have the same kind of offspring; there is no check. But if you take members of two distinct species, however similar they may be to each other, and make them breed together, you will find a check, with some modifications and exceptions, however, which I shall speak of presently. If you cross two such species with each other, then,—although you may get offspring in the case of the first cross, yet, if you attempt to breed from the products of that crossing, which are what are called HYBRIDS—that is, if you couple a male and a female hybrid—then the result is that in ninety-nine cases out of a hundred you will get no offspring at all: there will be no result whatsoever.

The reason of this is quite obvious in some cases; the male hybrids, although possessing all the external appearances and characteristics of perfect animals, are physiologically imperfect and deficient in the structural parts of the reproductive elements necessary to generation. It is said to be invariably the case with the male mule, the cross between the Ass and the Mare; and hence it is, that, although crossing the Horse with the

Ass is easy enough, and is constantly done, as far as I am aware, if you take two mules, a male and a female, and endeavour to breed from them, you get no offspring whatever; no generation will take place. This is what is called the sterility of the hybrids between two distinct species.

You see that this is a very extraordinary circumstance; one does not see why it should be. The common teleological explanation is, that it is to prevent the impurity of the blood resulting from the crossing of one species with another, but you see it does not in reality do anything of the kind. There is nothing in this fact that hybrids cannot breed with each other, to establish such a theory; there is nothing to prevent the Horse breeding with the Ass, or the Ass with the Horse. So that this explanation breaks down, as a great many explanations of this kind do, that are only founded on mere assumptions.

Thus you see that there is a great difference between "mongrels," which are crosses between distinct races, and "hybrids," which are crosses between distinct species. The mongrels are, so far as we know, fertile with one another. But between species, in many cases, you cannot succeed in obtaining even the first cross: at any rate it is quite certain that the hybrids are often absolutely infertile one with another.

Here is a feature, then, great or small as it may be, which distinguishes natural species of animals. Can we find any approximation to this in the different races known to be produced by selective breeding from a common stock? Up to the present time the answer to that question is absolutely a negative one. As far as we know at present, there is nothing approximating to this check. In crossing the breeds between the Fantail and the Pouter, the Carrier and the Tumbler, or any other variety or race you may name—so far as we know at present—there is no difficulty in breeding together the mongrels. Take the Carrier and the Fantail, for instance, and let them represent the Horse and the Ass in the case of distinct species; then you have, as the result of their breeding, the Carrier-Fantail mongrel,—we will say the male and female mongrel,—and, as far as we know, these two when crossed would not be less fertile than the original cross, or than Carrier with Carrier. Here, you see, is a physiological contrast between the races produced by selective modification and natural species. I shall inquire into the value of this fact, and of some modifying circumstances by and by; for the present I merely put it broadly before you.

But while considering this question of the limitations of species, a word must be said about what is called RECURRENCE—the tendency of races which have been developed by selective breeding from varieties to return to their primitive type. This is supposed by many to put an absolute limit to the extent of selective and all other variations. People say, " It is all very well to talk about producing these different races, but you know very well that if you turned all these birds wild, these Pouters, and Carriers, and so on, they would all return to their primitive stock." This is very commonly assumed to be a fact, and it is an argument that is commonly brought forward as conclusive; but if you will take the trouble to inquire into it rather closely, I think you will find that it is not worth very much. The first question of course is, Do they thus return to the primitive stock? And commonly as the thing is assumed and accepted, it is extremely difficult to get anything like good evidence of it. It is constantly said, for example, that if domesticated Horses are turned wild, as they have been in some parts of Asia Minor and South America, that they return at once to the primitive stock from which they were bred. But the first answer that you make to this assumption is, to ask who knows what the primitive stock was; and the second answer is, that in that case the wild Horses of Asia Minor ought to be exactly like the wild Horses of South America. If they are both like the same thing, they ought manifestly to be like each other! The best authorities, however, tell you that it is quite different. The wild Horse of Asia is said to be of a dun colour, with a largish head, and a great many other peculiarities; while the best authorities on the wild Horses of South America tell you that there is no similarity between their wild Horses and those of Asia Minor; the cut of their heads is very different, and they are commonly chestnut or bay-coloured. It is quite clear, therefore, that as by these facts there ought to have been two primitive stocks, they go for nothing in support of the assumption that races recur to one primitive stock, and so far as this evidence is concerned, it falls to the ground.

Suppose for a moment that it were so, and that domesticated races, when turned wild, did return to some common condition, I cannot see that this would prove much more than that similar conditions are likely to produce similar results ; and that when you take back domesticated animals into what we call natural conditions, you do exactly the same thing as if you carefully undid all the work you had gone through, for the purpose of bringing the animal from its wild to its domesticated state. I do not see anything very wonderful in the fact, if it took all that trouble to get it from a wild state, that it should go back into its original state as soon as you removed the conditions which produced the variation to the domesticated form. There is an important fact, however, forcibly brought forward by Mr. Darwin, which has been noticed in connection with the breeding of domesticated pigeons ; and it is, that however different these breeds of pigeons may be from each other, and we have already noticed the great differences in these breeds, that if, among any of those variations, you chance to have a blue pigeon turn up, it will be sure to have the black bars across the wings, which are characteristic of the original wild stock, the Rock Pigeon.

Now, this is certainly a very remarkable circumstance ; but I do not see myself how it tells very strongly either one way or the other. I think, in fact, that this argument in favour of recurrence to the primitive type might prove a great deal too much for those who so constantly bring it forward. For example, Mr. Darwin has very forcibly urged, that nothing is commoner than if you examine a dun horse—and I had an opportunity of verifying this illustration lately, while in the islands of the West Highlands, where there are a great many dun horses —to find that horse exhibit a long black stripe down his back, very often stripes on his shoulder, and very often stripes on his legs. I, myself, saw a pony of this description a short time ago, in a baker's cart, near Rothesay, in Bute: it had the long stripe down the back, and stripes on the shoulders and legs, just like those of the Ass, the Quagga, and the Zebra. Now, if we interpret the theory of recurrence as applied to this case, might it not be said that here was a case of a variation exhibiting the characters and conditions of an animal occupying something like an intermediate position between the Horse, the Ass, the Quagga, and the Zebra, and from which these had been developed? In the same way with regard even to Man. Every anatomist will tell you that there is nothing commoner, in dissecting the human body, than to meet with what are called muscular variations—that is, if you dissect two bodies very carefully, you will probably find that the modes of attachment and insertion of the muscles are not exactly the same in both, there being great peculiarities in the mode in which the muscles are arranged; and it is very singular, that in some dissections of the human body you will come upon arrangements of the muscles very similar indeed to the same parts in the Apes. Is the conclusion in that case to be, that this is like the black bars in the case of the Pigeon, and that it indicates a recurrence to the primitive type from which the animals have been probably developed? Truly, I think that the opponents of modification and variation had better leave the argument of recurrence alone, or it may prove altogether too strong for them.

To sum up,—the evidence as far as we have gone is against the argument as to any limit to divergences, so far as structure is concerned; and in favour of a physiological limitation. By selective breeding we can produce structural divergences as great as those of species, but we cannot produce equal physiological divergences. For the present I leave the question there.

Now, the next problem that lies before us—and it is an extremely important one—is this: Does this selective breeding occur in nature? Because, if there is no proof of it, all that I have been telling you goes for nothing in accounting for the origin of species. Are natural causes competent to play the part of selection in perpetuating varieties? Here we labour under very great difficulties. In the last lecture I had occasion to point out to you the extreme difficulty of obtaining evidence even of the first origin of those varieties which we know to have occurred in domesticated animals. I told you, that almost always the origin of these varieties is overlooked, so that I could only produce two or three cases, as that of Gratio Kelleia and of the Ancon sheep. People forget, or do not take notice of them until they come to have a prominence; and if that is true of artificial cases, under our own eyes, and in animals in our own care, how much more difficult it must be to have at first hand good evidence of the origin of varieties in nature! Indeed, I do not know that it is possible by direct evidence to prove the origin of a variety in nature, or to prove selective breeding; but I will tell you what we can prove—and this comes to the same thing —that varieties exist in nature within the limits of species, and, what is more, that when a variety has come into existence in nature, there are natural causes and conditions, which are amply competent to play the part of a selective breeder; and although that is not quite the evidence that one would like to have—though it is not direct testimony—yet it is exceeding good and exceedingly powerful evidence in its way.

As to the first point, of varieties existing among natural species, I might appeal to the universal experience of every naturalist, and of any person who has ever turned any attention at all to the characteristics of plants and animals in a state of nature; but I may as well take a few definite cases, and I will begin with Man himself.

I am one of those who believe that, at present, there is no evidence whatever for saying, that mankind sprang originally from any more than a single pair; I must say, that I cannot see any good ground whatever, or even any tenable sort of evidence, for believing that there is more than one species of Man. Nevertheless, as you know, just as there are numbers of varieties in animals, so there are remarkable varieties of men. I speak not merely of those broad and distinct variations which you see at a glance. Everybody, of course, knows the difference

between a Negro and a white man, and can tell a China-
man from an Englishman. They each have peculiar
characteristics of colour and physiognomy ; but you must
recollect that the characters of these races go very far
deeper—they extend to the bony structure, and to the
characters of that most important of all organs to us—
the brain ; so that, among men belonging to different
races, or even within the same race, one man shall have
a brain a third, or half, or even seventy per cent. bigger
than another ; and if you take the whole range of human
brains, you will find a variation in some cases of a hundred per cent. Apart from these variations in the size of
the brain, the characters of the skull vary. Thus if I
draw the figures of a Mongul and of a Negro head on the
blackboard, in the case of the last the breadth would be
about seven-tenths, and in the other it would be nine-
tenths of the total length. So that you see there is
abundant evidence of variation among men in their
natural condition. And if you turn to other animals
there is just the same thing. The fox, for example,
which has a very large geographical distribution all over
Europe, and parts of Asia, and on the American Continent, varies greatly. There are mostly large foxes in
the North, and smaller ones in the South. In Germany
alone, the foresters reckon some eight different sorts.

Of the tiger, no one supposes that there is more
than one species ; they extend from the hottest parts of
Bengal, into the dry, cold, bitter steppes of Siberia, into
a latitude of 50°,—so that they may even prey upon the
reindeer. These tigers have exceedingly different characteristics, but still they all keep their general features, so
that there is no doubt as to their being tigers. The
Siberian tiger has a thick fur, a small mane, and a longitudinal stripe down the back, while the tigers of Java and
Sumatra differ in many important respects from the tigers
of Northern Asia. So lions vary ; so birds vary ; and so,
if you go further back and lower down in creation, you
find that fishes vary. In different streams, in the same
country even, you will find the trout to be quite different
to each other and easily recognizable by those who fish
in the particular streams. There is the same differences

in leeches; leech collectors can easily point out to you the differences and the peculiarities which you yourself would probably pass by; so with fresh-water mussels; so, in fact, with every animal you can mention.

In plants there is the same kind of variation. Take such a case even as the common bramble. The botanists are all at war about it; some of them wanting to make out that there are many species of it, and others maintaining that they are but many varieties of one species; and they cannot settle to this day which is a species and which is a variety!

So that there can be no doubt whatsoever that any plant and any animal may vary in nature; that varieties may arise in the way I have described,—as spontaneous varieties,—and that those varieties may be perpetuated in the same way that I have shown you spontaneous varieties are perpetuated; I say, therefore, that there can be no doubt as to the origin and perpetuation of varieties in nature.

But the question now is:—Does selection take place in nature? is there anything like the operation of man in exercising selective breeding, taking place in nature? You will observe that, at present, I say nothing about species; I wish to confine myself to the consideration of the production of those natural races which everybody admits to exist. The question is, whether in nature there are causes competent to produce races, just in the same way as man is able to produce, by selection, such races of animals as we have already noticed.

When a variety has arisen, the CONDITIONS OF EXISTENCE are such as to exercise an influence which is exactly comparable to that of artificial selection. By Conditions of Existence I mean two things,—there are conditions which are furnished by the physical, the inorganic world, and there are conditions of existence which are furnished by the organic world. There is, in the first place, CLIMATE; under that head I include only temperature and the varied amount of moisture of particular places. In the next place there is what is technically called STATION, which means—given the climate, the particular kind of place in which an animal or a plant lives or grows;

for example, the station of a fish is in the water, of a fresh-water fish in fresh water; the station of a marine fish is in the sea, and a marine animal may have a station higher or deeper. So again with land animals: the differences in their stations are those of different soils and neighbour-hoods; some being best adapted to a calcareous, and others to an arenaceous soil. The third condition of existence is FOOD, by which I mean food in the broadest sense, the supply of the materials necessary to the exist-ence of an organic being; in the case of a plant the inorganic matters, such as carbonic acid, water, ammonia, and the earthy salts or salines; in the case of the animal the inorganic and organic matters, which we have seen they require; then these are all, at least the two first, what we may call the inorganic or physical conditions of existence. Food takes a mid-place, and then come the organic conditions; by which I mean the conditions which depend upon the state of the rest of the organic creation, upon the number and kind of living beings, with which an animal is surrounded. You may class these under two heads: there are organic beings, which operate as *opponents*, and there are organic beings which operate as *helpers* to any given organic creature. The opponents may be of two kinds: there are the *indirect opponents*, which are what we may call *rivals;* and there are the *direct opponents*, those which strive to destroy the creature; and these we call *enemies*. By rivals I mean, of course, in the case of plants, those which require for their support the same kind of soil and station, and, among animals, those which require the same kind of station, or food, or climate; those are the indirect opponents; the direct opponents are, of course, those which prey upon an animal or vegetable. The *helpers* may also be regarded as direct and indirect: in the case of a carnivorous animal, for example, a particular herbaceous plant may in multiply-ing be an indirect helper, by enabling the herbivora on which the carnivore preys to get more food, and thus to nourish the carnivore more abundantly; the direct helper may be best illustrated by reference to some parasitic creature, such as the tape-worm. The tape-worm exists in the human intestines, so that the fewer there are of men the fewer there will be of tape-worms, other things being alike. It is a humiliating reflection, perhaps, that we may be classed as direct helpers to the tape-worm, but the fact is so : we can all see that if there were no men there would be no tape-worms.

It is extremely difficult to estimate, in a proper way, the importance and the working of the Conditions of Existence. I do not think there were any of us who had the remotest notion of properly estimating them until the publication of Mr. Darwin's work, which has placed them before us with remarkable clearness ; and I must endeavour, as far as I can in my own fashion, to give you some notion of how they work. We shall find it easiest to take a simple case, and one as free as possible from every kind of complication.

I will suppose, therefore, that all the habitable part of this globe—the dry land, amounting to about 51,000,000 square miles,—I will suppose that the whole of that dry land has the same climate, and that it is composed of the same kind of rock or soil, so that there will be the same station everywhere ; we thus get rid of the peculiar influence of different climates and stations. I will then imagine that there shall be but one organic being in the world, and that shall be a plant. In this we start fair. Its food is to be carbonic acid, water and ammonia, and the saline matters in the soil, which are, by the supposition, everywhere alike. We take one single plant, with no opponents, no helpers, and no rivals ; it is to be a "fair field, and no favour." Now, I will ask you to imagine further that it shall be a plant which shall produce every year fifty seeds, which is a very moderate number for a plant to produce ; and that, by the action of the winds and currents, these seeds shall be equally and gradually distributed over the whole surface of the land. I want you now to trace out what will occur, and you will observe that I am not talking fallaciously any more than a mathematician does when he expounds his problem. If you show that the conditions of your problem are such as may actually occur in nature and do not transgress any of the known laws of nature in working out your proposition, then you are as safe in the conclusion you arrive at as is the mathematician in arriving at the solution of his problem. In science, the only way of getting rid of the complications with which a subject of this kind is environed, is to work in this deductive method. What will be the result, then? I will suppose that every plant requires one square foot of ground to live upon; and the result will be that, in the course of nine years, the plant will have occupied every single available spot in the whole globe! I have chalked upon the blackboard the figures by which I arrive at the result:—

		Plants.					Plants.
1	×	50	in	1st year	=		50
50	×	50	,,	2nd ,,	=		2,500
2,500	×	50	,,	3rd ,,	=		125,000
125,000	×	50	,,	4th ,,	=		6,250,000
6,250,000	×	50	,,	5th ,,	=		312,500,000
312,500,000	×	50	,,	6th ,,	=		15,625,000,000
15,625,000,000	×	50	,,	7th ,,	=		781,250,000,000
781,250,000,000	×	50	,,	8th ,,	=		39,062,500,000,000
39,062,500,000,000	×	50	,,	9th ,,	=		1,953,125,000,000,000

$$\left. \begin{array}{l} \text{51,000,000 sq. miles—the dry sur-} \\ \text{face of the earth} \times \text{27,878,400—} \\ \text{the number of sq. ft. in 1 sq. mile} \end{array} \right\} = \text{sq. ft. } 1,421,798,400,000,000$$

being 531,326,600,000,000 square feet less than would be required at the end of the ninth year.

You will see from this that, at the end of the first year the single plant will have produced fifty more of its kind; by the end of the second year these will have increased to 2500; and so on, in succeeding years, you get beyond even trillions; and I am not at all sure that I could tell you what the proper arithmetical denomination of the total number really is; but, at any rate, you will understand the meaning of all those noughts. Then you see that, at the bottom, I have taken the 51,000,000 of square miles, constituting the surface of the dry land; and as the number of square feet are placed under and subtracted from the number of seeds that would be produced in the ninth year, you can see at once that there would be an immense number more of plants than there would be square feet of ground for their accommodation. This is certainly quite enough to prove my point; that between the eighth and ninth year after being planted the single plant would have stocked the whole available surface of the earth.

This is a thing which is hardly conceivable—it seems hardly imaginable—yet it is so. It is indeed simply the law of Malthus exemplified. Mr. Malthus was a clergyman, who worked out this subject most minutely and truthfully some years ago; he showed quite clearly,—and although he was much abused for his conclusions at the time, they have never yet been disproved and never will be—he showed that in consequence of the increase in the number of organic beings in a geometrical ratio, while the means of existence cannot be made to increase in the same ratio, that there must come a time when the number of organic beings will be in excess of the power of production of nutriment, and that thus some check must arise to the further increase of those organic beings. At the end of the ninth year we have seen that each plant would not be able to get its full square foot of ground, and at the end of another year it would have to share that space with fifty others the produce of the seeds which it would give off.

What, then, takes place? Every plant grows up, flourishes, occupies its square foot of ground, and gives off its fifty seeds; but notice this, that out of this number only one can come to anything; there is thus, as it were, forty-nine chances to one against its growing up; it depends upon the most fortuitous circumstances whether any one of these fifty seeds shall grow up and flourish, or whether it shall die and perish. This is what Mr. Darwin has drawn attention to, and called the " STRUGGLE FOR EXISTENCE "; and I have taken this simple case of a plant because some people imagine that the phrase seems to imply a sort of fight.

I have taken this plant and shown you that this is the result of the ratio of the increase, the necessary result of the arrival of a time coming for every species when exactly as many members must be destroyed as are born; that is the inevitable ultimate result of the rate of production. Now, what is the result of all this? I have said that there are forty-nine struggling against every one; and it amounts to this, that the smallest possible start given to any one seed may give it an advantage which will enable it to get ahead of all the others ; anything that will enable any one of these seeds to germinate six hours before any of the others will, other things being alike, enable it to choke them out altogether. I have shown you that there is no particular in which plants will not vary from each other; it is quite possible that one of our imaginary plants may vary in such a character as the thickness of the integument of its seeds; it might happen that one of the plants might produce seeds having a thinner integument, and that would enable the seeds of that plant to germinate a little quicker than those of any of the others, and those seeds would most inevitably extinguish the forty-nine times as many that were struggling with them.

I have put it in this way, but you see the practical result of the process is the same as if some person had nurtured the one and destroyed the other seeds. It does not matter how the variation is produced, so long as it is once allowed to occur. The variation in the plant once fairly started tends to become hereditary and repro- duce itself ; the seeds would spread themselves in the same way and take part in the struggle with the forty- nine hundred, or forty-nine thousand, with which they might be exposed. Thus, by degrees, this variety with some slight organic change or modification, must spread itself over the whole surface of the habitable globe, and extirpate or replace the other kinds. That is what is meant by NATURAL SELECTION ; that is the kind of argument by which it is perfectly demonstrable that the conditions of existence may play exactly the same part for natural varieties as man does for domesticated varieties. No one doubts at all that particular circum- stances may be more favourable for one plant and less so for another, and the moment you admit that, you admit the selective power of nature. Now, although I have been putting a hypothetical case, you must not suppose that I have been reasoning hypothetically. There are plenty of direct experiments which bear out what we may call the theory of natural selection; there is extremely good authority for the statement that if you take the seed of mixed varieties of wheat and sow it, collecting the seed next year and sowing it again, at length you will find that out of all your varieties only two or three have lived, or perhaps even only one. There were one or two varieties which were best fitted to get on, and they have killed out the other kinds in just the same way and with just the same certainty as if you had taken the trouble to remove them. As I have already said, the operation of nature is exactly the same as the artificial operation of man.

But if this be true of that simple case, which I put before you, where there is nothing but the rivalry of one member of a species with others, what must be the operation of selective conditions, when you recollect as a matter of fact, that for every species of animal or plant there are fifty or a hundred species which might all, more or less, be comprehended in the same climate, food, and station;—that every plant has multitudinous animals which prey upon it, and which are its direct opponents; and that these have other animals preying upon them,— that every plant has its indirect helpers in the birds that scatter abroad its seed, and the animals that manure it with their dung;—I say, when these things are considered, it seems impossible that any variation which may arise in a species in nature should not tend in some way or other either to be a little better or worse than the previous stock; if it is a little better it will have an advantage over and tend to extirpate the latter in this crush and struggle; and if it is a little worse it will itself be extirpated.

I know nothing that more appropriately expresses this, than the phrase, "the struggle for existence"; because it brings before your minds, in a vivid sort of way, some of the simplest possible circumstances connected with it. When a struggle is intense there must be some who are sure to be trodden down, crushed, and overpowered by others; and there will be some who just manage to get through only by the help of the slightest accident. I recollect reading an account of the famous retreat of the

French troops, under Napoleon, from Moscow. Worn out, tired, and dejected, they at length came to a great river over which there was but one bridge for the passage of the vast army. Disorganized and demoralized as that army was, the struggle must certainly have been a terrible one — every one heeding only himself, and crushing through the ranks and treading down his fellows. The writer of the narrative, who was himself one of those who were fortunate enough to succeed in getting over, and not among the thousands who were left behind or forced into the river, ascribed his escape to the fact that he saw striding onward through the mass a great strong fellow,—one of the French Cuirassiers, who had on a large blue cloak—and he had enough presence of mind to catch and retain a hold of this strong man's cloak. He says, "I caught hold of his cloak, and although he swore at me and cut at and struck me by turns, and at last, when he found he could not shake me off, fell to entreating me to leave go or I should prevent him from escaping, besides not assisting myself, I still kept tight hold of him, and would not quit my grasp until he had at last dragged me through." Here you see was a case of selective saving—if we may so term it—depending for its success on the strength of the cloth of the Cuirassier's cloak. It is the same in nature; every species has its bridge of Beresina; it has to fight its way through and struggle with other species; and when well nigh overpowered, it may be that the smallest chance, something in its colour, perhaps—the minutest circumstance—will turn the scale one way or the other.

Suppose that by a variation of the black race it had produced the white man at any time—you know that the Negroes are said to believe this to have been the case, and to imagine that Cain was the first white man, and that we are his descendants—suppose that this had ever happened, and that the first residence of this human being was on the West Coast of Africa. There is no great structural difference between the white man and the Negro, and yet there is something so singularly different in the constitution of the two, that the malarias of that country, which do not hurt the black at all, cut off and destroy the white. Then you see there would have been a selective operation performed; if the white man had risen in that way, he would have been selected out and removed by means of the malaria. Now there really is a very curious case of selection of this sort among pigs, and it is a case of selection of colour, too. In the woods of Florida there are a great many pigs, and it is a very curious thing that they are all black, every one of them. Professor Wyman was there some years ago, and on noticing no pigs but these black ones, he asked some of the people how it was that they had no white pigs, and the reply was that in the woods of Florida there was a root which they called the Paint Root, and that if the white pigs were to eat any of it, it had the effect of making their hoofs crack, and they died, but if the black pigs ate any of it, it did not hurt them at all. Here was a very simple case of natural selection. A skilful breeder could not more carefully develop the black breed of pigs, and weed out all the white pigs, than the Paint Root does.

To show you how remarkably indirect may be such natural selective agencies as I have referred to, I will conclude by noticing a case mentioned by Mr. Darwin, and which is certainly one of the most curious of its kind. It is that of the Humble Bee. It has been noticed that there are a great many more humble bees in the neighbourhood of towns, than out in the open country; and the explanation of the matter is this: the humble bees build nests, in which they store their honey and deposit the larvæ and eggs. The field mice are amazingly fond of the honey and larvæ; therefore, wherever there are plenty of field mice, as in the country, the humble bees are kept down; but in the neighbourhood of towns, the number of cats which prowl about the fields eat up the field mice, and of course the more mice they eat up the less there are to prey upon the larvæ of the bees—the cats are therefore the INDIRECT HELPERS of the bees.[1]

---

[1] The humble bees, on the other hand, are direct helpers of some plants, such as the heartsease and red clover, which are fertilized by the visits of the bees; and they are indirect helpers of the numerous insects which are more or less completely supported by the heartsease and red clover.

Coming back a step farther we may say that the old maids are also indirect friends of the humble bees, and indirect enemies of the field mice, as they keep the cats which eat up the latter! This is an illustration somewhat beneath the dignity of the subject, perhaps, but it occurs to me in passing, and with it I will conclude this lecture.

IX

A CRITICAL EXAMINATION OF THE POSITION OF MR. DARWIN'S WORK, "ON THE ORIGIN OF SPECIES," IN RELATION TO THE COMPLETE THEORY OF THE CAUSES OF THE PHENOMENA OF ORGANIC NATURE.

In the preceding lectures I have endeavoured to give you an account of those facts, and of those reasonings from facts, which form the data upon which all theories regarding the causes of the phenomena of organic nature must be based. And, although I have had frequent occasion to quote Mr. Darwin—as all persons hereafter, in speaking upon these subjects, will have occasion to quote his famous book on the "Origin of Species,"—you must yet remember that, wherever I have quoted him, it has not been upon theoretical points, or for statements in any way connected with his particular speculations, but on matters of fact, brought forward by himself, or collected by himself, and which appear incidentally in his book. If a man *will* make a book, professing to discuss a single question, an encyclopædia, I cannot help it.

Now, having had an opportunity of considering in this sort of way the different statements bearing upon all theories whatsoever, I have to lay before you, as fairly as I can, what is Mr. Darwin's view of the matter and what position his theories hold, when judged by the principles which I have previously laid down, as deciding our judgments upon all theories and hypotheses.

I have already stated to you that the inquiry respecting the causes of the phenomena of organic nature resolves itself into two problems—the first being the question of the

origination of living or organic beings; and the second
being the totally distinct problem of the modification and
perpetuation of organic beings when they have already
come into existence.   The first question Mr. Darwin does
not touch; he does not deal with it at all; but he says :—
"Given the origin of organic matter—supposing its
creation to have already taken place, my object is to show
in consequence of what laws and what demonstrable
properties of organic matter, and of its environments, such
states of organic nature as those with which we are acquainted must have come about."   This, you will observe,
is a perfectly legitimate proposition; every person has a
right to define the limits of the inquiry which he sets
before himself; and yet it is a most singular thing that in
all the multifarious, and, not unfrequently, ignorant attacks
which have been made upon the "Origin of Species," there
is nothing which has been more speciously criticised than
this particular limitation.   If people have nothing else to
urge against the book, they say—"Well, after all, you see
Mr. Darwin's explanation of the 'Origin of Species' is not
good for much, because, in the long run, he admits that
he does not know how organic matter began to exist.
But if you admit any special creation for the first particle
of organic matter you may just as well admit it for all the
rest; five hundred or five thousand distinct creations are
just as intelligible, and just as little difficult to understand,
as one."   The answer to these cavils is two-fold.   In the
first place, all human inquiry must stop somewhere; all
our knowledge and all our investigation cannot take
us beyond the limits set by the finite and restricted
character of our faculties, or destroy the endless unknown, which accompanies, like its shadow, the endless
procession of phenomena.   So far as I can venture to
offer an opinion on such a matter, the purpose of our
being in existence, the highest object that human beings
can set before themselves, is not the pursuit of any such
chimera as the annihilation of the unknown; but it is
simply the unwearied endeavour to remove its boundaries
a little further from our little sphere of action.

I wonder if any historian would for a moment admit
the objection, that it is preposterous to trouble ourselves

about the history of the Roman Empire, because we do not know anything positive about the origin and first building of the city of Rome! Would it be a fair objection to urge, respecting the sublime discoveries of a Newton, or a Kepler, those great philosophers, whose discoveries have been of the profoundest benefit and service to all men,—to say to them—"After all that you have told us as to how the planets revolve, and how they are maintained in their orbits, you cannot tell us what is the cause of the origin of the sun, moon, and stars. So what is the use of what you have done?" Yet these objections would not be one whit more preposterous than the objections which have been made to the "Origin of Species." Mr. Darwin, then, had a perfect right to limit his inquiry as he pleased, and the only question for us— the inquiry being so limited—is to ascertain whether the method of his inquiry is sound or unsound; whether he has obeyed the canons which must guide and govern all investigation, or whether he has broken them; and it was because our inquiry this evening is essentially limited to that question, that I spent a good deal of time in a former lecture (which, perhaps some of you thought might have been better employed) in endeavouring to illustrate the method and nature of scientific inquiry in general. We shall now have to put in practice the principles that I then laid down.

I stated to you in substance, if not in words, that wherever there are complex masses of phenomena to be inquired into, whether they be phenomena of the affairs of daily life, or whether they belong to the more abstruse and difficult problems laid before the philosopher, our course of proceeding in unravelling that complex chain of phenomena with a view to get at its cause, is always the same; in all cases we must invent an hypothesis; we must place before ourselves some more or less likely supposition respecting that cause; and then, having assumed an hypothesis, having supposed a cause for the phenomena in question, we must endeavour, on the one hand, to demonstrate our hypothesis, or, on the other, to upset and reject it altogether, by testing it in three ways. We must, in the first place, be prepared to prove that the supposed causes of the phenomena exist in nature; that they are what the logicians call *vera causæ*—true causes;—in the next place, we should be prepared to show that the assumed causes of the phenomena are competent to produce such phenomena as those which we wish to explain by them; and in the last place, we ought to be able to show that no other known causes are competent to produce these phenomena. If we can succeed in satisfying these three conditions we shall have demonstrated our hypothesis; or rather I ought to say, we shall have proved it as far as certainty is possible for us; for, after all, there is no one of our surest convictions which may not be upset, or at any rate modified by a further accession of knowledge. It was because it satisfied these conditions that we accepted the hypothesis as to the disappearance of the tea-pot and spoons in the case I supposed in a previous lecture; we found that our hypothesis on that subject was tenable and valid, because the supposed cause existed in nature, because it was competent to account for the phenomena, and because no other known cause was competent to account for them; and it is upon similar grounds that any hypothesis you choose to name is accepted in science as tenable and valid.

What is Mr. Darwin's hypothesis? As I apprehend it —for I have put it into a shape more convenient for common purposes than I could find *verbatim* in his book —as I apprehend it, I say, it is, that all the phenomena of organic nature, past and present, result from, or are caused by, the inter-action of those properties of organic matter, which we have called ATAVISM and VARIABILITY, with the CONDITIONS OF EXISTENCE; or, in other words, —given the existence of organic matter, its tendency to transmit its properties, and its tendency occasionally to vary; and, lastly, given the conditions of existence by which organic matter is surrounded—that these put together are the causes of the Present and of the Past conditions of ORGANIC NATURE.

Such is the hypothesis as I understand it. Now let us see how it will stand the various tests which I laid down just now. In the first place, do these supposed causes of the phenomena exist in nature? Is it the fact that in nature these properties of organic matter—atavism and variability—and those phenomena which we have called the conditions of existence,—is it true that they exist? Well, of course, if they do not exist, all that I have told you in the last three or four lectures must be incorrect, because I have been attempting to prove that they do exist, and I take it that there is abundant evidence that they do exist; so far, therefore, the hypothesis does not break down.

But in the next place comes a much more difficult inquiry:—Are the causes indicated competent to give rise to the phenomena of organic nature? I suspect that this is indubitable to a certain extent. It is demonstrable, I think, as I have endeavoured to show you, that they are perfectly competent to give rise to all the phenomena which are exhibited by RACES in nature. Furthermore, I believe that they are quite competent to account for all that we may call purely structural phenomena which are exhibited by SPECIES in nature. On that point also I have already enlarged somewhat. Again, I think that the causes assumed are competent to account for most of the physiological characteristics of species, and I not only think that they are competent to account for them, but I think that they account for many things which otherwise remain wholly unaccountable and inexplicable, and I may say incomprehensible. For a full exposition of the grounds on which this conviction is based, I must refer you to Mr. Darwin's work; all that I can do now is to illustrate what I have said by two or three cases taken almost at random.

I drew your attention, on a previous evening, to the facts which are embodied in our systems of Classification, which are the results of the examination and comparison of the different members of the animal kingdom one with another. I mentioned that the whole of the animal kingdom is divisible into five sub-kingdoms; that each of these sub-kingdoms is again divisible into provinces; that each province may be divided into classes, and the classes into the successively smaller groups, orders, families, genera, and species.

Now, in each of these groups, the resemblance in struc-

ture among the members of the group is closer in proportion as the group is smaller. Thus, a man and a
worm are members of the animal kingdom in virtue of
certain apparently slight though really fundamental resemblances which they present. But a man and a fish
are members of the same Sub-kingdom *Vertebrata*, because they are much more like one another than either
of them is to a worm, or a snail, or any member of the
other sub-kingdoms. For similar reasons men and horses
are arranged as members of the same Class, *Mammalia;*
men and apes as members of the same Order, *Primates;*
and if there were any animals more like men than they
were like any of the apes, and yet different from men in
important and constant particulars of their organization,
we should rank them as members of the same Family, or
of the same Genus, but as of distinct Species.

That it is possible to arrange all the varied forms of
animals into groups, having this sort of singular subordination one to the other, is a very remarkable circumstance; but, as Mr. Darwin remarks, this is a result which
is quite to be expected, if the principles which he lays
down be correct. Take the case of the races which are
known to be produced by the operation of atavism and
variability, and the conditions of existence which check
and modify these tendencies. Take the case of the
pigeons that I brought before you: there it was shown
that they might be all classed as belonging to some one
of five principal divisions, and that within these divisions
other subordinate groups might be formed. The members of these groups are related to one another in just
the same way as the genera of a family, and the groups
themselves as the families of an order, or the orders of
a class; while all have the same sort of structural relations
with the wild Rock-pigeon, as the members of any great
natural group have with a real or imaginary typical form.
Now, we know that all varieties of pigeons of every kind
have arisen by a process of selective breeding from a
common stock, the Rock-pigeon; hence, you see, that if
all species of animals have proceeded from some common
stock, the general character of their structural relations,
and of our systems of classification, which express those

relations, would be just what we find them to be. In other words, the hypothetical cause is, so far, competent to produce effects similar to those of the real cause.

Take, again, another set of very remarkable facts,—the existence of what are called rudimentary organs, organs for which we can find no obvious use, in the particular animal economy in which they are found, and yet which are there.

Such are the splint-like bones in the leg of the horse, which I here show you, and which correspond with bones which belong to certain toes and fingers in the human hand and foot. In the horse you see they are quite rudimentary, and bear neither toes nor fingers; so that the horse has only one "finger" in his fore-foot and one "toe" in his hind-foot. But it is a very curious thing that the animals closely allied to the horse show more toes than he; as the rhinoceros, for instance: he has these extra toes well formed, and anatomical facts show very clearly that he is very closely related to the horse indeed. So we may say that animals, in an anatomical sense nearly related to the horse, have those parts which are rudimentary in him, fully developed.

Again, the sheep and the cow have no cutting-teeth, but only a hard pad in the upper jaw. That is the common characteristic of ruminants in general. But the calf has in its upper jaw some rudiments of teeth which never are developed, and never play the part of teeth at all. Well, if you go back in time, you find some of the older, now extinct, allies of the ruminants have well-developed teeth in their upper jaws; and at the present day the pig (which is in structure closely connected with ruminants) has well-developed teeth in its upper jaw; so that here is another instance of organs well developed and very useful, in one animal, represented by rudimentary organs, for which we can discover no purpose whatsoever, in another closely allied animal. The whalebone whale, again, has horny "whalebone" plates in its mouth, and no teeth; but the young fœtal whale, before it is born, has teeth in its jaws; they, however, are never used, and they never come to anything. But other members of the group to which the whale belongs have well-developed teeth in both jaws.

Upon any hypothesis of special creation, facts of this kind appear to me to be entirely unaccountable and inexplicable, but they cease to be so if you accept Mr. Darwin's hypothesis, and see reason for believing that the whalebone whale and the whale with teeth in its mouth both sprang from a whale that had teeth, and that the teeth of the fœtal whale are merely remnants—recollections, if we may so say—of the extinct whale. So in the case of the horse and the rhinoceros : suppose that both have descended by modification from some earlier form which had the normal number of toes, and the persistence of the rudimentary bones which no longer support toes in the horse becomes comprehensible.

In the language that we speak in England, and in the language of the Greeks, there are identical verbal roots, or elements entering into the composition of words. That fact remains unintelligible so long as we suppose English and Greek to be independently created tongues ; but when it is shown that both languages are descended from one original, the Sanscrit, we give an explanation of that resemblance. In the same way the existence of identical structural roots, if I may so term them, entering into the composition of widely different animals, is striking evidence in favour of the descent of those animals from a common original.

To turn to another kind of illustration :—If you regard the whole series of stratified rocks—that enormous thickness of sixty or seventy thousand feet that I have mentioned before, constituting the only record we have of a most prodigious lapse of time, that time being, in all probability, but a fraction of that of which we have no record ;—if you observe in these successive strata of rocks successive groups of animals arising and dying out, a constant succession, giving you the same kind of impression, as you travel from one group of strata to another, as you would have in travelling from one country to another ;—when you find this constant succession of forms, their traces obliterated except to the man of science,—when you look at this wonderful history, and ask what it means, it is only a paltering with words if you are offered the reply,—" They were so created."

But if, on the other hand, you look on all forms of organized beings as the results of the gradual modification of a primitive type, the facts receive a meaning, and you see that these older conditions are the necessary predecessors of the present. Viewed in this light the facts of palæontology receive a meaning—upon any other hypothesis, I am unable to see, in the slightest degree, what knowledge or signification we are to draw out of them. Again, note as bearing upon the same point, the singular likeness which obtains between the successive Faunæ and Floræ, whose remains are preserved on the rocks: you never find any great and enormous difference between the immediately successive Faunæ and Floræ, unless you have reason to believe there has also been a great lapse of time or a great change of conditions. The animals, for instance, of the newest tertiary rocks, in any part of the world, are always, and without exception, found to be closely allied with those which now live in that part of the world. For example, in Europe, Asia, and Africa, the large mammals are at present rhinoceri, hippopotami, elephants, lions, tigers, oxen, horses, &c.; and if you examine the newest tertiary deposits, which contain the animals and plants which immediately preceded those which now exist in the same country, you do not find gigantic specimens of ant-eaters and kangaroos, but you find rhinoceroses, elephants, lions, tigers, &c.,—of different species to those now living,—but still their close allies. If you turn to South America, where, at the present day, we have great sloths and armadilloes and creatures of that kind, what do you find in the newest tertiaries? You find the great sloth-like creature, the *Megatherium*, and the great armadillo, the *Glyptodon*, and so on. And if you go to Australia you find the same law holds good, namely, that that condition of organic nature which has preceded the one which now exists, presents differences perhaps of species, and of genera, but that the great types of organic structure are the same as those which now flourish.

What meaning has this fact upon any other hypothesis or supposition than one of successive modification? But if the population of the world, in any age, is the result of the gradual modification of the forms which peopled it in the preceding age,—if that has been the case, it is intelligible enough; because we may expect that the creature that results from the modification of an elephantine mammal shall be something like an elephant, and the creature which is produced by the modification of an armadillo-like mammal shall be like an armadillo. Upon that supposition, I say, the facts are intelligible; upon any other, that I am aware of, they are not.

So far, the facts of palæontology are consistent with almost any form of the doctrine of progressive modification; they would not be absolutely inconsistent with the wild speculations of De Maillet, or with the less objectionable hypothesis of Lamarck. But Mr. Darwin's views have one peculiar merit; and that is, that they are perfectly consistent with an array of facts which are utterly inconsistent with and fatal to, any other hypothesis of progressive modification which has yet been advanced. It is one remarkable peculiarity of Mr. Darwin's hypothesis that it involves no necessary progression or incessant modification, and that it is perfectly consistent with the persistence for any length of time of a given primitive stock, contemporaneously with its modifications. To return to the case of the domestic breeds of pigeons, for example; you have the Dove-cot pigeon, which closely resembles the Rock-pigeon, from which they all started, existing at the same time with the others. And if species are developed in the same way in nature, a primitive stock and its modifications may, occasionally, all find the conditions fitted for their existence; and though they come into competition, to a certain extent, with one another, the derivative species may not necessarily extirpate the primitive one, or *vice versâ*.

Now palæontology shows us many facts which are perfectly harmonious with these observed effects of the process by which Mr. Darwin supposes species to have originated, but which appear to me to be totally inconsistent with any other hypothesis which has been proposed. There are some groups of animals and plants, in the fossil world, which have been said to belong to "persistent types," because they have persisted, with very little change indeed, through a very great range of time, while everything about them has changed largely. There are families of fishes whose type of construction has persisted all the way from the carboniferous rock right up to the cretaceous; and others which have lasted through almost the whole range of the secondary rocks, and from the lias to the older tertiaries. It is something stupendous this — to consider a genus lasting without essential modifications through all this enormous lapse of time while almost everything else was changed and modified.

Thus I have no doubt that Mr. Darwin's hypothesis will be found competent to explain the majority of the phenomena exhibited by species in nature; but in an earlier lecture I spoke cautiously with respect to its power of explaining all the physiological peculiarities of species.

There is, in fact, one set of these peculiarities which the theory of selective modification, as it stands at present, is not wholly competent to explain, and that is the group of phenomena which I mentioned to you under the name of Hybridism, and which I explained to consist in the sterility of the offspring of certain species when crossed one with another. It matters not one whit whether this sterility is universal, or whether it exists only in a single case. Every hypothesis is bound to explain, or, at any rate, not be inconsistent with, the whole of the facts which it professes to account for; and if there is a single one of these facts which can be shown to be inconsistent with (I do not merely mean inexplicable by, but contrary to,) the hypothesis, the hypothesis falls to the ground,— it is worth nothing. One fact with which it is positively inconsistent is worth as much, and as powerful in nega-tiving the hypothesis, as five hundred. If I am right in thus defining the obligations of an hypothesis, Mr. Darwin, in order to place his views beyond the reach of all possible assault, ought to be able to demonstrate the possibility of developing from a particular stock by selective breeding, two forms, which should either be unable to cross one with another, or whose cross-bred offspring should be infertile with one another.

For, you see, if you have not done that you have not strictly fulfilled all the conditions of the problem; you have not shown that you can produce, by the cause assumed, all the phenomena which you have in nature. Here are the phenomena of Hybridism staring you in the face, and you cannot say, "I can, by selective modification, produce these same results." Now, it is admitted on all hands that, at present, so far as experiments have gone, it has not been found possible to produce this complete physiological divergence by selective breeding. I stated this very clearly before, and I now refer to the point, because, if it could be proved, not only that this *has* not been done, but that it *cannot* be done; if it could be demonstrated that it is impossible to breed selectively, from any stock, a form which shall not breed with another, produced from the same stock; and if we were shown that this must be the necessary and inevitable result of all experiments, I hold that Mr. Darwin's hypothesis would be utterly shattered.

But has this been done? or what is really the state of the case? It is simply that, so far as we have gone yet with our breeding, we have not produced from a common stock two breeds which are not more or less fertile with one another.

I do not know that there is a single fact which would justify any one in saying that any degree of sterility has been observed between breeds absolutely known to have been produced by selective breeding from a common stock. On the other hand, I do not know that there is a single fact which can justify any one in asserting that such sterility cannot be produced by proper experimentation. For my own part, I see every reason to believe that it may, and will be so produced. For, as Mr. Darwin has very properly urged, when we consider the phenomena of sterility, we find they are most capricious; we do not know what it is that the sterility depends on. There are some animals which will not breed in captivity; whether it arises from the simple fact of their being shut up and deprived of their liberty, or not, we do not know, but they certainly will not breed. What an astounding thing this is, to find one of the most important of all functions annihilated by mere imprisonment!

So, again, there are cases known of animals which have been thought by naturalists to be undoubted species, which have yielded perfectly fertile hybrids; while there are other species which present what everybody believes to be varieties [1] which are more or less infertile with one another. There are other cases which are truly extraordinary; there is one, for example, which has been carefully examined,—of two kinds of sea-weed, of which the male element of the one, which we may call A, fertilizes the female element of the other, B; while the male element of B will not fertilize the female element of A; so that, while the former experiment seems to show us that they are *varieties*, the latter leads to the conviction that they are *species*.

When we see how capricious and uncertain this sterility is, how unknown the conditions on which it depends, I say that we have no right to affirm that those conditions will not be better understood by and by, and we have no ground for supposing that we may not be able to experiment so as to obtain that crucial result which I mentioned just now. So that though Mr. Darwin's hypothesis does not completely extricate us from this difficulty at present, we have not the least right to say it will not do so.

There is a wide gulf between the thing you cannot explain and the thing that upsets you altogether. There is hardly any hypothesis in this world which has not some fact in connection with it which has not been explained, but that is a very different affair to a fact that entirely opposes your hypothesis; in this case all you can say is, that your hypothesis is in the same position as a good many others.

Now, as to the third test, that there are no other causes competent to explain the phenomena, I explained to you that one should be able to say of an hypothesis, that no other known causes than those supposed by it

---

[1] And as I conceive with very good reason; but if any objector urges that we cannot prove that they have been produced by artificial or natural selection, the objection must be admitted—ultra-sceptical as it is. But in science, scepticism is a duty.

are competent to give rise to the phenomena. Here, I think, Mr. Darwin's view is pretty strong. I really believe that the alternative is either Darwinism or nothing, for I do not know of any rational conception or theory of the organic universe which has any scientific position at all beside Mr. Darwin's. I do not know of any proposition that has been put before us with the intention of explaining the phenomena of organic nature, which has in its favour a thousandth part of the evidence which may be adduced in favour of Mr. Darwin's views. Whatever may be the objections to his views, certainly all other theories are absolutely out of court.

Take the Lamarckian hypothesis, for example. Lamarck was a great naturalist, and to a certain extent went the right way to work; he argued from what was undoubtedly a true cause of some of the phenomena of organic nature. He said it is a matter of experience that an animal may be modified more or less in consequence of its desires and consequent actions. Thus, if a man exercise himself as a blacksmith, his arms will become strong and muscular; such organic modification is a result of this particular action and exercise. Lamarck thought that by a very simple supposition based on this truth he could explain the origin of the various animal species: he said, for example, that the short-legged birds which live on fish, had been converted into the long-legged waders by desiring to get the fish without wetting their feathers, and so stretching their legs more and more through successive generations. If Lamarck could have shown experimentally, that even races of animals could be produced in this way, there might have been some ground for his speculations. But he could show nothing of the kind, and his hypothesis has pretty well dropped into oblivion, as it deserved to do. I said in an earlier lecture that there are hypotheses and hypotheses, and when people tell you that Mr. Darwin's strongly-based hypothesis is nothing but a mere modification of Lamarck's, you will know what to think of their capacity for forming a judgment on this subject.

But you must recollect that when I say I think it is either Mr. Darwin's hypothesis or nothing; that either we must take his view, or look upon the whole of organic nature as an enigma, the meaning of which is wholly hidden from us; you must understand that I mean that I accept it provisionally, in exactly the same way as I accept any other hypothesis.   Men of science do not pledge themselves to creeds; they are bound by articles of no sort; there is not a single belief that it is not a bounden duty with them to hold with a light hand and to part with it, cheerfully, the moment it is really proved to be contrary to any fact, great or small.   And if in course of time I see good reasons for such a proceeding, I shall have no hesitation in coming before you, and pointing out any change in my opinion without finding the slightest occasion to blush for so doing.   So I say that we accept this view as we accept any other, so long as it will help us, and we feel bound to retain it only so long as it will serve our great purpose—the improvement of Man's estate and the widening of his knowledge. The moment this, or any other conception, ceases to be useful for these purposes, away with it to the four winds; we care not what becomes of it !

But to say truth, although it has been my business to attend closely to the controversies roused by the publication of Mr. Darwin's book, I think that not one of the enormous mass of objections and obstacles which have been raised is of any very great value, except that sterility case which I brought before you just now.   All the rest are misunderstandings of some sort, arising either from prejudice, or want of knowledge, or still more from want of patience and care in reading the work.

For you must recollect that it is not a book to be read, with as much ease, as its pleasant style may lead you to imagine.   You spin through it as if it were a novel the first time you read it, and think you know all about it; the second time you read it you think you know rather less about it ; and the third time, you are amazed to find how little you have really apprehended its vast scope and objects.   I can positively say that I never take it up without finding in it some new view, or light, or suggestion that I have not noticed before.   That is the best characteristic of a thorough and profound book ; and I believe this feature of the "Origin of Species" explains why so many persons have ventured to pass judgment and criticisms upon it which are by no means worth the paper they are written on.

Before concluding these lectures there is one point to which I must advert,—though, as Mr. Darwin has said nothing about man in his book, it concerns myself rather than him ;—for I have strongly maintained on sundry occasions that if Mr. Darwin's views are sound, they apply as much to man as to the lower mammals, seeing that it is perfectly demonstrable that the structural differences which separate man from the apes are not greater than those which separate some apes from others. There cannot be the slightest doubt in the world that the argument which applies to the improvement of the horse from an earlier stock, or of ape from ape, applies to the improvement of man from some simpler and lower stock than man. There is not a single faculty—functional or structural, moral, intellectual, or instinctive,—there is no faculty whatever that is not capable of improvement ; there is no faculty whatsoever which does not depend upon structure, and as structure tends to vary, it is capable of being improved.

Well, I have taken a good deal of pains at various times to prove this, and I have endeavoured to meet the objections of those who maintain, that the structural differences between man and the lower animals are of so vast a character and enormous extent, that even if Mr. Darwin's views are correct, you cannot imagine this particular modification to take place. It is, in fact, easy matter to prove that, so far as structure is concerned, man differs to no greater extent from the animals which are immediately below him than these do from other members of the same order. Upon the other hand, there is no one who estimates more highly than I do the dignity of human nature, and the width of the gulf in intellectual and moral matters, which lies between man and the whole of the lower creation.

But I find this very argument brought forward vehemently by some. "You say that man has proceeded from a modification of some lower animal, and you take pains to prove that the structural differences which are said to exist in his brain do not exist at all, and you teach that all functions, intellectual, moral, and others, are the expression or the result, in the long run, of structures, and of the molecular forces which they exert." It is quite true that I do so.

"Well, but," I am told at once, somewhat triumphantly, "you say in the same breath that there is a great moral and intellectual chasm between man and the lower animals. How is this possible when you declare that moral and intellectual characteristics depend on structure, and yet tell us that there is no such gulf between the structure of man and that of the lower animals?"

I think that objection is based upon a misconception of the real relations which exist between structure and function, between mechanism and work. Function is the expression of molecular forces and arrangements no doubt; but, does it follow from this, that variation in function so depends upon variation in structure that the former is always exactly proportioned to the latter? If there is no such relation, if the variation in function which follows on a variation in structure, may be enormously greater than the variation of the structure, then, you see, the objection falls to the ground.

Take a couple of watches—made by the same maker, and as completely alike as possible; set them upon the table, and the function of each—which is its rate of going —will be performed in the same manner, and you shall be able to distinguish no difference between them; but let me take a pair of pincers, and if my hand is steady enough to do it, let me just lightly crush together the bearings of the balance-wheel, or force to a slightly different angle the teeth of the escapement of one of them, and of course you know the immediate result will be that the watch, so treated, from that moment will cease to go. But what proportion is there between the structural alteration and the functional result? Is it not perfectly obvious that the alteration is of the minutest kind, yet that slight as it is, it has produced an infinite difference in the performance of the functions of these two instruments?

*K 47

Well, now, apply that to the present question. What is it that constitutes and makes man what he is? What is it but his power of language—that language giving him the means of recording his experience — making every generation somewhat wiser than its predecessor,—more in accordance with the established order of the universe?

What is it but this power of speech, of recording experience, which enables men to be men—looking before and after and, in some dim sense, understanding the working of this wondrous universe—and which distinguishes man from the whole of the brute world? I say that this functional difference is vast, unfathomable, and truly infinite in its consequences; and I say at the same time, that it may depend upon structural differences which shall be absolutely inappreciable to us with our present means of investigation. What is this very speech that we are talking about? I am speaking to you at this moment, but if you were to alter, in the minutest degree, the proportion of the nervous forces now active in the two nerves which supply the muscles of my glottis, I should become suddenly dumb. The voice is produced only so long as the vocal chords are parallel; and these are parallel only so long as certain muscles contract with exact equality; and that again depends on the equality of action of those two nerves I spoke of. So that a change of the minutest kind in the structure of one of these nerves, or in the structure of the part in which it originates, or of the supply of blood to that part, or of one of the muscles to which it is distributed, might render all of us dumb. But a race of dumb men, deprived of all communication with those who could speak, would be little indeed removed from the brutes. And the moral and intellectual difference between them and ourselves would be practically infinite, though the naturalist should not be able to find a single shadow of even specific structural difference.

But let me dismiss this question now, and, in conclusion, let me say that you may go away with it as my mature conviction, that Mr. Darwin's work is the greatest contribution which has been made to biological science since the publication of the "Règne Animal" of Cuvier,

and since that of the "History of Development," of Von
Baer. I believe that if you strip it of its theoretical
part it still remains one of the greatest encyclopædias of
biological doctrine that any one man ever brought forth;
and I believe that, if you take it as the embodiment of
an hypothesis, it is destined to be the guide of biological
and psychological speculation for the next three or four
generations.

X

ON THE EDUCATIONAL VALUE OF THE NATURAL HISTORY SCIENCES

THE subject to which I have to beg your attention during the ensuing hour is "The Relation of Physiological Science to other branches of knowledge."

Had circumstances permitted of the delivery, in their strict logical order, of that series of discourses of which the present lecture is a member, I should have preceded my friend and colleague Mr. Henfrey, who addressed you on Monday last; but while, for the sake of that order, I must beg you to suppose that this discussion of the Educational bearings of Biology in general *does* precede that of Special Zoology and Botany, I am rejoiced to be able to take advantage of the light thus already thrown upon the tendency and methods of Physiological Science.

Regarding Physiological Science then, in its widest sense—as the equivalent of *Biology*—the Science of Individual Life—we have to consider in succession:

1. Its position and scope as a branch of knowledge.
2. Its value as a means of mental discipline.
3. Its worth as practical information.

And lastly,

4. At what period it may best be made a branch of Education.

Our conclusions on the first of these heads must depend, of course, upon the nature of the subject-matter of Biology; and I think a few preliminary considerations will place before you in a clear light the vast difference which exists between the living bodies with which Physiological science is concerned, and the remainder of the

universe ;—between the phænomena of Number and
Space, of Physical and of Chemical force, on the one
hand, and those of Life on the other.

The mathematician, the physicist, and the chemist con-
template things in a condition of rest; they look upon a
state of equilibrium as that to which all bodies normally
tend.

The mathematician does not suppose that a quantity
will alter, or that a given point in space will change its
direction with regard to another point, spontaneously.
And it is the same with the physicist. When Newton saw
the apple fall, he concluded at once that the act of falling
was not the result of any power inherent in the apple, but
that it was the result of the action of something else on
the apple. In a similar manner, all physical force is
regarded as the disturbance of an equilibrium to which
things tended before its exertion,—to which they will tend
again after its cessation.

The chemist equally regards chemical change in a
body, as the effect of the action of something external to
the body changed. A chemical compound once formed
would persist for ever, if no alteration took place in surrounding conditions.

But to the student of Life the aspect of nature is
reversed. Here, incessant, and, so far as we know,
spontaneous change is the rule, rest the exception—the
anomaly to be accounted for. Living things have no
inertia and tend to no equilibrium.

Permit me, however, to give more force and clearness
to these somewhat abstract considerations, by an illustration or two.

Imagine a vessel full of water, at the ordinary temperature, in an atmosphere saturated with vapour. The
quantity and the *figure* of that water will not change, so
far as we know, for ever.

Suppose a lump of gold be thrown into the vessel
—motion and disturbance of figure exactly proportional
to the momentum of the gold will take place. But after
a time the effects of this disturbance will subside—equilibrium will be restored, and the water will return to its
passive state.

Expose the water to cold—it will solidify—and in so doing its particles will arrange themselves in definite crystalline shapes. But once formed, these crystals change no further.

Again, substitute for the lump of gold some substance capable of entering into chemical relations with the water:—say, a mass of that substance which is called "protein"—the substance of flesh:—a very considerable disturbance of equilibrium will take place—all sorts of chemical compositions and decompositions will occur; but in the end, as before, the result will be the resumption of a condition of rest.

Instead of such a mass of *dead* protein, however, take a particle of *living* protein—one of those minute microscopic living things which throng our pools, and are known as Infusoria—such a creature, for instance, as an Euglena, and place it in our vessel of water. It is a round mass provided with a long filament, and except in this peculiarity of shape, presents no appreciable physical or chemical difference whereby it might be distinguished from the particle of dead protein.

But the difference in the phænomena to which it will give rise is immense: in the first place it will develope a vast quantity of physical force—cleaving the water in all directions, with considerable rapidity, by means of the vibrations of the long filament or cilium.

Nor is the amount of chemical energy which the little creature possesses less striking. It is a perfect laboratory in itself, and it will act and react upon the water and the matters contained therein; converting them into new compounds resembling its own substance and, at the same time, giving up portions of its own substance which have become effete.

Furthermore, the Euglena will increase in size; but this increase is by no means unlimited, as the increase of a crystal might be. After it has grown to a certain extent it divides, and each portion assumes the form of the original and proceeds to repeat the process of growth and division.

Nor is this all. For after a series of such divisions and subdivisions, these minute points assume a totally new form, lose their long tails—round themselves, and secrete a sort of envelope or box, in which they remain shut up for a time, eventually to resume, directly or indirectly, their primitive mode of existence.

Now, so far as we know, there is no natural limit to the existence of the Euglena, or of any other living germ. A living species once launched into existence tends to live for ever.

Consider how widely different this living particle is from the dead atoms with which the physicist and chemist have to do!

The particle of gold falls to the bottom and rests—the particle of dead protein decomposes and disappears—it also rests : but the *living* protein mass neither tends to exhaustion of its forces nor to any permanency of form, but is essentially distinguished as a disturber of equilibrium so far as force is concerned,— as undergoing continual metamorphosis and change, in point of form.

Tendency to equilibrium of force, and to permanency of form then, are the characters of that portion of the universe which does not live the domain of the chemist and physicist.

Tendency to disturb existing equilibrium,—to take on forms which succeed one another in definite cycles, is the character of the living world.

What is the cause of this wonderful difference between the dead particle and the living particle of matter appearing in other respects identical? that difference to which we give the name of Life?

I, for one, cannot tell you. It may be that, by and bye, philosophers will discover some higher laws of which the facts of life are particular cases—very possibly they will find out some bond between physico-chemical phæ-nomena on the one hand, and vital phænomena on the other. At present, however, we assuredly know of none; and I think we shall exercise a wise humility in confessing that, for us at least, this successive assumption of different states—(external conditions remaining the same) —this *spontaneity of action*—if I may use a term which implies more than I would be answerable for—which constitutes so vast and plain a practical distinction between living bodies and those which do not live, is an ultimate fact; indicating as such, the existence of a broad line of demarcation between the subject-matter of Biological and that of all other sciences.

For I would have it understood that this simple Euglena is the type of *all* living things, so far as the distinction between these and inert matter is concerned. That cycle of changes, which is constituted by perhaps not more than two or three steps in the Euglena, is as clearly manifested in the multitudinous stages through which the germ of an oak or of a man passes. Whatever forms the Living Being may take on, whether simple or complex, — *production, growth, reproduction,* — are the phænomena which distinguish it from that which does not live.

If this be true, it is clear that the student, in passing from the physico-chemical to the physiological sciences, enters upon a totally new order of facts; and it will next be for us to consider how far these new facts involve *new* methods, or require a modification of those with which he is already acquainted. Now a great deal is said about the peculiarity of the scientific method in general, and of the different methods which are pursued in the different sciences. The Mathematics are said to have one special method; Physics another, Biology a third, and so forth. For my own part, I must confess that I do not understand this phraseology. So far as I can arrive at any clear comprehension of the matter, Science is not, as many would seem to suppose, a modification of the black art, suited to the tastes of the nineteenth century, and flourishing mainly in consequence of the decay of the Inquisition.

Science is, I believe, nothing but *trained and organized common sense,* differing from the latter only as a veteran may differ from a raw recruit: and its methods differ from those of common sense only so far as the guardsman's cut and thrust differ from the manner in which a savage wields his club. The primary power is the same in each case, and perhaps the untutored savage has the more brawny arm of the two. The *real* advantage lies in the point and polish of the swordsman's weapon; in the trained eye quick to spy out the weakness of the adversary; in the ready hand prompt to follow it on the instant. But after all, the sword exercise is only the hewing and poking of the clubman developed and perfected.

So, the vast results obtained by Science are won by no mystical faculties, by no mental processes, other than those which are practised by every one of us, in the humblest and meanest affairs of life. A detective police-man discovers a burglar from the marks made by his shoe, by a mental process identical with that by which Cuvier restored the extinct animals of Montmartre from fragments of their bones. Nor does that process of induction and deduction by which a lady, finding a stain of a peculiar kind upon her dress, concludes that somebody has upset the inkstand thereon, differ in any way, in kind, from that by which Adams and Leverrier discovered a new planet.

The man of science, in fact, simply uses with scrupulous exactness, the methods which we all, habitually and at every moment, use carelessly; and the man of business must as much avail himself of the scientific method— must be as truly a man of science—as the vericst book-worm of us all; though I have no doubt that the man of business will find himself out to be a philosopher with as much surprise as M. Jourdain exhibited when he dis-covered that he had been all his life talking prose. If, however, there be no real difference between the methods of science and those of common life, it would seem on the face of the matter highly improbable that there should be any difference between the methods of the different sciences; nevertheless, it is constantly taken for granted, that there is a very wide difference between the Physio-logical and other sciences in point of method.

In the first place it is said—and I take this point first, because the imputation is too frequently admitted by Physiologists themselves—that Biology differs from the Physico-chemical and Mathematical sciences, in being "inexact."

Now, this phrase "inexact" must refer either to the *methods* or to the *results* of Physiological science.

It cannot be correct to apply it to the methods; for, as

I hope to show you by and bye, these are identical in all sciences, and whatever is true of Physiological method is true of Physical and Mathematical method.

Is it then the *results* of Biological science which are "inexact"? I think not. If I say that respiration is performed by the lungs; that digestion is effected in the stomach; that the eye is the organ of sight; that the jaws of a vertebrated animal never open sideways, but always up and down; while those of an annulose animal always open sideways, and never up and down—I am enumerating propositions which are as exact as anything in Euclid. How then has this notion of the inexactness of Biological science come about? I believe from two causes: first, because, in consequence of the great complexity of the science and the multitude of interfering conditions, we are very often only enabled to predict approximately what will occur under given circumstances; and secondly, because, on account of the comparative youth of the Physiological sciences, a great many of their laws are still imperfectly worked out. But in an educational point of view, it is most important to distinguish between the essence of a science and the accidents which surround it; and essentially, the methods and results of Physiology are as exact as those of Physics or Mathematics.

It is said that the Physiological method is especially *comparative* [1]; and this dictum also finds favour in the eyes of many. I should be sorry to suggest that the

---

[1] "In the third place, we have to review the method of Comparison, which is so specially adapted to the study of living bodies, and by which, above all others, that study must be advanced. In Astronomy, this method is necessarily inapplicable; and it is not till we arrive at Chemistry that this third means of investigation can be used, and then only in subordination to the two others. It is in the study, both statical and dynamical, of living bodies that it first acquires its full development; and its use elsewhere can be only through its application here."—*Comte's Positive Philosophy*, translated by Miss Martineau. Vol. i. p. 372.

By what method does M. Comte suppose that the equality or inequality of forces and quantities and the dissimilarity or similarity of forms—points of some slight importance not only in Astronomy and Physics, but even in Mathematics,—are ascertained, if not by Comparison?

speculators on scientific classification have been misled by the accident of the name of one leading branch of Biology—*Comparative Anatomy;* but I would ask whether *comparison*, and that classification which is the result of comparison, are not the essence of every science whatsoever? How is it possible to discover a relation of cause and effect of *any* kind without comparing a series of cases together in which the supposed cause and effect occur singly, or combined? So far from comparison being in any way peculiar to Biological science, it is, I think, the essence of every science.

A speculative philosopher again tells us that the Biological sciences are distinguished by being sciences of observation and not of experiment![1]

Of all the strange assertions into which speculation without practical acquaintance with a subject may lead even an able man, I think this is the very strangest. Physiology not an experimental science! Why, there is not a function of a single organ in the body which has not been determined wholly and solely by experiment? How did Harvey determine the nature of the circulation, except by experiment? How did Sir Charles Bell determine the functions of the roots of the spinal nerves, save by experiment? How do we know the use of a nerve at all, except by experiment? Nay, how do you know even that your eye is your seeing apparatus, unless you make the experiment of shutting it; or that your ear is your hearing apparatus, unless you close it up and thereby discover that you become deaf?

It would really be much more true to say that Physiology is *the* experimental science *par excellence* of all sciences; that in which there is least to be learnt by mere observa-

---

[1] " Proceeding to the second class of means,—Experiment cannot but be less and less decisive, in proportion to the complexity of the phænomena to be explored; and therefore we saw this resource to be less effectual in chemistry than in physics: and we now find that it is eminently useful in chemistry in comparison with physiology. *In fact, the nature of the phænomena seems to offer almost insurmountable impediments to any extensive and prolific application of such a procedure in biology.*"—COMTE, vol. i. p. 367.

M. Comte, as his manner is, contradicts himself two pages further on, but that will hardly relieve him from the responsibility of such a paragraph as the above.

tion, and that which affords the greatest field for the exercise of those faculties which characterize the experimental philosopher. I confess, if any one were to ask me for a model application of the logic of experiment, I should know no better work to put into his hands than Bernard's late Researches on the Functions of the Liver.[1]

Not to give this lecture a too controversial tone however, I must only advert to one more doctrine, held by a thinker of our own age and country, whose opinions are worthy of all respect. It is, that the Biological sciences differ from all others, inasmuch as in *them*, classification takes place by type and not by definition.[2]

It is said, in short, that a natural-history class is not capable of being defined—that the class Rosaceæ, for instance, or the class of Fishes, is not accurately and absolutely definable, inasmuch as its members will present exceptions to every possible definition; and that the members of the class are united together only by the circumstance that they are all more like some imaginary average rose or average fish, than they resemble anything else.

But here, as before, I think the distinction has arisen entirely from confusing a transitory imperfection with an essential character. So long as our information concerning them is imperfect, we class all objects together according to resemblances which we *feel*, but cannot *define*: we group them round *types*, in short. Thus, if

---

[1] Nouvelle Fonction du Foie considéré comme organe producteur de matière sucrée chez l'Homme et les Animaux, par M. Claude Bernard.

[2] "*Natural Groups given by Type, not by Definition.* . . . The class is steadily fixed, though not precisely limited; it is given, though not circumscribed; it is determined, not by a boundary-line without, but by a central point within; not by what it strictly excludes, but what it eminently includes; by an example, not by a precept; in short, instead of Definition we have a *Type* for our director. A type is an example of any class, for instance, a species of a genus, which is considered as eminently possessing the characters of the class. All the species which have a greater affinity with this type-species than with any others, form the genus, and are ranged about it, deviating from it in various directions and different degrees."—*Whewell, The Philosophy of the Inductive Sciences*, vol. i. pp. 476–7.

you ask an ordinary person what kinds of animals there are, he will probably say, beasts, birds, reptiles, fishes, insects, &c. Ask him to define a beast from a reptile, and he cannot do it; but he says, things like a cow or a horse are beasts, and things like a frog or a lizard are reptiles. You see *he does* class by type, and not by definition. But how does this classification differ from that of the scientific Zoologist? How does the meaning of the scientific class-name of "Mammalia" differ from the unscientific of "Beasts"?

Why, exactly because the former depends on a definition, the latter on a type. The class Mammalia is scientifically defined as "all animals which have a vertebrated skeleton and suckle their young." Here is no reference to type, but a definition rigorous enough for a geometrician. And such is the character which every scientific naturalist recognizes as that to which his classes must aspire— knowing, as he does, that classification by type is simply an acknowledgment of ignorance and a temporary device.

So much in the way of negative argument as against the reputed differences between Biological and other methods. No such differences, I believe, really exist. The subject-matter of Biological science is different from that of other sciences, but the methods of all are identical; and these methods are—

1. *Observation* of facts—including under this head that *artificial observation* which is called *experiment*.

2. That process of tying up similar facts into bundles, ticketed and ready for use, which is called *Comparison* and *Classification*,—the results of the process, the ticketed bundles, being named *General propositions*.

3. *Deduction*, which takes us from the general proposition to facts again—teaches us, if I may so say, to anticipate from the ticket what is inside the bundle. And finally—

4. *Verification*, which is the process of ascertaining whether, in point of fact, our anticipation is a correct one.

Such are the methods of all science whatsoever; but perhaps you will permit me to give you an illustration of their employment in the science of Life; and I will take as a special case, the establishment of the doctrine of the *Circulation of the Blood*.

In this case, *simple observation* yields us a knowledge of the existence of the blood from some accidental hæmorrhage, we will say : we may even grant that it informs us of the localisation of this blood in particular vessels, the heart, &c., from some accidental cut or the like. It teaches also the existence of a pulse in various parts of the body, and acquaints us with the structure of the heart and vessels.

Here, however, *simple observation* stops, and we must have recourse to *experiment*.

You tie a vein, and you find that the blood accumulates on the side of the ligature opposite the heart. You tie an artery, and you find that the blood accumulates on the side near the heart. Open the chest, and you see the heart contracting with great force. Make openings into its principal cavities, and you will find that all the blood flows out, and no more pressure is exerted on either side of the arterial or venous ligature.

Now all these facts, taken together, constitute the evidence that the blood is propelled by the heart through the arteries, and returns by the veins—that, in short, the blood circulates.

Suppose our experiments and observations have been made on horses, then we group and ticket them into a general proposition, thus :—*all horses have a circulation of their blood*.

Henceforward a horse is a sort of indication or label, telling us where we shall find a peculiar series of phæno-mena called the circulation of the blood.

Here is our *general proposition* then.

How and when are we justified in making our next step—a *deduction* from it ?

Suppose our physiologist, whose experience is limited to horses, meets with a zebra for the first time,—will he suppose that his generalization holds good for zebras also ?

That depends very much on his turn of mind. But we will suppose him to be a bold man. He will say, " The zebra is certainly not a horse, but it is very like

one,—so like, that it must be the 'ticket' or mark of a
blood-circulation also ; and, I conclude that the zebra
has a circulation."

That is a deduction, a very fair deduction, but by no
means to be considered scientifically secure. This last
quality in fact can only be given by *verification*—that is,
by making a zebra the subject of all the experiments performed on the horse. Of course in the present case the
deduction would be *confirmed* by this process of verification,
and the result would be, not merely a positive widening
of knowledge, but a fair increase of confidence in the
truth of one's generalizations in other cases.

Thus, having settled the point in the zebra and horse,
our philosopher would have great confidence in the existence of a circulation in the ass. Nay, I fancy most
persons would excuse him, if in this case he did not take
the trouble to go through the process of verification at
all ; and it would not be without a parallel in the history
of the human mind, if our imaginary physiologist now
maintained that he was acquainted with asinine circulation
à priori.

However, if I might impress any caution upon your
minds, it is, the utterly conditional nature of all our
knowledge,—the danger of neglecting the process of
verification under any circumstances ; and the film upon
which we rest, the moment our deductions carry us
beyond the reach of this great process of verification.
There is no better instance of this than is afforded by
the history of our knowledge of the circulation of the
blood in the animal kingdom until the year 1824. In
every animal possessing a circulation at all, which had
been observed up to that time, the current of the blood
was known to take one definite and invariable direction.
Now, there is a class of animals called *Ascidians*, which
possess a heart and a circulation, and up to the period
of which I speak, no one would have dreamt of question-
ing the propriety of the deduction, that these creatures
have a circulation in one direction ; nor would any one
have thought it worth while to verify the point. But, in
that year, M. von Hasselt happening to examine a transparent animal of this class, found to his infinite surprise,

that after the heart had beat a certain number of times, it stopped, and then began beating the opposite way—so as to reverse the course of the current, which returned by and bye to its original direction.

I have myself timed the heart of these little animals. I found it as regular as possible in its periods of reversal: and I know no spectacle in the animal kingdom more wonderful than that which it presents—all the more wonderful that to this day it remains an unique fact, peculiar to this class among the whole animated world. At the same time I know of no more striking case of the necessity of the *verification* of even those deductions which seem founded on the widest and safest inductions.

Such are the methods of Biology—methods which are obviously identical with those of all other sciences, and therefore wholly incompetent to form the ground of any distinction between it and them.[1]

But I shall be asked at once, do you mean to say that there is no difference between the habit of mind of a mathematician and that of a naturalist? Do you imagine that Laplace might have been put into the Jardin des Plantes, and Cuvier into the Observatory, with equal advantage to the progress of the sciences they professed?

To which I would reply, that nothing could be further from my thoughts. But different habits and various special tendencies of two sciences do not imply different methods. The mountaineer and the man of the plains have very different habits of progression, and each would be at a loss in the other's place; but the method of progression, by putting one leg before the other, is the same in each case. Every step of each is a combination of a lift and a push; but the mountaineer lifts more and the lowlander pushes more. And I think the case of two sciences resembles this.

I do not question for a moment, that while the Mathematician is busy with deductions *from* general propositions, the Biologist is more especially occupied with observation, comparison, and those processes which lead

[1] Save for the pleasure of doing so, I need hardly point out my obligations to Mr. J. S. Mill's "System of Logic," in this view of scientific method.

to general propositions. All I wish to insist upon is, that this difference depends not on any fundamental distinction in the sciences themselves, but on the accidents of their subject-matter, of their relative complexity, and consequent relative perfection.

The Mathematician deals with two properties of objects only, number and extension, and all the inductions he wants have been formed and finished ages ago. He is occupied now with nothing but deduction and verification.

The biologist deals with a vast number of properties of objects, and his inductions will not be completed, I fear, for ages to come; but when they are, his science will be as deductive and as exact as the Mathematics themselves.

Such is the relation of Biology to those sciences which deal with objects having fewer properties than itself. But as the student in reaching Biology looks back upon sciences of a less complex and therefore more perfect nature, so on the other hand does he look forward to other more complex and less perfect branches of knowledge. Biology deals only with living beings as isolated things treats only of the life of the individual : but there is a higher division of science still, which considers living beings as aggregates—which deals with the relation of living beings one to another—the science which *observes* men—whose *experiments* are made by nations one upon another, in battle-fields—whose *general propositions* are embodied in history, morality, and religion—whose *deductions* lead to our happiness or our misery,—and whose *verifications* so often come too late, and serve only

> " To point a moral or adorn a tale "—

I mean the science of Society or *Sociology*.

I think it is one of the grandest features of Biology, that it occupies this central position in human knowledge. There is no side of the human mind which physiological study leaves uncultivated. Connected by innumerable ties with abstract science, Physiology is yet in the most intimate relation with humanity ; and by teaching us that law and order, and a definite scheme of development, regulate even the strangest and wildest manifestations of individual life, she prepares the student to look for a goal even amidst the erratic wanderings of mankind, and to believe that history offers something more than an entertaining chaos—a journal of a toilsome, tragi-comic march nowhither.

The preceding considerations have, I hope, served to indicate the replies which befit the two first of the questions which I set before you at starting, viz. what is the range and position of Physiological Science as a branch of knowledge, and what is its value as a means of mental discipline?

Its *subject-matter* is a large moiety of the universe—its *position* is midway between the physico-chemical and the social sciences. Its *value* as a branch of discipline is partly that which it has in common with all sciences—the training and strengthening of common sense; partly that which is more peculiar to itself—the great exercise which it affords to the faculties of observation and comparison; and I may add, the *exactness* of knowledge which it requires on the part of those among its votaries who desire to extend its boundaries.

If what has been said as to the position and scope of Biology be correct, our third question—what is the practical value of physiological instruction?—might, one would think, be left to answer itself.

On other grounds even, were mankind deserving of the title "rational," which they arrogate to themselves, there can be no question that they would consider as the most necessary of all branches of instruction for themselves and for their children—that which professes to acquaint them with the conditions of the existence they prize so highly—which teaches them how to avoid disease and to cherish health, in themselves and those who are dear to them.

I am addressing, I imagine, an audience of educated persons; and yet I dare venture to assert, that with the exception of those of my hearers who may chance to have received a medical education, there is not one who could tell me what is the meaning and use of an act which he performs a score of times every minute, and whose suspension would involve his immediate death;—I mean the act of breathing—or who could state in precise terms why it is that a confined atmosphere is injurious to health.

The *Practical value* of Physiological knowledge! Why is it that educated men can be found to maintain that a slaughter-house in the midst of a great city is rather a good thing than otherwise?—that mothers persist in exposing the largest possible amount of surface of their children to the cold, by the absurd style of dress they adopt, and then marvel at the peculiar dispensation of Providence, which removes their infants by bronchitis and gastric fever? Why is it that quackery rides rampant over the land; and that not long ago, one of the largest public rooms in this great city could be filled by an audience gravely listening to the reverend expositor of the doctrine—that the simple physiological phænomena known as spirit-rapping, table-turning, phreno-magnetism, and by I know not what other absurd and inappropriate names, are due to the direct and personal agency of Satan?

Why is all this, except from the utter ignorance as to the simplest laws of their own animal life, which prevails among even the most highly educated persons in this country?

But there are other branches of Biological Science, besides Physiology proper, whose practical influence, though less obvious, is not, as I believe, less certain. I have heard educated men speak with an ill-disguised contempt of the studies of the naturalist, and ask, not without a shrug, "What is the use of knowing all about these miserable animals—what bearing has it on human life?"

I will endeavour to answer that question. I take it that all will admit there is definite Government of this universe—that its pleasures and pains are not scattered at random, but are distributed in accordance with orderly and fixed laws, and that it is only in accordance with all we know of the rest of the world, that there should be an agreement between one portion of the sensitive creation and another in these matters.

Surely then it interests us to know the lot of other animal creatures—however far below us, they are still the sole created things which share with us the capability of pleasure and the susceptibility to pain.

I cannot but think that he who finds a certain proportion of pain and evil inseparably woven up in the life of the very worms, will bear his own share with more courage and submission; and will, at any rate, view with suspicion those weakly amiable theories of the Divine government, which would have us believe pain to be an oversight and a mistake,—to be corrected by and bye. On the other hand, the predominance of happiness among living things—their lavish beauty—the secret and wonderful harmony which pervades them all, from the highest to the lowest, are equally striking refutations of that modern Manichean doctrine, which exhibits the world as a slave-mill, worked with many tears, for mere utilitarian ends.

There is yet another way in which natural history may, I am convinced, take a profound hold upon practical life,—and that is, by its influence over our finer feelings, as the greatest of all sources of that pleasure which is derivable from beauty. I do not pretend that natural-history knowledge, as such, can increase our sense of the beautiful in natural objects. I do not suppose that the dead soul of Peter Bell, of whom the great poet of nature says,—

> " A primrose by the river's brim,
> A yellow primrose was to him,—
> And it was nothing more,"—

would have been a whit roused from its apathy, by the information that the primrose is a Dicotyledonous Exogen, with a monopetalous corolla and central placentation. But I advocate natural-history knowledge from this point of view, because it would lead us to *seek* the beauties of natural objects, instead of trusting to chance to force them on our attention. To a person uninstructed in natural history, his country or sea-side stroll is a walk through a gallery filled with wonderful works of art, nine-tenths of which have their faces turned to the wall. Teach him something of natural history, and you place in his hands a catalogue of those which are worth turning round. Surely our innocent pleasures are not so abundant in this life, that we can afford to despise this or any other source of them. We should fear being banished for our neglect to that limbo, where the great Florentine tells us are those who during this life "wept when they might be joyful."

But I shall be trespassing unwarrantably on your kindness, if I do not proceed at once to my last point—the time at which Physiological Science should first form a part of the Curriculum of Education.

The distinction between the teaching of the facts of a science as instruction, and the teaching it systematically as knowledge, has already been placed before you in a previous lecture : and it appears to me, that, as with other sciences, the *common facts* of Biology—the uses of parts of the body—the names and habits of the living creatures which surround us—may be taught with advantage to the youngest child. Indeed, the avidity of children for this kind of knowledge, and the comparative ease with which they retain it, is something quite marvellous. I doubt whether any toy would be so acceptable to young children as a vivarium, of the same kind as, but of course on a smaller scale than, those admirable devices in the Zoological Gardens.

On the other hand, systematic teaching in Biology cannot be attempted with success until the student has attained to a certain knowledge of physics and chemistry : for though the phænomena of life are dependent neither on physical nor on chemical, but on vital forces, yet they result in all sorts of physical and chemical changes, which can only be judged by their own laws.

And now to sum up in a few words the conclusions to which I hope you see reason to follow me.

Biology needs no apologist when she demands a place—and a prominent place—in any scheme of education worthy of the name. Leave out the Physiological sciences from your curriculum, and you launch the student into the world, undisciplined in that science whose subject-matter would best develope his powers of observation ; ignorant of facts of the deepest importance for his own and others' welfare ; blind to the richest sources of beauty in God's creation ; and unprovided with that belief in a living law, and an order manifesting itself in and through endless change and variety, which might serve to check and moderate that phase of despair through which, if he take an earnest interest in social problems, he will assuredly sooner or later pass.

Finally, one word for myself. I have not hesitated to speak strongly where I have felt strongly ; and I am but too conscious that the indicative and imperative moods have too often taken the place of the more becoming subjunctive and conditional. I feel, therefore, how necessary it is to beg you to forget the personality of him who has thus ventured to address you, and to consider only the truth or error in what has been said.

XI

ON THE PERSISTENT TYPES OF ANIMAL LIFE

THE successive modifications which the views of physical geologists have undergone since the infancy of their science, with regard to the amount and the nature of the changes which the crust of the globe has suffered, have all tended in one direction, viz. towards the establishment of the belief, that throughout that vast series of ages which was occupied by the deposition of the stratified rocks, and which may be called "geological time," (to distinguish it from the "historical time" which followed, and the "pre-geological time," which preceded it) the intensity and the character of the physical forces which have been in operation, have varied within but narrow limits; so that, even in Silurian or Cambrian times, the aspect of physical nature must have been much what it is now.

This uniformitarian view of telluric conditions, so far as geological time is concerned, is, however, perfectly consistent with the notion of a totally different state of things in antecedent epochs, and the strongest advocate of such "physical uniformity" during the time of which we have a record might, with perfect consistency, hold the so-called "nebular hypothesis," or any other view involving the conception of a long series of states very different from that which we now know, and whose succession occupied pre-geological time.

The doctrine of physical uniformity and that of physical progression are therefore perfectly consistent, if we regard geological time as having the same relation to pre-geological time as historical time has to it.

The accepted doctrines of palæontology are by no means

in harmony with these tendencies of physical geology. It is generally believed that there is a vast contrast between the ancient and the modern organic worlds—it is incessantly assumed that we are acquainted with the beginning of life, and with the primal manifestation of each of its typical forms : nor does the fact that the discoveries of every year oblige the holders of these views to change their ground, appear sensibly to affect the tenacity of their adhesion.

Without at all denying the considerable positive differences which really exist between the ancient and the modern forms of life, and leaving the negative ones to be met by the other lines of argument, an impartial examination of the facts revealed by palæontology seems to show that these differences and contrasts have been greatly exaggerated.

Thus, of some two hundred known orders of plants, not one is exclusively fossil. Among animals, there is not a single totally extinct class ; and of the orders, at the outside not more than seven per cent. are unrepresented in the existing creation.

Again, certain well marked forms of living beings have existed through enormous epochs, surviving not only the changes of physical conditions, but persisting comparatively unaltered, while other forms of life have appeared and disappeared. Some forms may be termed "persistent types" of life ; and examples of them are abundant enough in both the animal and the vegetable worlds.

Among plants, for instance, ferns, club mosses, and *Coniferæ*, some of them apparently generically identical with those now living, are met with as far back as the carboniferous epoch ; the cone of the oolitic *Araucaria* is hardly distinguishable from that of existing species ; a species of *Pinus* has been discovered in the Purbecks, and a walnut (*Juglans*) in the cretaceous rocks.[1] All these are types of vegetable structure, abounding at the present day ; and surely it is a most remarkable fact to find them persisting with so little change through such vast epochs.

Every sub-kingdom of animals yields instances of the

[1] I state these facts on the authority of my friend Dr. Hooker.— T. H. H.

same kind. The *Globigerina* of the Atlantic soundings is identical with the cretaceous species of the same genus; and the casts of lower Silurian *Foraminifera*, recently described by Ehrenberg, assure us of the very close resemblance between the oldest and the newest forms of many of the *Protozoa*.

Among the *Cælenterata*, the tabulate corals of the Silurian epoch are wonderfully like the millepores of our own seas, as every one may convince himself who compares *Heliolites* with *Heliopora*.

Turning to the *Mollusca*, the genera *Crania, Discina, Lingula*, have persisted from the Silurian epoch to the present day, with so little change, that very competent malacologists are sometimes puzzled to distinguish the ancient from the modern species. *Nautili* have a like range, and the shell of the liassic *Loligo* is similar to that of the "squid" of our own seas. Among the *Annulosa*, the carboniferous insects are in several cases referable to existing genera, as are the *Arachnida*, the highest group of which, the scorpions, is represented in the coal by a genus differing from its living congeners only in the disposition of its eyes.

The vertebrate sub-kingdom furnishes many examples of the same kind. The *Ganoidei* and *Elasmobranchii* are known to have persisted from at least the middle of the Palæozoic epoch to our own times, without exhibiting a greater amount of deviation from the typical characters of these orders, than may be found within their limits at the present day.

Among the *Reptilia*, the highest group, that of the *Crocodilia*, was represented at the beginning of the Mesozoic epoch, if not earlier, by species identical in the essential character of their organization with those now living, and presenting differences only in such points as the form of the articular faces of their vertebræ, in the extent to which the nasal passages are separated from the mouth by bone, and in the proportions of the limbs. Even such imperfect knowledge as we possess of the ancient mammalian fauna leads to the belief that certain of its types, such as that of the *Marsupialia*, have persisted with no greater change through as vast a lapse of time.

It is difficult to comprehend the meaning of such facts as these, if we suppose that each species of animal and plant, or each great type of organization, was formed and placed upon the surface of the globe at long intervals by a distinct act of creative power; and it is well to recollect that such an assumption is as unsupported by tradition or revelation as it is opposed to the general analogy of Nature.

If, on the other hand, we view " Persistent Types," in relation to that hypothesis which supposes the species of living beings living at any time to be the result of the gradual modification of pre-existing species—a hypothesis which though unproven, and sadly damaged by some of its supporters, is yet the only one to which physiology lends any countenance—their existence would seem to show, that the amount of modification which living beings have undergone during geological time is but very small in relation to the whole series of changes which they have suffered. In fact, palæontology and physical geology are in perfect harmony, and coincide in indicating that all we know of the conditions in our world during geological time, is but the last term of a vast and, so far as our present knowledge reaches, unrecorded progression.

XII

TIME AND LIFE

Mr. Darwin's "Origin of Species"

EVERYONE knows that that superficial film of the earth's substance, hardly ten miles thick, which is accessible to human investigation, is composed for the most part of beds or strata of stone, the consolidated muds and sands of former seas and lakes, which have been deposited one upon the other, and hence are the older the deeper they lie. These multitudinous strata present such resemblances and differences among themselves that they are capable of classification into groups or formations, and these formations again are brigaded together into still larger assemblages, called by the older geologists, primary, secondary, and tertiary; by the moderns, palæozoic, mesozoic, and cainozoic: the basis of the former nomenclature being the relative age of the groups of strata; that of the latter, the kinds of living forms contained in them.

Though but a film if compared with the total diameter of our planet, the total series of formations is vast indeed when measured by any human standard, and, as all action implies time, so are we compelled to regard these mineral masses as a measure of the time which has elapsed during their accumulation. The amount of the time which they represent is, of course, in the inverse proportion of the intensity of the forces which have been in operation. If, in the ancient world, mud and sand accumulated on sea-bottoms at tenfold their present rate, it is clear that a bed of mud or sand ten feet thick would have been formed then in the same time as a stratum of similar materials one foot thick would be formed now, and *vice versâ*.

At the outset of his studies, therefore, the physical
geologist had to choose between two hypotheses; either,
throughout the ages which are represented by the accumulated strata, and which we may call *geologic time*, the
forces of nature have operated with much the same
average intensity as at present, and hence the lapse of
time which they represent must be something prodigious
and inconceivable, or, in the primeval epochs, the natural
powers were infinitely more intense than now, and hence
the time through which they acted to produce the effects
we see was comparatively short.

The earlier geologists adopted the latter view almost
with one consent. For they had little knowledge of the
present workings of nature, and they read the records of
geologic time as a child reads the history of Rome or
Greece, and fancies that antiquity was grand, heroic, and
unlike the present because it is unlike his little experience
of the present.

Even so the earlier observers were moved with wonder
at the seeming contrast between the ancient and the
present order of nature. The elemental forces seemed
to have been grander and more energetic in primeval
times. Upheaved and contorted, rifted and fissured,
pierced by dykes of molten matter or worn away over vast
areas by aqueous action, the older rocks appeared to bear
witness to a state of things far different from that exhibited
by the peaceful epoch on which the lot of man has fallen.

But by degrees thoughtful students of geology have
been led to perceive that the earliest efforts of nature
have been by no means the grandest. Alps and Andes
are children of yesterday when compared with Snowdon
and the Cumberland hills; and the so-called glacial epoch
—that in which perhaps the most extensive physical
changes of which any record remains occurred—is the
last and the newest of the revolutions of the globe. And
in proportion as physical geography—which is the geology
of our own epoch—has grown into a science, and the
present order of nature has been ransacked to find what,
hibernicè, we may call precedents for the phenomena of
the past, so the apparent necessity of supposing the past
to be widely different from the present has diminished.

The transporting power of the greatest deluge which can be imagined sinks into insignificance beside that of the slowly floating, slowly melting iceberg, or the glacier creeping along at its snail's pace of a yard a day. The study of the deltas of the Nile, the Ganges, and the Mississippi has taught us how slow is the wearing action of water, how vast its effects when time is allowed for its operation. The reefs of the Pacific, the deep-sea soundings of the Atlantic, show that it is to the slow-growing coral and to the imperceptible animalcule, which lives its brief space and then adds its tiny shell to the muddy cairn left by its brethren and ancestors, that we must look as the agents in the formation of limestone and chalk, and not to hypothetical oceans saturated with calcareous salts and suddenly depositing them.

And while the inquirer has thus learnt that existing forces—*give them time*—are competent to produce all the physical phenomena we meet with in the rocks, so, on the other side, the study of the marks left in the ancient strata by past physical actions shows that these were similar to those which now obtain. Ancient beaches are met with whose pebbles are like those found on modern shores; the hardened sea-sands of the oldest epochs show ripple-marks, such as may now be found on every sandy coast; nay, more, the pits left by ancient rain-drops prove that even in the very earliest ages, the " bow in the clouds " must have adorned the palæozoic firmament. So that if we could reverse the legend of the Seven Sleepers, —if we could sleep back through the past, and awake a million ages before our own epoch, in the midst of the earliest geologic times,—there is no reason to believe that sea, or sky, or the aspect of the land would warn us of the marvellous retrospection.

Such are the beliefs which modern physical geologists hold, or, at any rate, tend towards holding. But, in so doing, it is obvious that they by no means prejudge the question, as to what the physical condition of the globe may have been before our chapters of its history begin, in what may be called (with that licence which is implied in the often-used term "prehistoric epoch") "pregeologic time." The views indicated, in fact, are not only quite consistent with the hypothesis, that, in the still earlier period referred to, the condition of our world was very different; but they may be held by some to necessitate that hypothesis. The physical philosopher who is accurately acquainted with the velocity of a cannon-ball, and the precise character of the line which it traverses for a yard of its course, is necessitated by what he knows of the laws of nature to conclude that it came from a certain spot, whence it was impelled by a certain force, and that it has followed a certain trajectory. In like manner, the student of physical geology, who fully believes in the uniformity of the general condition of the earth through geologic time, may feel compelled by what he knows of causation, and by the general analogy of nature, to suppose that our solar system was once a nebulous mass, that it gradually condensed, that it broke up into that wonderful group of harmoniously rolling balls we call planets and satellites, and that then each of these underwent its appointed metamorphosis, until at last our own share of the cosmic vapour passed into that condition in which we first meet with definite records of its state, and in which it has since, with comparatively little change, remained.

The doctrine of uniformity and the doctrine of progression are, therefore, perfectly consistent; perhaps, indeed, they might be shown to be necessarily connected with one another.

If, however, the condition of the world, which has obtained throughout geologic time, is but the sequel to a vast series of changes which took place in pregeologic time, then it seems not unlikely that the duration of this latter is to that of the former as the vast extent of geologic time is to the length of the brief epoch we call the historical period; and that even the oldest rocks are records of an epoch almost infinitely remote from that which could have witnessed the first shaping of our globe.

It is probable that no modern geologist would hesitate to admit the general validity of these reasonings when applied to the physics of his subject, whence it is the more remarkable that the moment the question changes from one of physics and chemistry to one of natural history, scientific opinions and the popular prejudices, which reflect them in a distorted form, undergo a sudden metamorphosis. Geologists and palæontologists write about the "beginning of life" and the "first-created forms of living beings," as if they were the most familiar things in the world; and even cautious writers seem to be on quite friendly terms with the "archetype" whereby the Creator was guided "amidst the crash of falling worlds." Just as it used to be imagined that the ancient universe was physically opposed to the present, so it is still widely assumed that the living population of our globe, whether animal or vegetable, in the older epochs, exhibited forms so strikingly contrasted with those which we see around us, that there is hardly anything in common between the two. It is constantly tacitly assumed that we have before us all the forms of life which have ever existed; and though the progress of knowledge, yearly and almost monthly, drives the defenders of that position from their ground, they entrench themselves in the new line of defences as if nothing had happened, and proclaim that the *new* beginning is the *real* beginning.

Without for an instant denying or endeavouring to soften down the considerable positive differences (the negative ones are met by another line of argument) which undoubtedly obtain between the ancient and the modern worlds of life, we believe they have been vastly overstated and exaggerated, and this belief is based upon certain facts whose value does not seem to have been fully appreciated, though they have long been more or less completely known.

The multitudinous kinds of animals and plants, both recent and fossil, are, as is well known, arranged by zoologists and botanists, in accordance with their natural relations, into groups which receive the names of sub-kingdoms, classes, orders, families, genera and species. Now it is a most remarkable circumstance that, viewed on the great scale, living beings have differed so little throughout all geologic time that there is no sub-kingdom and no class wholly extinct or without living representatives.

If we descend to the smaller groups, we find that the number of orders of plants is about two hundred; and

I have it on the best authority that not one of these is exclusively fossil; so that there is absolutely not a single extinct ordinal type of vegetable life; and it is not until we descend to the next group, or the families, that we find types which are wholly extinct. The number of orders of animals, on the other hand, may be reckoned at a hundred and twenty, or thereabouts, and of these, eight or nine have no living representatives. The proportion of extinct ordinal types of animals to the existing types, therefore, does not exceed seven per cent.—a marvellously small proportion when we consider the vastness of geologic time.

Another class of considerations—of a different kind, it is true, but tending in the same direction—seems to have been overlooked. Not only is it true that the general plan of construction of animals and plants has been the same in all recorded time as at present, but there are particular kinds of animals and plants which have existed throughout vast epochs, sometimes through the whole range of recorded time, with very little change. By reason of this persistency, the typical form of such a kind might be called a "persistent type," in contradistinction to those types which have appeared for but a short time in the course of the world's history. Examples of these persistent types are abundant enough in both the vegetable and the animal kingdoms. The oldest group of plants with which we are well acquainted is that of whose remains coal is constituted; and, so far as they can be identified, the carboniferous plants are ferns, or club-mosses, or Coniferæ, in many cases generically identical with those now living!

Among animals, instances of the same kind may be found in every sub-kingdom. The *Globigerina* of the Atlantic soundings is identical with that which occurs in the chalk; and the casts of lower silurian *Foraminifera*, which Ehrenberg has recently described, seem to indicate the existence at that remote period of forms singularly like those which now exist. Among the corals, the palæozoic *Tabulata* are constructed on precisely the same type as the modern millepores; and if we turn to molluscs, the most competent malacologists fail to discover any generic distinction between the *Craniæ*, *Lingulæ*, and *Discinæ* of the silurian rocks and those which now live. Our existing *Nautilus* has its representative species in every great formation, from the oldest to the newest; and *Loligo*, the squid of modern seas, appears in the lias, or at the bottom of the mesozoic series, in a form, at most, specifically different from its living congeners. In the great assemblage of annulose animals, the two highest classes, the insects and spider tribe, exhibit a wonderful persistency of type. The cockroaches of the carboniferous epoch are exceedingly similar to those which now run about our coal-cellars; and its locusts, termites, and dragon-flies are closely allied to the members of the same groups which now chirrup about our fields, undermine our houses, or sail with swift grace about the banks of our sedgy pools. And, in like manner, the palæozoic scorpions can only be distinguished by the eye of a naturalist from the modern ones.

Finally, with respect to the *Vertebrata*, the same law holds good: certain types, such as those of the ganoid and placoid fishes, having persisted from the palæozoic epoch to the present time without a greater amount of deviation from the normal standard than that which is seen within the limits of the group as it now exists. Even among the *Reptilia*—the class which exhibits the largest proportion of entirely extinct forms of any—one type, that of the *Crocodilia*, has persisted from at least the commencement of the Mesozoic epoch up to the present time with so much constancy, that the amount of change which it exhibits may fairly, in relation to the time which has elapsed, be called insignificant. And the imperfect knowledge we have of the ancient mammalian population of our earth leads to the belief that certain of its types, such as that of the *Marsupialia*, have persisted with correspondingly little change through a similar range of time.

Thus it would appear to be demonstrable, that, notwithstanding the great change which is exhibited by the animal population of the world as a whole, certain types have persisted comparatively without alteration, and the question arises, What bearing have such facts as these on our notions of the history of life through geological time?

*L 47

The answer to this question would seem to depend on the view we take respecting the origin of species in general. If we assume that every species of animal and of plant was formed by a distinct act of creative power, and if the species which have incessantly succeeded one another were placed upon the globe by these separate acts, then the existence of persistent types is simply an unintelligible irregularity. Such assumption, however, is as unsupported by tradition or by Revelation as it is opposed by the analogy of the rest of the operations of nature; and those who imagine that, by adopting any such hypothesis, they are strengthening the hands of the advocates of the letter of the Mosaic account, are simply mistaken. If, on the other hand, we adopt that hypothesis to which alone the study of physiology lends any support—that hypothesis which, having struggled beyond the reach of those fatal supporters, the Telliameds and Vestigiarians, who so nearly caused its suffocation by wind in early infancy, is now winning at least the provisional assent of all the best thinkers of the day—the hypothesis that the forms or species of living beings, as we know them, have been produced by the gradual modification of pre-existing species—then the existence of persistent types seems to teach us much. Just as a small portion of a great curve appears straight, the apparent absence of change in direction of the line being the exponent of the vast extent of the whole, in proportion to the part we see; so, if it be true that all living species are the result of the modification of other and simpler forms, the existence of these little altered persistent types, ranging through all geological time, must indicate that they are but the final terms of an enormous series of modifications, which had their being in the great lapse of pregeologic time, and are now perhaps for ever lost.

In other words, when rightly studied, the teachings of palæontology are at one with those of physical geology. Our farthest explorations carry us back but a little way above the mouth of the great river of Life: where it arose, and by what channels the noble tide has reached the point when it first breaks upon our view, is hidden from us.

The foregoing pages contain the substance of a lecture delivered before the Royal Institution of Great Britain many months ago, and of course long before the appearance of the remarkable work on the "Origin of Species," just published by Mr. Darwin, who arrives at very similar conclusions. Although, in one sense, I might fairly say that my own views have been arrived at independently, I do not know that I can claim any equitable right to property in them; for it has long been my privilege to enjoy Mr. Darwin's friendship, and to profit by corresponding with him, and by, to some extent, becoming acquainted with the workings of his singularly original and well-stored mind. It was in consequence of my knowledge of the general tenor of the researches in which Mr. Darwin had been so long engaged; because I had the most complete confidence in his perseverance, his knowledge, and, above all things, his high-minded love of truth; and, moreover, because I found that the better I became acquainted with the opinions of the best naturalists regarding the vexed question of species, the less fixed they seemed to be, and the more inclined they were to the hypothesis of gradual modification, that I ventured to speak as strongly as I have done in the final paragraphs of my discourse.

Thus, my daw having so many borrowed plumes, I see no impropriety in making a tail to this brief paper by taking another handful of feathers from Mr. Darwin; endeavouring to point out in a few words, in fact, what, as I gather from the perusal of his book, his doctrines really are, and on what sort of basis they rest. And I do this the more willingly, as I observe that already the hastier sort of critics have begun, not to review my friend's book, but to howl over it in a manner which must tend greatly to distract the public mind.

No one will be better satisfied than I to see Mr. Darwin's book refuted, if any person be competent to perform that feat; but I would suggest that refutation is retarded, not aided, by mere sarcastic misrepresentation. Every one who has studied cattle-breeding, or turned pigeon-fancier, or "pomologist," must have been struck by the extreme modifiability or plasticity of those kinds of animals and plants which have been subjected to such artificial conditions as are imposed by domestication. Breeds of dogs are more different from one another than are the dog and the wolf; and the purely artificial races of pigeons, if their origin were unknown, would most assuredly be reckoned by naturalists as distinct species and even genera.

These breeds are always produced in the same way. The breeder selects a pair, one or other, or both, of which present an indication of the peculiarity he wishes to perpetuate, and then selects from the offspring of them those which are most characteristic, rejecting the others. From the selected offspring he breeds again, and, taking the same precautions as before, repeats the process until he has obtained the precise degree of divergence from the primitive type at which he aimed.

If he now breeds from the variety thus established for some generations, taking care always to keep the stock pure, the tendency to produce this particular variety becomes more and more strongly hereditary; and it does not appear that there is any limit to the persistency of the race thus developed.

Men like Lamarck, apprehending these facts, and knowing that varieties comparable to those produced by the breeder are abundantly found in nature, and finding it impossible to discriminate in some cases between varieties and true species, could hardly fail to divine the possibility that species even the most distinct were, after all, only exceedingly persistent varieties, and that they had arisen by the modification of some common stock, just as it is with good reason believed that turnspits and greyhounds, carrier and tumbler pigeons, have arisen.

But there was a link wanting to complete the parallel. Where in nature was the analogue of the breeder to be found? How could that operation of selection, which is his essential function, be carried out by mere natural agencies? Lamarck did not value this problem; neither did he admit his impotence to solve it; but he guessed a solution. Now, guessing in science is a very hazardous proceeding, and Lamarck's reputation has suffered woefully for the absurdities into which his baseless suppositions led him.

Lamarck's conjectures, equipped with a new hat and stick, as Sir Walter Scott was wont to say of an old story renovated, formed the foundation of the biological speculations of the "Vestiges," a work which has done more harm to the progress of sound thought on these matters than any that could be named ; and, indeed, I mention it here simply for the purpose of denying that it has anything in common with what essentially characterises Mr. Darwin's work.

The peculiar feature of the latter is, in fact, that it professes to tell us what in nature takes the place of the breeder ; what it is that favours the development of one variety into which a species may run, and checks that of another ; and, finally, shows how this natural selection, as it is termed, may be the physical cause of the production of species by modification.

That which takes the place of the breeder and selector in nature is Death. In a most remarkable chapter, "On the Struggle for Existence," Mr. Darwin draws attention to the marvellous destruction of life which is constantly going on in nature. For every species of living thing, as for man, *"Eine Bresche ist ein jeder Tag."*—Every species has its enemies ; every species has to compete with others for the necessaries of existence ; the weakest goes to the wall, and death is the penalty inflicted on all laggards and stragglers. Every variety to which a species may give rise is either worse or better adapted to surrounding circumstances than its parent. If worse, it cannot maintain itself against death, and speedily vanishes again. But if better adapted, it must, sooner or later, "improve" its progenitor from the face of the earth, and take its place. If circumstances change, the victor will be similarly supplanted by its own progeny ; and thus, by the operation of natural causes, unlimited modification may in the lapse of long ages occur.

For an explanation of what I have here called vaguely "surrounding circumstances," and of why they continually change—for ample proof that the "struggle for existence" is a very great reality, and assuredly *tends* to exert the influence ascribed to it—I must refer to Mr. Darwin's book. I believe I have stated fairly the position upon which his whole theory must stand or fall ; and it is not my purpose to anticipate a full review of his work. If it can be proved that the process of natural selection, operating upon any species, can give rise to varieties of species so different from one another that none of our tests will distinguish them from true species, Mr. Darwin's hypothesis of the origin of species will take its place among the established theories of science, be its consequences whatever they may. If, on the other hand, Mr. Darwin has erred, either in fact or in reasoning, his fellow-workers will soon find out the weak points in his doctrines, and their extinction by some nearer approximation to the truth will exemplify his own principle of natural selection.

In either case the question is one to be settled only by the painstaking, truth-loving investigation of skilled naturalists. It is the duty of the general public to await the result in patience ; and, above all things, to discourage, as they would any other crimes, the attempt to enlist the prejudices of the ignorant, or the uncharitableness of the bigoted, on either side of the controversy.

XIII

DARWIN ON THE ORIGIN OF SPECIES

MR. DARWIN'S long-standing and well-earned scientific
eminence probably renders him indifferent to that social
notoriety which passes by the name of success; but if
the calm spirit of the philosopher have not yet wholly
superseded the ambition and the vanity of the carnal
man within him, he must be well satisfied with the results
of his venture in publishing the "Origin of Species."
Overflowing the narrow bounds of purely scientific
circles, the "species question" divides with Italy and
the Volunteers the attention of general society. Everybody has read Mr. Darwin's book, or, at least, has given
an opinion upon its merits or demerits; pietists, whether
lay or ecclesiastic, decry it with the mild railing which
sounds so charitable; bigots denounce it with ignorant
invective; old ladies, of both sexes, consider it a decidedly
dangerous book, and even savans, who have no better
mud to throw, quote antiquated writers to show that its
author is no better than an ape himself; while every
philosophical thinker hails it as a veritable Whitworth
gun in the armoury of liberalism, and all competent
naturalists and physiologists, whatever their opinions as
to the ultimate fate of the doctrines put forth, acknowledge that the work in which they are embodied is a solid
contribution to knowledge and inaugurates a new epoch
in natural history.

Nor has the discussion of the subject been restrained
within the limits of conversation. When the public is
eager and interested, reviewers must minister to its wants,
and the genuine *littérateur* is too much in the habit of
acquiring his knowledge from the book he judges—as the

Abyssinian is said to provide himself with steaks from the ox which carries him—to be withheld from criticism of a profound scientific work by the mere want of the requisite preliminary scientific acquirement; while, on the other hand, the men of science who wish well to the new views, no less than those who dispute their validity, have naturally sought opportunities of expressing their opinions. Hence it is not surprising that almost all the critical journals have noticed Mr. Darwin's work at greater or less length, and so many disquisitions, of every degree of excellence, from the poor product of ignorance, too often stimulated by prejudice, to the fair and thoughtful essay of the candid student of nature, have appeared, that it seems an almost hopeless task to attempt to say anything new upon the question.

But it may be doubted if the knowledge and acumen of prejudged scientific opponents, or the subtlety of orthodox special pleaders, have yet exerted their full force in mystifying the real issues of the great controversy which has been set afoot, and whose end is hardly likely to be seen by this generation; so that at this eleventh hour, and even failing anything new, it may be useful to state afresh that which is true, and to put the fundamental positions advocated by Mr. Darwin in such a form that they may be grasped by those whose special studies lie in other directions; and the adoption of this course may be the more advisable, because notwithstanding its great deserts, and indeed partly on account of them, the " Origin of Species " is by no means an easy book to read—if by reading is implied the full comprehension of an author's meaning.

We do not speak jestingly in saying that it is Mr. Darwin's misfortune to know more about the question he has taken up than any man living. Personally and practically exercised in zoology, in minute anatomy, in geology; a student of geographical distribution, not on maps and in museums only, but by long voyages and laborious collection; having largely advanced each of these branches of science, and having spent many years in gathering and sifting materials for his present work, the store of accurately registered facts upon which the author of the "Origin of Species" is able to draw at will is prodigious.

But this very superabundance of matter must have been embarrassing to a writer who, for the present, can only put forward an abstract of his views, and thence it arises, perhaps, that notwithstanding the clearness of the style, those who attempt fairly to digest the book find much of it a sort of intellectual pemmican—a mass of facts crushed and pounded into shape, rather than held together by the ordinary medium of an obvious logical bond : due attention will, without doubt, discover this bond, but it is often hard to find.

Again, from sheer want of room, much has to be taken for granted which might readily enough be proved, and hence, while the adept, who can supply the missing links in the evidence from his own knowledge, discovers fresh proof of the singular thoroughness with which all difficulties have been considered and all unjustifiable supposition avoided, at every reperusal of Mr. Darwin's pregnant paragraphs, the novice in biology is apt to complain of the frequency of what he fancies is gratuitous assumption.

Thus while it may be doubted if, for some years, any one is likely to be competent to pronounce judgment on all the issues raised by Mr. Darwin, there is assuredly abundant room for him, who, assuming the humbler, though perhaps as useful, office of an interpreter between the "Origin of Species" and the public, contents himself with endeavouring to point out the nature of the problems which it discusses ; to distinguish between the ascertained facts and the theoretical views which it contains ; and finally, to show the extent to which the explanation it offers satisfies the requirements of scientific logic. At any rate, it is this office which we purpose to undertake in the following pages.

It may be safely assumed that our readers have a general conception of the nature of the objects to which the word "species" is applied ; but it has, perhaps, occurred to few, even of those who are naturalists *ex professo*, to reflect, that, as commonly employed, the term has a double sense and denotes two very different

orders of relations.   When we call a group of animals, or
of plants, a species, we may imply thereby either, that all
these animals or plants have some common peculiarity of
form or structure; or, we may mean that they possess
some common functional character.   That part of biological science which deals with form and structure is
called Morphology—that which concerns itself with function, Physiology—so that we may conveniently speak of
these two senses or aspects of "species"—the one as
morphological, the other as physiological.   Regarded from
the former point of view, a species is nothing more than
a kind of animal or plant, which is distinctly definable
from all others, by certain constant and not merely sexual,
morphological peculiarities.   Thus horses form a species,
because the group of animals to which that name is
applied is distinguished from all others in the world by
the following constantly associated characters.   They
have 1. A vertebral column; 2. Mammæ; 3. A placental
embryo; 4. Four legs; 5. A single well-developed toe in
each foot provided with a hoof; 6. A bushy tail; and
7. Callosities on the inner sides of both the fore and
the hind legs.   The asses again, form a distinct species,
because, with the same characters, as far as the fifth in
the above list, all asses have tufted tails, and have
callosities only on the inner side of the fore-legs.   If
animals were discovered having the general characters
of the horse, but sometimes with callosities only on the
fore legs, and more or less tufted tails; or animals having
the general characters of the ass, but with more or less
bushy tails, and sometimes with callosities on both pairs
of legs, besides being intermediate in other respects—the
two species would have to be merged into one.   They
could no longer be regarded as morphologically distinct
species, for they would not be distinctly definable one
from the other.

However bare and simple this definition of species
may appear to be, we confidently appeal to all practical
naturalists, whether zoologists, botanists, or palæontologists, to say if, in the vast majority of cases, they know,
or mean to affirm, anything more of the group of animals
or plants they so denominate than what has just been

stated. Even the most decided advocates of the received doctrines respecting species admit this.

"I apprehend," says Professor Owen,[1] "that few naturalists now-a-days, in describing and proposing a name for what they call 'a new *species*,' use that term to signify what was meant by it twenty or thirty years ago, that is, an originally distinct creation, maintaining its primitive distinction by obstructive generative peculiarities. The proposer of the new species now intends to state no more than he actually knows; as for example, that the differences in which he founds the specific character are constant in individuals of both sexes, so far as observation has reached; and that they are not due to domestication or to artificially superinduced external circumstances, or to any outward influence within his cognizance; that the species is wild, or is such as it appears by nature."

If we consider, in fact, that by far the largest proportion of recorded existing species are known only by the study of their skins, or bones, or other lifeless exuvia; that we are acquainted with none, or next to none, of their physiological peculiarities, beyond those which can be deduced from their structure, or are open to cursory observation; and that we cannot hope to learn more of any of those extinct forms of life which now constitute no inconsiderable proportion of the known Flora and Fauna of the world; it is obvious that the definitions of these species can be only of a purely structural or morphological character. It is probable that naturalists would have avoided much confusion of ideas if they had more frequently borne these necessary limitations of our knowledge in mind. But while it may safely be admitted that we are acquainted with only the morphological characters of the vast majority of species—the functional or physiological peculiarities of a few have been carefully investigated, and the result of that study forms a large and most interesting portion of the physiology of reproduction.

The student of nature wonders the more and is

[1] "On the Osteology of the Chimpanzees and Orangs." Transactions of the Zoological Society, 1858.

astonished the less, the more conversant he becomes with her operations; but of all the perennial miracles she offers to his inspection, perhaps the most worthy of admiration is the development of a plant or of an animal from its embryo. Examine the recently laid egg of some common animal, such as a salamander or a newt. It is a minute spheroid in which the best microscope will reveal nothing but a structureless sac, enclosing a glairy fluid, holding granules in suspension. But strange possibilities lie dormant in that semi-fluid globule. Let a moderate supply of warmth reach its watery cradle, and the plastic matter undergoes changes so rapid and yet so steady and purpose-like in their succession, that one can only compare them to those operated by a skilled modeller upon a formless lump of clay. As with an invisible trowel, the mass is divided and subdivided into smaller and smaller portions, until it is reduced to an aggregation of granules not too large to build withal the finest fabrics of the nascent organism. And, then, it is as if a delicate finger traced out the line to be occupied by the spinal column, and moulded the contour of the body; pinching up the head at one end, the tail at the other, and fashioning flank and limb into due salamandrine proportions, in so artistic a way, that, after watching the process hour by hour, one is almost involuntarily possessed by the notion, that some more subtle aid to vision than an achromatic would show the hidden artist, with his plan before him, striving with skilful manipulation to perfect his work.

As life advances, and the young amphibian ranges the waters, the terror of his insect contemporaries, not only are the nutritious particles supplied by its prey, by the addition of which to its frame growth takes place, laid down, each in its proper spot, and in such due proportion to the rest, as to reproduce the form, the colour and the size, characteristic of the parental stock; but even the wonderful powers of reproducing lost parts possessed by these animals are controlled by the same governing tendency. Cut off the legs, the tail, the jaws, separately or all together, and, as Spallanzani showed long ago, these parts not only grow again, but the redintegrated limb is

formed on the same type as those which were lost.   The
new jaw or leg is a newt's, and never by any accident
more like that of a frog.   What is true of the newt is true
of every animal and of every plant ; the acorn tends to
build itself up again into a woodland giant such as that
from whose twig it fell ; the spore of the humblest lichen
reproduces the green or brown incrustation which gave it
birth ; and at the other end of the scale of life, the child
that resembled neither the paternal nor the maternal side
of the house would be regarded as a kind of monster.

So that the one end to which in all living beings the
formative impulse is tending—the one scheme which the
Archæus of the old speculators strives to carry out, seems
to be to mould the offspring into the likeness of the
parent.   It is the first great law of reproduction, that the
offspring tends to resemble its parent or parents, more
closely than anything else.

Science will some day show us how this law is a necessary consequence of the more general laws which govern
matter ; but for the present, more can hardly be said than
that it appears to be in harmony with them.   We know
that the phenomena of vitality are not something apart
from other physical phenomena, but one with them ; and
matter and force are the two names of the one artist who
fashions the living as well as the lifeless.   Hence living
bodies should obey the same great laws as other matter—
nor, throughout nature, is there a law of wider application
than this, that a body impelled by two forces takes the
direction of their resultant.   But living bodies may be
regarded as nothing but extremely complex bundles of
forces held in a mass of matter, as the complex forces of
a magnet are held in the steel by its coercive force ; and
since the differences of sex are comparatively slight, or,
in other words, the sum of the forces in each has a
very similar tendency, their resultant, the offspring, may
reasonably be expected to deviate but little from a
course parallel to either, or to both.

Represent the reason of the law to ourselves by what
physical metaphor or analogy we will, however, the great
matter is to apprehend its existence and the importance
of the consequences deducible from it.   For things which

are like to the same are like to one another, and if, in a great series of generations, every offspring is like its parent, it follows that all the offspring and all the parents must be like one another; and that, given an original parental stock with the opportunity of undisturbed multiplication, the law in question necessitates the production, in course of time, of an indefinitely large group, the whole of whose members are at once very similar and are blood relations, having descended from the same parent, or pair of parents. The proof that all the members of any given group of animals, or plants, had thus descended, would be ordinarily considered sufficient to entitle them to the rank of physiological species, for most physiologists consider species to be definable as "the offspring of a single primitive stock."

But though it is quite true that all those groups we call species *may*, according to the known laws of reproduction, have descended from a single stock, and though it is very likely they really have done so, yet this conclusion rests on deduction and can hardly hope to establish itself upon a basis of observation. And the primitiveness of the supposed single stock, which, after all, is the essential part of the matter, is not only a hypothesis, but one which has not a shadow of foundation, if by "primitive" be meant "independent of any other living being." A scientific definition, of which an unwarrantable hypothesis forms an essential part, carries its condemnation within itself; but even supposing such a definition were, in form, tenable, the physiologist who should attempt to apply it in nature would soon find himself involved in great, if not inextricable difficulties. As we have said, it is indubitable that offspring *tend* to resemble the parental organism, but it is equally true that the similarity attained never amounts to identity, either in form or in structure. There is always a certain amount of deviation, not only from the precise characters of a single parent, but when, as in most animals and many plants, the sexes are lodged in distinct individuals, from an exact mean between the two parents. And, indeed, on general principles, this slight deviation seems as intelligible as the general similarity, if we reflect how complex the co-operating "bundles of forces" are,

and how improbable it is that, in any case, their true resultant shall coincide with any mean between the more
obvious characters of the two parents. Whatever be its
cause, however, the co-existence of this tendency to minor
variation with the tendency to general similarity, is of vast
importance in its bearing on the question of the origin of
species.

As a general rule, the extent to which an offspring
differs from its parent is slight enough ; but, occasionally,
the amount of difference is much more strongly marked,
and then the divergent offspring receives the name of a
Variety. Multitudes, of what there is every reason to
believe are such varieties, are known, but the origin of
very few has been accurately recorded, and of these we
will select two as more especially illustrative of the main
features of variation. The first of them is that of the
"Ancon," or "Otter" sheep, of which a careful account
is given by Colonel David Humphreys, F.R.S., in a letter
to Sir Joseph Banks, published in the Philosophical
Transactions for 1813. It appears that one Seth Wright,
the proprietor of a farm on the banks of the Charles
River, in Massachusetts, possessed a flock of fifteen ewes
and a ram of the ordinary kind. In the year 1791, one
of the ewes presented her owner with a male lamb, differing, for no assignable reason, from its parents by a proportionally long body and short bandy legs, whence it was
unable to emulate its relatives in those sportive leaps over
the neighbours' fences, in which they were in the habit of
indulging, much to the good farmer's vexation.

The second case is that detailed by a no less unexcep-
tionable authority than Réaumur, in his "Art de faire
éclorre les poulets." A Maltese couple, named Kelleia,
whose hands and feet were constructed upon the ordinary
human model, had born to them a son, Gratio, who possessed six perfectly moveable fingers on each hand and six
toes, not quite so well formed, on each foot. No cause
could be assigned for the appearance of this unusual
variety of the human species.

Two circumstances are well worthy of remark in both
these cases. In each, the variety appears to have arisen
in full force, and, as it were, *per saltum ;* a wide and

definite difference appearing, at once, between the Ancon ram and the ordinary sheep ; between the six-fingered and six-toed Gratio Kelleia and ordinary men. In neither case is it possible to point out any obvious reason for the appearance of the variety. Doubtless there were determining causes for these as for all other phenomena ; but they do not appear, and we can be tolerably certain that what are ordinarily understood as changes in physical conditions, as in climate, in food, or the like, did not take place and had nothing to do with the matter. It was no case of what is commonly called adaptation to circumstances ; but, to use a conveniently erroneous phrase, the variations arose spontaneously. The fruitless search after final causes leads their pursuers a long way ; but even those hardy teleologists, who are ready to break through all the laws of physics in chase of their favourite will-o'-the-wisp, may be puzzled to discover what purpose could be attained by the stunted legs of Seth Wright's ram or the hexadactyle members of Gratio Kelleia.

Varieties then arise we know not why ; and it is more than probable that the majority of varieties have arisen in the spontaneous manner, though we are, of course, far from denying that they may be traced, in some cases, to distinct external influences, which are assuredly competent to alter the character of the tegumentary covering, to change colour, to increase or diminish the size of muscles, to modify constitution, and, among plants, to give rise to the metamorphosis of stamens into petals, and so forth. But however they may have arisen, what especially interests us at present is, to remark that, once in existence, varieties obey the fundamental law of reproduction that like tends to produce like, and their offspring exemplify it by tending to exhibit the same deviation from the parental stock as themselves. Indeed, there seems to be, in many instances, a pre-potent influence about a newly-arisen variety which gives it what one may call an unfair advantage over the normal descendants from the same stock. This is strikingly exemplified by the case of Gratio Kelleia, who married a woman with the ordinary pentadactyle extremities, and had by her four children, Salvator, George, André, and Marie. Of these children

Salvator, the eldest boy, had six fingers and six toes, like his father; the second and third, also boys, had five fingers and toes, like their mother, though the hands and feet of George were slightly deformed; the last, a girl, had five fingers and toes, but the thumbs were slightly deformed. The variety thus reproduced itself purely in the eldest, while the normal type reproduced itself purely in the third, and almost purely in the second and last: so that it would seem, at first, as if the normal type were more powerful than the variety. But all these children grew up and intermarried with normal wives and husbands, and then, note what took place: Salvator had four children, three of whom exhibited the hexadactyle members of their grandfather and father, while the youngest had the pentadactyle limbs of the mother and grandmother; so that here, notwithstanding a double pentadactyle dilution of the blood, the hexadactyle variety had the best of it. The same pre-potency of the variety was still more markedly exemplified in the progeny of two of the other children, Marie and George. Marie (whose thumbs only were deformed) gave birth to a boy with six toes, and three other normally formed children; but George, who was not quite so pure a pentadactyle, begot, first, two girls, each of whom had six fingers and toes; then a girl with six fingers on each hand and six toes on the right foot, but only five toes on the left; and lastly, a boy with only five fingers and toes. In these instances, therefore, the variety, as it were, leaped over one generation to reproduce itself in full force in the next. Finally, the purely pentadactyle André was the father of many children, not one of whom departed from the normal parental type.

If a variation which approaches the nature of a monstrosity can strive thus forcibly to reproduce itself, it is not wonderful that less aberrant modifications should tend to be preserved even more strongly; and the history of the Ancon sheep is, in this respect, particularly instructive. With the "'cuteness" characteristic of their nation, the neighbours of the Massachusetts farmer imagined it would be an excellent thing if all his sheep were imbued with the stay-at-home tendencies enforced by nature upon the newly-arrived ram; and they advised Wright to kill the old patriarch of his fold, and instal the Ancon ram in his place. The result justified their sagacious anticipations, and coincided very nearly with what occurred to the progeny of Gratio Kelleia. The young lambs were almost always either pure Ancons, or pure ordinary sheep.[1] But when sufficient Ancon sheep were obtained to interbreed with one another, it was found that the offspring was always pure Ancon. Colonel Humphreys, in fact, states that he was acquainted with only "one questionable case of a contrary nature." Here, then, is a remarkable and well-established instance, not only of a very distinct race being established *per saltum*, but of that race breeding "true" at once, and showing no mixed forms, even when crossed with another breed.

By taking care to select Ancons of both sexes, for breeding from, it thus became easy to establish an extremely well-marked race, so peculiar that even when herded with other sheep, it was noted that the Ancons kept together, and there is every reason to believe that the existence of this breed might have been indefinitely protracted; but the introduction of the Merino sheep, which were not only very superior to the Ancons in wool and meat, but quite as quiet and orderly, led to the complete neglect of the new breed, so that, in 1813, Colonel Humphreys found it difficult to obtain the specimen whose skeleton was presented to Sir Joseph Banks. We believe that, for many years, no remnant of it has existed in the United States.

Gratio Kelleia was not the progenitor of a race of six-fingered men, as Seth Wright's ram became a nation of

[1] Colonel Humphreys' statements are exceedingly explicit on this point:—"When an Ancon ewe is impregnated by a common ram the increase resembles wholly either the ewe or the ram. The increase of the common ewe impregnated by an Ancon ram follows entirely the one or the other, without blending any of the distinguishing and essential peculiarities of both. Frequent instances have happened where common ewes have had twins by Ancon rams, when one exhibited the complete marks and features of the ewe, the other of the ram. The contrast has been rendered singularly striking, when one short-legged and one long-legged lamb, produced at a birth, have been seen sucking the dam at the same time."—Philosophical Transactions, 1813, Pt. I. pp. 89, 90.

Ancon sheep, though the tendency of the variety to perpetuate itself appears to have been fully as strong in the one case as in the other. And the reason of the difference is not far to seek. Seth Wright took care not to weaken the Ancon blood by matching his Ancon ewes with any but males of the same variety, while Gratio Kelleia's sons were too far removed from the patriarchal times to intermarry with their sisters; and his grand-children seem not to have been attracted by their six-fingered cousins. In other words, in the one example a race was produced, because, for several generations, care was taken to *select* both parents of the breeding stock, from animals exhibiting a tendency to vary in the same direction, while in the other no race was evolved, because no such selection was exercised. A race is a propagated variety, and as, by the laws of reproduction, offspring tend to assume the parental form, they will be more likely to propagate a variation exhibited by both parents than that possessed by only one.

There is no organ of the body of an animal which may not, and does not, occasionally, vary more or less from the normal type; and there is no variation which may not be transmitted, and which, if selectively transmitted, may not become the foundation of a race. This great truth, some-times forgotten by philosophers, has long been familiar to practical agriculturists and breeders : and upon it rest all the methods of improving the breeds of domestic animals, which for the last century have been followed with so much success in England. Colour, form, size, texture of hair or wool, proportions of various parts, strength or weakness of constitution, tendency to fatten or to remain lean, to give much or little milk, speed, strength, temper, intelligence, special instincts; there is not one of these characters whose transmission is not an every-day occurrence within the experience of cattle-breeders, stock-farmers, horse-dealers, and dog and poultry fanciers. Nay, it is only the other day that an eminent physiologist, Dr. Brown Sequard, communicated to the Royal Society his discovery that epilepsy, artificially pro-duced in guinea-pigs, by a means which he has discovered, is transmitted to their offspring.

But a race, once produced, is no more a fixed and immutable entity than the stock whence it sprang; variations arise among its members, and as these variations are transmitted like any others, new races may be developed out of the pre-existing ones *ad infinitum*, or, at least, within any limit at present determined. Given sufficient time and sufficiently careful selection, and the multitude of races which may arise from a common stock is as astonishing as are the extreme structural differences which they may present. A remarkable example of this is to be found in the rock-pigeon, which Mr. Darwin has, in our opinion, satisfactorily demonstrated to be the progenitor of all our domestic pigeons, of which there are certainly more than a hundred well-marked races. The most noteworthy of these races are, the four great stocks known to the "fancy" as tumblers, pouters, carriers, and fantails; birds which not only differ most singularly in size, colour, and habits, but in the form of the beak and of the skull; in the proportions of the beak to the skull; in the number of tail-feathers; in the absolute and relative size of the feet; in the presence or absence of the uropygial gland; in the number of vertebræ in the back; in short, in precisely those characters in which the genera and species of birds differ from one another.

And it is most remarkable and instructive to observe, that none of these races can be shown to have been originated by the action of changes in what are commonly called external circumstances, upon the wild rock-pigeon. On the contrary, from time immemorial, pigeon fanciers have had essentially similar methods of treating their pets, which have been housed, fed, protected and cared for in much the same way in all pigeonries. In fact, there is no case better adapted than that of the pigeons, to refute the doctrine which one sees put forth on high authority, that "no other characters than those founded on the development of bone for the attachment of muscles" are capable of variation. In precise contradiction of this hasty assertion, Mr. Darwin's researches prove that the skeleton of the wings in domestic pigeons has hardly varied at all from that of the wild type; while, on the other hand, it is in exactly those respects, such as the relative length of the beak and skull, the number of the vertebræ, and the number of the tail-feathers, in which muscular exertion can have no important influence, that the utmost amount of variation has taken place.

We have said that the following out of the properties exhibited by physiological species would lead us into difficulties, and at this point they begin to be obvious ; for, if, as a result of spontaneous variation and of selective breeding, the progeny of a common stock may become separated into groups distinguished from one another by constant, not sexual, morphological characters, it is clear that the physiological definition of species is likely to clash with the morphological definition. No one would hesitate to describe the pouter and the tumbler as distinct species, if they were found fossil, or if their skins and skeletons were imported, as those of exotic wild birds commonly are—and, without doubt, if considered alone, they are good and distinct morphological species. On the other hand, they are not physiological species, for they are descended from a common stock, the rock-pigeon.

Under these circumstances, as it is admitted on all sides that races occur in nature, how are we to know whether any apparently distinct animals are really of different physiological species, or not, seeing that the amount of morphological difference is no safe guide? Is there any test of a physiological species? The usual answer of physiologists is in the affirmative. It is said that such a test is to be found in the phenomena of hybridization —in the results of crossing races as compared with the results of crossing species.

So far as the evidence goes at present, individuals, of what are certainly known to be mere races produced by selection, however distinct they may appear to be, not only breed freely together, but the offspring of such crossed races are also perfectly fertile with one another. Thus, the spaniel and the greyhound, the dray-horse and the Arab, the pouter and the tumbler, breed together with perfect freedom, and their mongrels, if matched with other mongrels of the same kind, are equally fertile.

On the other hand, there can be no doubt that the individuals of many natural species are either absolutely infertile, if crossed with individuals of other species, or, if they give rise to hybrid offspring, the hybrids so produced are infertile when paired together. The horse and the ass, for instance, if so crossed, give rise to the mule, and there is no certain evidence of offspring ever having been produced by a male and female mule. The unions of the rock-pigeon and the ring-pigeon appear to be equally barren of result. Here, then, says the physiologist, we have a means of distinguishing any two true species from any two varieties. If a male and a female, selected from each group, produce offspring, and that offspring is fertile with others produced in the same way, the groups are races and not species. If, on the other hand, no result ensues, or if the offspring are infertile with others produced in the same way, they are true physiological species. The test would be an admirable one, if, in the first place, it were always practicable to apply it, and if, in the second, it always yielded results susceptible of a definite interpretation. Unfortunately, in the great majority of cases, this touchstone for species is wholly inapplicable.

The constitution of many wild animals is so altered by confinement that they will not even breed with their own females, so that the negative results obtained from crosses are of no value, and the antipathy of wild animals of different species for one another, or even of wild and tame members of the same species, is ordinarily so great, that it is hopeless to look for such unions in nature. The hermaphrodism of most plants, the difficulty in the way of ensuring the absence of their own, or the proper working of other pollen, are obstacles of no less magnitude in applying the test to them. And in both animals and plants is superadded the further difficulty, that experiments must be continued over a long time for the purpose of ascertaining the fertility of the mongrel or hybrid progeny, as well as of the first crosses from which they spring.

Not only do these great practical difficulties lie in the way of applying the hybridization test, but even when this oracle can be questioned, its replies are sometimes as doubtful as those of Delphi. For example, cases are cited by Mr. Darwin, of plants which are more fertile with the pollen of another species than with their own; and there are others, such as certain *fuci*, whose male element will fertilize the ovule of a plant of distinct species, while the males of the latter species are ineffective with the females of the first. So that, in the last-named instance, a physiologist, who should cross the two species in one way, would decide that they were true species; while another, who should cross them in the reverse way, would, with equal justice, according to the rule, pronounce them to be mere races. Several plants, which there is great reason to believe are mere varieties, are almost sterile when crossed; while both animals and plants, which have always been regarded by naturalists as of distinct species, turn out, when the test is applied, to be perfectly fertile. Again, the sterility or fertility of crosses seems to bear no relation to the structural resemblances or differences of the members of any two groups.

Mr. Darwin has discussed this question with singular ability and circumspection, and his conclusions are summed up as follows at page 276 of his work:—

"First crosses between forms sufficiently distinct to be ranked as species, and their hybrids, are very generally, but not universally, sterile. The sterility is of all degrees, and is often so slight that the two most careful experimentalists who have ever lived have come to diametrically opposite conclusions in ranking forms by this test. The sterility is innately variable in individuals of the same species, and is eminently susceptible of favourable and unfavourable conditions. The degree of sterility does not strictly follow systematic affinity, but is governed by several curious and complex laws. It is generally different, and sometimes widely different, in reciprocal crosses between the same two species. It is not always equal in degree in a first cross, and in the hybrid produced from this cross.

In the same manner as in grafting trees, the capacity of one species or variety to take on another is incidental on generally unknown differences in their vegetative systems, so in crossing, the greater or less facility of one species to unite with another is incidental on unknown differences in their reproductive systems. There is no more reason to think that species have been specially endowed with various degrees of sterility to prevent them crossing and breeding in nature, than to think that trees have been specially endowed with various and somewhat analogous degrees of difficulty in being grafted together, in order to prevent them becoming inarched in our forests.

The sterility of first crosses between pure species, which have their reproductive systems perfect, seems to depend on several circumstances; in some cases largely on the early death of the embryo. The sterility of hybrids which have their reproductive systems imperfect, and which have had this system and their whole organization disturbed by being compounded of two distinct species, seems closely allied to that sterility which so frequently affects pure species when their natural conditions of life have been disturbed. This view is supported by a parallelism of another kind; namely, that the crossing of forms only slightly different is favourable to the vigour and fertility of the offspring; and that slight changes in the conditions of life are apparently favourable to the vigour and fertility of all organic beings. It is not surprising that the degree of difficulty in uniting two species, and the degree of sterility of their hybrid offspring should generally correspond, though due to distinct causes; for both depend on the amount of difference of some kind between the species which are crossed. Nor is it surprising that the facility of effecting a first cross, the fertility of hybrids produced from it, and the capacity of being grafted together—though this latter capacity evidently depends on widely different circumstances—should all run to a certain extent parallel with the systematic affinity of the forms which are subjected to experiment; for systematic affinity attempts to express all kinds of resemblance between all species.

First crosses between forms known to be varieties, or sufficiently alike to be considered as varieties, and their mongrel offspring, are very generally, but not quite universally, fertile. Nor is this nearly general and perfect fertility surprising, when we remember how liable we are to argue in a circle with respect to varieties in a state of nature; and when we remember that the greater number of varieties have been produced under domestication by the selection of mere external differences, and not of differences in the reproductive system. In all other respects, excluding fertility, there is a close general resemblance between hybrids and mongrels" (pp. 276–8).

We fully agree with the general tenor of this weighty passage, but forcible as are these arguments, and little as the value of fertility or infertility as a test of species may be, it must not be forgotten that the really important fact, so far as the inquiry into the origin of species goes, is, that there are such things in nature as groups of animals and of plants, whose members are incapable of fertile union with those of other groups; and that there are such things as hybrids, which are absolutely sterile when crossed with other hybrids. For if such phenomena as these were exhibited by only two of those assemblages of living objects, to which the name of species (whether it be used in its physiological or in its morphological sense) is given, it would have to be accounted for by any theory of the origin of species, and every theory which could not account for it would be, so far, imperfect.

Up to this point we have been dealing with matters of fact, and the statements which we have laid before the reader would, to the best of our knowledge, be admitted to contain a fair exposition of what is at present known respecting the essential properties of species, by all who have studied the question. And whatever may be his theoretical views, no naturalist will probably be disposed to demur to the following summary of that exposition :—

Living beings, whether animals or plants, are divisible into multitudes of distinctly definable kinds, which are morphological species. They are also divisible into groups of individuals, which breed freely together, tending to reproduce their like, and are physiological species. Normally, resembling their parents, the offspring of members of these species are still liable to vary, and the variation may be perpetuated by selection, as a race, which race, in many cases, presents all the characteristics of a morphological species. But it is not as yet proved that a race ever exhibits, when crossed with another race of the same species, those phenomena of hybridization which are exhibited by many species when crossed with other species. On the other hand, not only is it not proved that all species give rise to hybrids infertile *inter se*, but there is much reason to believe that, in crossing, species exhibit every gradation from perfect sterility to perfect fertility.

Such are the most essential characteristics of species. Even were man not one of them—a member of the same system and subject to the same laws—the question of their origin, their causal connexion, that is, with the other phenomena of the universe, must have attracted his attention, as soon as his intelligence had raised itself above the level of his daily wants.

Indeed history relates that such was the case, and has embalmed for us the speculations upon the origin of living beings, which were among the earliest products of the dawning intellectual activity of man. In those early days positive knowledge was not to be had, but the craving after it needed, at all hazards, to be satisfied, and according to the country, or the turn of thought of the speculator, the suggestion that all living things arose from the mud of the Nile, from a primeval egg, or from some more anthropomorphic agency, afforded a sufficient resting-place for his curiosity. The myths of Paganism are as dead as Osiris or Zeus, and the man who should revive them, in opposition to the knowledge of our time, would be justly laughed to scorn; but the coeval imaginations current among the rude inhabitants of Palestine, recorded by writers whose very name and age are admitted by every scholar to be unknown, have unfortunately not yet shared their fate, but, even at this day, are regarded by nine-tenths of the civilized world as the authoritative standard of fact and the criterion of the justice of scientific conclusions, in all that relates to the origin of things, and, among them, of species. In this nineteenth century, as at the dawn of modern physical science, the cosmogony of the semi-barbarous Hebrew is the incubus of the philosopher and the opprobrium of the orthodox. Who shall number the patient and earnest seekers after truth from the days of Galileo until now, whose lives have been embittered and their good name blasted by the mistaken zeal of Bibliolaters? Who shall count the host of weaker men whose sense of truth has been destroyed in the effort to harmonize impossibilities—whose life has been wasted in the attempt to force the generous new wine of science into the old bottles of Judaism, compelled by the outcry of the same strong party?

It is true that if philosophers have suffered, their cause has been amply avenged. Extinguished theologians lie about the cradle of every science as the strangled snakes beside that of Hercules, and history records that whenever science and dogmatism have been fairly opposed, the latter has been forced to retire from the lists, bleeding and crushed, if not annihilated; scotched, if not slain. But orthodoxy is the Bourbon of the world of thought. It learns not, neither can it forget; and though at present bewildered and afraid to move, it is as willing as ever to insist that the first chapter of Genesis contains the beginning and the end of sound science, and to visit with such petty thunderbolts as its half-paralysed hands can hurl, those who refuse to degrade nature to the level of primitive Judaism.

Philosophers, on the other hand, have no such aggressive tendencies. With eyes fixed on the noble goal to which "per aspera et ardua" they tend, they may, now and then, be stirred to momentary wrath by the unnecessary obstacles with which the ignorant, or the malicious, encumber, if they cannot bar, the difficult path; but why should their souls be deeply vexed? The majesty of Fact is on their side, and the elemental forms of matter are working for them. Not a star comes to the meridian at its calculated time but testifies to the justice of their methods—their beliefs are "one with the falling rain and with the growing corn." By doubt they are established, and open inquiry is their bosom friend. Such men have no fear of traditions however venerable, and no respect for them when they become mischievous and obstructive; but they have better than mere antiquarian business in hand, and if dogmas, which ought to be fossil but are not, are not forced upon their notice, they are too happy to treat them as non-existent.

The hypotheses respecting the origin of species, which profess to stand upon a scientific basis, and, as such, alone demand serious attention, are of two kinds. The one, the "special creation" hypothesis, presumes every species to have originated from one or more stocks, these not being the result of the modification of any other form of living matter — or arising by natural agencies—but being produced, as such, by a supernatural creative act.

The other, the so-called "transmutation" hypothesis, considers that all existing species are the result of the modification of pre-existing species and those of their predecessors, by agencies similar to those which at the present day produce varieties and races, and therefore in an altogether natural way; and it is a probable, though not a necessary consequence of this hypothesis, that all living beings have arisen from a single stock. With respect to the origin of this primitive stock or stocks, the doctrine of the origin of species is obviously not necessarily concerned. The transmutation hypothesis, for example, is perfectly consistent either with the conception of a special creation of the primitive germ, or with the supposition of its having arisen, as a modification of inorganic matter, by natural causes.

The doctrine of special creation owes its existence very largely to the supposed necessity of making science accord with the Hebrew cosmogony; but it is curious to observe that, as the doctrine is at present maintained by men of science, it is as hopelessly inconsistent with the Hebrew view as any other hypothesis.

If there be any result which has come more clearly out of geological investigation than another, it is, that the vast series of extinct animals and plants is not divisible, as it was once supposed to be, into distinct groups, separated by sharply marked boundaries. There are no great gulfs between epochs and formations — no successive periods marked by the appearance of plants, of water animals, and of land animals, *en masse.* Every year adds to the list of links between what the older geologists supposed to be widely separated epochs; witness the crags linking the drift with the older tertiaries; the Maestricht beds linking the tertiaries with the chalk; the St. Cassian beds exhibiting an abundant fauna of mixed mesozoic and paleozoic types, in rocks of an epoch once supposed to be eminently poor in life; witness, lastly, the incessant disputes as to whether a given stratum shall be reckoned devonian or carboniferous, silurian or devonian, cambrian or silurian.

This truth is further illustrated in a most interesting manner by the impartial and highly competent testimony of M. Pictet, from whose calculations of what percentage of the genera of animals existing in any formation lived during the preceding formation, it results that in no case is the proportion less than *one-third,* or 33 per cent. It is the triassic formation, or the commencement of the mesozoic epoch, which has received this smallest inheritance from preceding ages. The other formations not uncommonly exhibit 60, 80, or even 94 per cent. of genera in common with those whose remains are imbedded in their predecessor. Not only is this true, but the subdivisions of each formation exhibit new species characteristic of, and found only in, them, and in many cases, as in the lias for example, the separate beds of these subdivisions are distinguished by well marked and peculiar forms of life. A section, a hundred feet thick, will exhibit at different heights a dozen species of ammonite, none of which passes beyond its particular zone of limestone or clay into the zone below it or into that above it; so that those who adopt the doctrine of special creation must be prepared to admit, that at intervals of time, corresponding with the thickness of these beds, the Creator thought fit to interfere with the natural course of events for the purpose of making a new ammonite. It is not easy to transplant oneself into the frame of mind of those who can accept such a conclusion as this, on any evidence, short of absolute demonstration; and it is difficult to see what is to be gained by so doing, since, as we have said, it is obvious that such a view of the origin of living beings is utterly opposed to the Hebrew cosmogony. Deserving no aid from the powerful arm of bibliolatry, then, does the received form of the hypothesis of special creation derive any support from science or sound logic? Assuredly not much. The arguments brought forward in its favour all take one form: If species were not supernaturally created, we cannot understand the facts x, or y, or z; we cannot understand the structure of animals or plants, unless we suppose they were contrived for special ends; we cannot understand the structure of the eye, except by supposing it to have been made to see with; we cannot understand instincts, unless we suppose animals to have been miraculously endowed with them.

As a question of dialectics, it must be admitted that this sort of reasoning is not very formidable to those who are not to be frightened by consequences. It is an argumentum ad ignorantiam—take this explanation or be ignorant. But suppose we prefer to admit our ignorance rather than adopt a hypothesis at variance with all the teachings of nature? Or suppose for a moment we admit the explanation, and then seriously ask ourselves how much the wiser are we? what does the explanation explain? Is it any more than a grandiloquent way of announcing the fact, that we really know nothing about the matter? A phenomenon is explained, when it is shown to be a case of some general law of nature; but the supernatural interposition of the Creator can by the nature of the case exemplify no law, and if species have really arisen in this way, it is absurd to attempt to discuss their origin.

Or, lastly, let us ask ourselves whether any amount of evidence which the nature of our faculties permits us to attain, can justify us in asserting that any phenomenon is out of the reach of natural causation. To this end it is obviously necessary that we should know all the consequences to which all possible combinations, continued through unlimited time, can give rise. If we knew these, and found none competent to originate species, we should have good ground for denying their origin by natural causation. Till we know them, any hypothesis is better than one which involves us in such miserable presumption.

But the hypothesis of special creation is not only a mere specious mask for our ignorance; its existence in Biology marks the youth and imperfection of the science. For what is the history of every science but the history of the elimination of the notion of creative, or other interferences, with the natural order of the phenomena which are the subject-matter of that science? When Astronomy was young "the morning stars sang together for joy," and the planets were guided in their courses by celestial hands. Now, the harmony of the stars has resolved itself into gravitation according to the inverse squares of the distances, and the orbits of the planets are deducible from the laws of the forces which allow a schoolboy's stone to break a window. The lightning was the angel of the Lord; but it has pleased Providence, in these modern times, that science should make it the humble messenger of man, and we know that every flash that skimmers about the horizon on a summer's evening is determined by ascertainable conditions, and that its direction and brightness might, if our knowledge of these were great enough, have been calculated.

The solvency of great mercantile companies rests on the validity of the laws, which have been ascertained to govern the seeming irregularity of that human life which the moralist bewails as the most uncertain of things; plague, pestilence, and famine are admitted, by all but fools, to be the natural result of causes for the most part fully within human control, and not the unavoidable tortures inflicted by wrathful Omnipotence upon his helpless handiwork.

Harmonious order governing eternally continuous progress—the web and woof of matter and force interweaving by slow degrees, without a broken thread, that veil which lies between us and the Infinite—that universe which alone we know, or can know;—such is the picture which science draws of the world, and in proportion as any part of that picture is in unison with the rest, so may we feel sure that it is rightly painted. Shall Biology alone remain out of harmony with her sister sciences?

Such arguments against the hypothesis of the direct creation of species as these are plainly enough deducible from general considerations, but there are, in addition, phenomena exhibited by species themselves, and yet not so much a part of their very essence as to have required earlier mention, which are in the highest degree perplexing, if we adopt the popularly accepted hypothesis. Such are the facts of distribution in space and in time ; the singular phenomena brought to light by the study of development ; the structural relations of species upon which our systems of classification are founded ; the great doctrines of philosophical anatomy, such as that of homology, or of the community of structural plan exhibited by large groups of species differing very widely in their habits and functions.

The species of animals which inhabit the sea on opposite sides of the isthmus of Panama are wholly distinct ; the animals and plants which inhabit islands are commonly distinct from those of the neighbouring mainlands, and yet have a similarity of aspect. The mammals of the latest tertiary epoch in the Old and New Worlds belong to the same genera, or family groups, as those which now inhabit the same great geographical area. The crocodilian reptiles which existed in the earliest secondary epoch were similar in general structure to those now living, but exhibit slight differences in their vertebræ, nasal passages, and one or two other points. The guinea-pig has teeth which are shed before it is born, and hence can never subserve the masticatory purpose for which they seem contrived, and, in like manner, the female dugong has tusks which never cut the gum. All the members of the same great group run through similar conditions in their development, and all their parts, in the adult state, are arranged according to the same plan. Man is more like a gorilla than a gorilla is like a lemur. Such are a few, taken at random, among the multitudes of similar facts which modern research has established ; but when the student seeks for an explanation of them from the supporters of the received hypothesis of the origin of species, the reply he receives is, in substance, of oriental simplicity and brevity—"Mashallah ! it so pleases God !" There are different species on opposite sides of the isthmus of Panama, because they were created different on the two sides.

The pliocene mammals are like the existing ones, because such was the plan of creation ; and we find rudimental organs and similarity of plan, because it has pleased the Creator to set before himself a " divine exemplar or archetype," and to copy it in his works ; and somewhat ill, those who hold this view imply, in some of them. That such verbal hocus-pocus should be received as science will one day be regarded as evidence of the low state of intelligence in the nineteenth century, just as we amuse ourselves with the phraseology about Nature's abhorrence of a vacuum, wherewith Torricelli's compatriots were satisfied to explain the rise of water in a pump. And be it recollected that this sort of satisfaction works not only negative but positive ill, by discouraging inquiry, and so depriving man of the usufruct of one of the most fertile fields of his great patrimony, Nature.

The objections to the doctrine of origin of species by special creation which have been detailed, must have occurred with more or less force to the mind of every one who has seriously and independently considered the subject. It is therefore no wonder that, from time to time, this hypothesis should have been met by counter hypotheses, all as well, and some better, founded than itself ; and it is curious to remark that the inventors of the opposing views seem to have been led into them as much by their knowledge of geology as by their acquaintance with biology. In fact, when the mind has once admitted the conception of the gradual production of the present physical state of our globe, by natural causes operating through long ages of time, it will be little disposed to allow that living beings have made their appearance in another way, and the speculations of De Maillet and his successors are the natural complement of Scilla's demonstration of the true nature of fossils.

A contemporary of Newton and of Leibnitz, sharing therefore in the intellectual activity of the remarkable age which witnessed the birth of modern physical science, Benoît de Maillet spent a long life as a consular agent of the French Government in various Mediterranean ports. For sixteen years, in fact, he held the office of Consul-General in Egypt, and the wonderful phenomena offered by the valley of the Nile appear to have strongly impressed his mind, to have directed his attention to all facts of a similar order which came within his observation, and to have led him to speculate on the origin of the present condition of our globe and of its inhabitants. But, with all his ardour for science, De Maillet seems to have hesitated to publish views which, notwithstanding the ingenious attempts to reconcile them with the Hebrew hypothesis contained in the preface to "Telliamed" (and which we recommend for Mr. MacCausland's perusal), were hardly likely to be received with favour by his contemporaries.

But a short time had elapsed since more than one of the great anatomists and physicists of the Italian school had paid dearly for their endeavours to dissipate some of the prevalent errors; and their illustrious pupil, Harvey, the founder of modern physiology, had not fared so well, in a country less oppressed by the benumbing influences of theology, as to tempt any man to follow his example. Probably not uninfluenced by these considerations, his Catholic majesty's Consul-General for Egypt kept his theories to himself throughout a long life, for "Telliamed," the only scientific work which is known to have proceeded from his pen, was not printed till 1735, when its author had reached the ripe age of seventy-nine; and though De Maillet lived three years longer, his book was not given to the world before 1748. Even then it was anonymous to those who were not in the secret of the anagrammatic character of its title, and the preface and dedication are so worded as, in case of necessity, to give the printer a fair chance of falling back on the excuse that the work was intended for a mere jeu d'esprit.

The speculations of the supposititious Indian sage, though quite as sound as those of many a "Mosaic Geology" which sells exceedingly well, have no great value if we consider them by the light of modern science. The waters are supposed to have originally covered up the whole globe; to have deposited the rocky masses which compose its mountains by processes comparable to those which are now forming mud, sand, and shingle; and then to have gradually lowered their level, leaving the spoils of the animal and vegetable inhabitants embedded in the strata. As the dry land appeared, certain of the aquatic animals are supposed to have taken to it, and to have become gradually adapted to terrestrial and aerial modes of existence. But if we regard the general tenor and style of the reasoning in relation to the state of knowledge of the day, two circumstances appear very well worthy of remark. The first, that De Maillet had a notion of the modifiability of living forms (though without any precise information on the subject), and how such modifiability might account for the origin of species; the second, that he very clearly apprehended the great modern geological doctrine, so strongly insisted upon by Hutton, and so ably and comprehensively expounded by Lyell, that we must look to existing causes for the explanation of past geological events. The following passage of the preface indeed, in which De Maillet is supposed to speak of the Indian philosopher Telliamed, his *alter ego*, might have been written by the most philosophical uniformitarian of the present day.

"Ce qu'il y a d'étonnant, est que pour arriver à ces connoissances il semble avoir perverti l'ordre naturel, puisqu'au lieu de s'attacher d'abord à rechercher l'origine de notre globe il a commencé par travailler à s'instruire de la nature. Mais à l'entendre, ce renversement de l'ordre a eté pour lui l'effet d'un génie favorable qui l'a conduit pas à pas et comme par la main aux découvertes les plus sublimes. C'est en décomposant la substance de ce globe par une anatomie exacte de toutes ses parties qu'il a premièrement appris de quelles matières il était composé et quels arrangemens ces mêmes matières observaient entre elles. Ces lumières jointes à l'esprit de comparaison toujours nécessaire à quiconque entreprend de percer les voiles dont la nature aime à se cacher, ont servi de guide à notre philosophe pour parvenir à des connoissances plus intéressantes. Par la matière et l'arrangement de ces compositions il prétend avoir reconnu quelle est la véritable origine de ce globe que nous habitons, comment et par qui il a été formé."— (Pp. xix. xx.)

But De Maillet was before his age, and as could hardly fail to happen to one who speculated on a zoological and botanical question before Linnæus, and on a physiological problem before Haller, he fell into great errors here and there ; and hence, perhaps, the general neglect of his work. Robinet's speculations are rather behind than in advance of those of De Maillet, and though Linnæus may have played with the hypothesis of transmutation, it obtained no serious support until Lamarck adopted it, and advocated it with great ability in his " Philosophie Zoologique."

Impelled towards the hypothesis of the transmutation of species, partly by his general cosmological and geological views ; partly by the conception of a graduated, though irregularly branching scale of being, which had arisen out of his profound study of plants and of the lower forms of animal life, Lamarck, whose general line of thought often closely resembles that of De Maillet, made a great advance upon the crude and merely speculative manner in which that writer deals with the question of the origin of living beings, by endeavouring to find physical causes competent to effect that change of one species into another which De Maillet had only supposed to occur. And Lamarck conceived that he had found in nature such causes, amply sufficient for the purpose in view. It is a physiological fact, he says, that organs are increased in size by action, atrophied by inaction ; it is another physiological fact that modifications produced are transmissible to offspring. Change the actions of an animal, therefore, and you will change its structure, by increasing the development of the parts newly brought into use and by the diminution of those less used ; but by altering the circumstances which surround it you will alter its actions, and hence, in the long run, change of circumstance must produce change of organization. All the species of animals, therefore, are in Lamarck's view the result of the indirect action of changes of circumstance upon those primitive germs which he considered to have originally arisen, by spontaneous generation, within the waters of the globe. It is curious, however, that Lamarck should insist so strongly[1] as he has done,

[1] See Phil. Zoologique, vol. i. p. 222, et seq.

that circumstances never in any degree directly modify the form or the organization of animals, but only operate by changing their wants, and consequently their actions; for he thereby brings upon himself the obvious question, how, then, do plants, which cannot be said to have wants or actions, become modified? To this he replies, that they are modified by the changes in their nutritive processes, which are effected by changing circumstances; and it does not seem to have occurred to him that such changes might be as well supposed to take place among animals.

When we have said that Lamarck felt that mere speculation was not the way to arrive at the origin of species, but that it was necessary in order to the establishment of any sound theory on the subject, to discover by observation or otherwise, some *vera causa*, competent to give rise to them; that he affirmed the true order of classification to coincide with the order of their development one from another; that he insisted on the necessity of allowing sufficient time, very strongly; and that all the varieties of instinct and reason were traced back by him to the same cause as that which has given rise to species, we have enumerated his chief contributions to the advance of the question. On the other hand, from his ignorance of any power in nature competent to modify the structure of animals, except the development of parts, or atrophy of them, in consequence of a change of needs, Lamarck was led to attach infinitely greater weight than it deserves to this agency, and the absurdities into which he was led have met with deserved condemnation. Of the struggle for existence, on which as we shall see Mr. Darwin lays such great stress, he had no conception; indeed, he doubts whether there really are such things as extinct species, unless they be such large animals as may have met their death at the hands of man; and so little does he dream of there being any other destructive causes at work, that, in discussing the possible existence of fossil shells, he asks, "Pourquoi d'ailleurs seroient-ils perdues dès que l'homme n'a pu opérer leur destruction?" ("Phil. Zool.," vol. i. p. 77). Of the influence of selection Lamarck has as little notion, and he makes no use of the wonderful phenomena which are exhibited by domesticated animals, and illustrate its powers. The vast influence of Cuvier was employed against the Lamarckian views, and as the untenability of some of his conclusions was easily shown, his doctrines sank under the opprobrium of scientific as well as of theological heterodoxy. Nor have the efforts made of late years to revive them, tended to re-establish their credit in the minds of sound thinkers acquainted with the facts of the case; indeed it may be doubted whether Lamarck has not suffered more from his friends than from his foes.

Two years ago, in fact, though we venture to question if even the strongest supporters of the special creation hypothesis had not, now and then, an uneasy consciousness that all was not right, their position seemed more impregnable than ever, if not by its own inherent strength, at any rate by the obvious failure of all the attempts which had been made to carry it. On the other hand, however much the few, who thought deeply on the question of species, might be repelled by the generally received dogmas, they saw no way of escaping from them, save by the adoption of suppositions, so little justified by experiment or by observation, as to be at least equally distasteful. The choice lay between two absurdities and a middle condition of uneasy scepticism; which last, however unpleasant and unsatisfactory, was obviously the only justifiable state of mind under the circumstances.

Such being the general ferment in the minds of naturalists, it is no wonder that they mustered strong in the rooms of the Linnæan Society, on the first of July of the year 1858, to hear two papers by authors living on opposite sides of the globe, working out their results independently, and yet professing to have discovered one and the same solution of all the problems connected with species. The one of these authors was an able naturalist, Mr. Wallace, who had been employed for some years in studying the productions of the islands of the Indian Archipelago, and who had forwarded a memoir embodying his views to Mr. Darwin for communication to the Linnæan Society. On perusing the essay Mr. Darwin was not a little surprised to find that it embodied some of the leading ideas of a great work which he had been preparing for twenty years, and parts of which, containing a development of the very same views, had been perused by his private friends fifteen or sixteen years before. Perplexed in what manner to do full justice both to his friend and to himself, Mr. Darwin placed the matter in the hands of Dr. Hooker and Sir Charles Lyell, by whose advice he communicated a brief abstract of his own views to the Linnæan Society, at the same time that Mr. Wallace's paper was read. Of that abstract, the work on the "Origin of Species" is an enlargement, but a complete statement of Mr. Darwin's doctrine is looked for in the large and well-illustrated work which he is said to be preparing for publication.[1]

The Darwinian hypothesis has the merit of being eminently simple and comprehensible in principle, and its essential positions may be stated in a very few words: all species have been produced by the development of varieties from common stocks, by the conversion of these, first into permanent races and then into new species, by the process of *natural selection*, which process is essentially identical with that artificial selection by which man has originated the races of domestic animals—the *struggle for existence* taking the place of man, and exerting, in the case of natural selection, that selective action which he performs in artificial selection.

The evidence brought forward by Mr. Darwin in support of his hypothesis is of three kinds. First, he endeavours to prove that species may be originated by selection; secondly, he attempts to show that natural causes are competent to exert selection; and thirdly, he tries to prove that the most remarkable and apparently anomalous phenomena exhibited by the distribution, development, and mutual relations of species, can be shown to be deducible from the general doctrine of their origin, which he propounds, combined with the known facts of geological change; and that, even if not all these phenomena are at present explicable by it, none are necessarily inconsistent with it.

There cannot be a doubt that the method of inquiry

[1] The reader will remember that Huxley was writing in 1860.

which Mr. Darwin has adopted is not only rigorously in accordance with the canons of scientific logic, but that it is the only adequate method. Critics exclusively trained in classics or in mathematics, who have never determined a scientific fact in their lives by induction from experiment or observation, prate learnedly about Mr. Darwin's method, which is not inductive enough, not Baconian enough, forsooth, for them. But even if practical acquaintance with the process of scientific investigation is denied them, they may learn, by the perusal of Mr. Mill's admirable chapter "On the Deductive Method," that there are multitudes of scientific inquiries, in which the method of pure induction helps the investigator but a very little way.

"The mode of investigation" (says Mr. Mill) "which from the proved inapplicability of direct methods of observation and experiment remains to us as the main source of the knowledge we possess, or can acquire, respecting the conditions and laws of recurrence of the more complex phenomena, is called, in its most general expression, the deductive method, and consists of three operations : the first, one of direct induction ; the second, of ratiocination ; and the third, of verification."

Now, the conditions which have determined the existence of species are not only exceedingly complex, but, so far as the great majority of them are concerned, are necessarily beyond our cognisance. But what Mr. Darwin has attempted to do is in exact accordance with the rule laid down by Mr. Mill ; he has endeavoured to determine certain great facts inductively, by observation and experiment ; he has then reasoned from the data thus furnished; and lastly, he has tested the validity of his ratiocination by comparing his deductions with the observed facts of nature. Inductively, Mr. Darwin endeavours to prove that species arise in a given way. Deductively, he desires to show that, if they arise in that way, the facts of distribution, development, classification, &c., may be accounted for, *i.e.* may be deduced from their mode of origin, combined with admitted changes in physical geography and climate, during an indefinite period. And this explanation, or coincidence of observed with deduced facts, is, so far as it extends, a verification of the Darwinian view.

There is no fault to be found with Mr. Darwin's method, then; but it is another question whether he has fulfilled all the conditions imposed by that method. Is it satisfactorily proved, in fact, that species may be originated by selection? that there is such a thing as natural selection? that none of the phenomena exhibited by species are inconsistent with the origin of species in this way? If these questions can be answered in the affirmative, Mr. Darwin's view steps out of the ranks of hypotheses into those of proved theories; but so long as the evidence at present adduced falls short of enforcing that affirmation, so long, to our minds, must the new doctrine be content to remain among the former—an extremely valuable, and in the highest degree probable, doctrine, indeed the only extant hypothesis which is worth anything in a scientific point of view; but still a hypothesis, and not yet the theory of species.

After much consideration, and with assuredly no bias against Mr. Darwin's views, it is our clear conviction that, as the evidence stands, it is not absolutely proven that a group of animals, having all the characters exhibited by species in nature, has ever been originated by selection, whether artificial or natural. Groups having the morphological character of species, distinct and permanent races in fact, have been so produced over and over again; but there is no positive evidence at present that any group of animals has, by variation and selective breeding, given rise to another group which was even in the least degree infertile with the first. Mr. Darwin is perfectly aware of this weak point, and brings forward a multitude of ingenious and important arguments to diminish the force of the objection. We admit the value of these arguments to their fullest extent; nay, we will go so far as to express our belief that experiments, conducted by a skilful physiologist, would very probably obtain the desired production of mutually more or less infertile breeds from a common stock, in a comparatively few years; but still, as the case stands at present, this "little rift within the lute" is not to be disguised nor overlooked.

In the remainder of Mr. Darwin's argument our own private ingenuity has not hitherto enabled us to pick holes of any great importance; and judging by what we hear and read, other adventurers in the same field do not seem to have been much more fortunate. It has been urged, for instance, that in his chapters on the struggle for existence and on natural selection, Mr. Darwin does not so much prove that natural selection does occur, as that it must occur; but, in fact, no other sort of demonstration is attainable. A race does not attract our attention in nature until it has, in all probability, existed for a considerable time, and then it is too late to inquire into the conditions of its origin. Again, it is said that there is no real analogy between the selection which takes place under domestication, by human influence, and any operation which can be effected by nature, for man interferes intelligently. Reduced to its elements, this argument implies that an effect produced with trouble by an intelligent agent must, à fortiori, be more troublesome, if not impossible, to an unintelligent agent. Even putting aside the question whether nature, acting as she does according to definite and invariable laws, can be rightly called an unintelligent agent, such a position as this is wholly untenable. Mix salt and sand, and it shall puzzle the wisest of men with his mere natural appliances to separate all the grains of sand from all the grains of salt; but a shower of rain will effect the same object in ten minutes. And so while man may find it tax all his intelligence to separate any variety which arises, and to breed selectively from it, the destructive agencies incessantly at work in nature, if they find one variety to be more soluble in circumstances than the other, will inevitably in the long run eliminate it.

A frequent and a just objection to the Lamarckian hypothesis of the transmutation of species is based upon the absence of transitional forms between many species. But against the Darwinian hypothesis this argument has no force. Indeed, one of the most valuable and suggestive parts of Mr. Darwin's work is that in which he proves, that the frequent absence of transitions is a necessary consequence of his doctrine, and that the stock whence two or more species have sprung, need in no respect be intermediate between these species. If any two species have arisen from a common stock in the same way as the carrier and the pouter, say, have arisen from the rock-pigeon, then the common stock of these two species need be no more intermediate between the two than the rock-pigeon is between the carrier and pouter. Clearly appreciate the force of this analogy, and all the arguments against the origin of species by selection, based on the absence of transitional forms, fall to the ground. And Mr. Darwin's position might, we think, have been even stronger than it is if he had not embarrassed himself with the aphorism, "*Natura non facit saltum*," which turns up so often in his pages. We believe, as we have said above, that nature does make jumps now and then, and a recognition of the fact is of no small importance in disposing of many minor objections to the doctrine of transmutation.

But we must pause. The discussion of Mr. Darwin's arguments in detail would lead us far beyond the limits within which we proposed, at starting, to confine this article. Our object has been attained if we have given an intelligible, however brief, account of the established facts connected with species, and of the relation of the explanation of those facts offered by Mr. Darwin to the theoretical views held by his predecessors and his contemporaries, and, above all, to the requirements of scientific logic. We have ventured to point out that it does not, as yet, satisfy all those requirements; but we do not hesitate to assert that it is as superior to any preceding or contemporary hypothesis, in the extent of observational and experimental basis on which it rests, in its rigorously scientific method, and in its power of explaining biological phenomena, as was the hypothesis of Copernicus to the speculations of Ptolemy. But the planetary orbits turned out to be not quite circular after all, and grand as was the service Copernicus rendered to science, Kepler and Newton had to come after him. What if the orbit of Darwinism should be a little too circular? what if species should offer residual phenomena here and there, not explicable by natural selection?

Twenty years hence naturalists may be in a position to say whether this is, or is not, the case; but in either event they will owe the author of " The Origin of Species " an immense debt of gratitude. We should leave a very wrong impression on the reader's mind if we permitted him to suppose that the value of that work depends wholly on the ultimate justification of the theoretical views which it contains. On the contrary, if they were disproved to-morrow, the book would still be the best of its kind—the most compendious statement of well-sifted facts bearing on the doctrine of species that has ever appeared. The chapters on Variation, on the Struggle for Existence, on Instinct, on Hybridism, on the Imperfection of the Geological Record, on Geographical Distribution, have not only no equals, but, so far as our knowledge goes, no competitors, within the range of biological literature. And viewed as a whole, we do not believe that, since the publication of Von Baer's Researches on Development, thirty years ago, any work has appeared calculated to exert so large an influence, not only on the future of Biology, but in extending the domination of Science over regions of thought into which she has, as yet, hardly penetrated.

XIV

THE DARWINIAN HYPOTHESIS

DARWIN ON THE ORIGIN OF SPECIES

THERE is a growing immensity in the speculations of science to which no human thing or thought at this day is comparable. Apart from the results which science brings us home and securely harvests, there is an expansive force and latitude in its tentative efforts, which lifts us out of ourselves and transfigures our mortality. We may have a preference for moral themes, like the Homeric sage, who had seen and known much :—

> "Cities of men
> And manners, climates, councils, governments;"

yet we must end by confessing that

> "The windy ways of men
> Are but dust which rises up
> And is lightly laid again,"

in comparison with the work of nature, to which science testifies, but which has no boundaries in time or space to which science can approximate.

There is something altogether out of the reach of science, and yet the compass of science is practically illimitable. Hence it is that from time to time we are startled and perplexed by theories which have no parallel in the contracted moral world; for the generalizations of science sweep on in ever-widening circles, and more aspiring flights, though a limitless creation. While astronomy, with its telescope, ranges beyond the known stars, and physiology, with its microscope, is subdividing

infinite minutiæ, we may expect that our historic centuries
may be treated as inadequate counters in the history of
the planet on which we are placed. We must expect new
conceptions of the nature and relations of its denizens, as
science acquires the materials for fresh generalizations;
nor have we occasion for alarms if a highly advanced
knowledge, like that of the eminent Naturalist before us,
confronts us with an hypothesis as vast as it is novel.
This hypothesis may or may not be sustainable hereafter;
it may give way to something else, and higher science
may reverse what science has here built up with so much
skill and patience, but its sufficiency must be tried by the
tests of science *alone*, if we are to maintain our position
as the heirs of Bacon and the acquitters of Galileo. We
must weigh this hypothesis strictly in the controversy which
is coming, by the only tests which are appropriate, and
by no others whatsoever.

The hypothesis to which we point, and of which the
present work of Mr. Darwin is but the preliminary outline, may be stated in his own language as follows:—
"*Species originated by means of natural selection, or
through the preservation of the favoured races in the
struggle for life.*" To render this thesis intelligible, it is
necessary to interpret its terms. In the first place, what
is a species? The question is a simple one, but the
right answer to it is hard to find, even if we appeal to
those who should know most about it. It is all those
animals or plants which have descended from a single
pair of parents; it is the smallest distinctly definable
group of living organisms; it is an eternal and immutable entity; it is a mere abstraction of the human
intellect having no existence in nature. Such are a few
of the significations attached to this simple word which
may be culled from authoritative sources; and if, leaving
terms and theoretical subtleties aside, we turn to facts
and endeavour to gather a meaning for ourselves, by
studying the things to which, in practice, the name of
species is applied, it profits us little. For practice varies
as much as theory. Let the botanist or the zoologist
examine and describe the productions of a country, and
one will pretty certainly disagree with the other as to

the number, limits, and definitions of the species into which he groups the very same things. In these islands we are in the habit of regarding mankind as of one species, but a fortnight's steam will land us in a country where divines and savans, for once in agreement, vie with one another in loudness of assertion, if not in cogency of proof, that men are of different species; and, more particularly, that the species negro is so distinct from our own that the Ten Commandments have actually no reference to him. Even in the calm region of entomology, where, if anywhere in this sinful world, passion and prejudice should fail to stir the mind, one learned coleopterist will fill ten attractive volumes with descriptions of species of beetles, nine-tenths of which are immediately declared by his brother beetle-mongers to be no species at all.

The truth is that the number of distinguishable living creatures almost surpasses imagination. At least a hundred thousand such kinds of insects alone have been described and may be identified in collections, and the number of separable kinds of living things is under estimated at half a million. Seeing that most of these obvious kinds have their accidental varieties, and that they often shade into others by imperceptible degrees, it may well be imagined that the task of distinguishing between what is permanent and what fleeting, what is a species and what a mere variety, is sufficiently formidable.

But is it not possible to apply a test whereby a true species may be known from a mere variety? Is there no criterion of species? Great authorities affirm that there is—that the unions of members of the same species are always fertile, while those of distinct species are either sterile, or their offspring, called hybrids, are so. It is affirmed not only that this is an experimental fact, but that it is a provision for the preservation of the purity of species. Such a criterion as this would be invaluable; but, unfortunately, not only is it not obvious how to apply it in the great majority of cases in which its aid is needed, but its general validity is stoutly denied. The Hon. and Rev. Mr. Herbert, a most trustworthy authority, not only asserts as the result of his own obser-

vations and experiments that many hybrids are quite as
fertile as the parent species, but he goes so far as to
assert that the particular plant *Crinum capense* is much
more fertile when crossed by a distinct species than when
fertilised by its proper pollen ! On the other hand the
famous Gaertner, though he took the greatest pains to
cross the primrose and cowslip, succeeded only once or
twice in several years ; and yet it is a well-established fact
that the primrose and the cowslip are only varieties of the
same kind of plant. Again, such cases as the following
are well established. The female of species A if crossed
with the male of species B is fertile, but if the female of
B is crossed with the male of A, she remains barren.
Facts of this kind destroy the value of the supposed
criterion.

If, weary of the endless difficulties involved in the
determination of species, the investigator, contenting
himself with the rough practical distinction of separable
kinds, endeavours to study them as they occur in nature
—to ascertain their relations to the conditions which
surround them, their mutual harmonies and discordances
of structure, the bond of union of their parts and their
past history, he finds himself, according to the received
notions, in a mighty maze, and with, at most, the dim-
mest adumbration of a plan. If he starts with any one
clear conviction, it is that every part of a living creature
is cunningly adapted to some special use in its life. Has
not his Paley told him that that seemingly useless organ,
the spleen, is beautifully adjusted as so much packing
between the other organs ? And yet, at the outset of
his studies, he finds that no adaptive reason whatsoever
can be given for one-half of the peculiarities of vegetable
structure ; he also discovers rudimentary teeth, which are
never used, in the gums of the young calf and in those of
the fœtal whale ; insects which never bite have rudimental
jaws, and others which never fly have rudimental wings ;
naturally blind creatures have rudimentary eyes ; and the
halt have rudimentary limbs. So, again, no animal or
plant puts on its perfect form at once, but all have to start
from the same point, however various the course which
each has to pursue. Not only men and horses, and cats

and dogs, lobsters and beetles, periwinkles and mussels, but even the very sponges and animalcules commence their existence under forms which are essentially undistinguishable ; and this is true of all the infinite variety of plants.   Nay, more, all living beings march side by side along the high road of development, and separate the later the more like they are ; like people leaving church, who all go down the aisle, but having reached the door some turn into the parsonage, others go down the village, and others part only in the next parish.   A man in his development runs for a little while parallel with, though never passing through, the form of the meanest worm, then travels for a space beside the fish, then journeys along with the bird and the reptile for his fellow travellers ; and only at last, after a brief companionship with the highest of the four-footed and four-handed world, rises into the dignity of pure manhood. No competent thinker of the present day dreams of explaining these indubitable facts by the notion of the existence of unknown and undiscoverable adaptations to purpose.   And we would remind those who, ignorant of the facts, must be moved by authority, that no one has asserted the incompetence of the doctrine of final causes, in its application to physiology and anatomy, more strongly than our own eminent anatomist, Professor Owen, who, speaking of such cases, says (*On the Nature of Limbs*, pp. 39, 40) : "I think it will be obvious that the principle of final adaptations fails to satisfy all the conditions of the problem."

But, if the doctrine of final causes will not help us to comprehend the anomalies of living structure, the principle of adaptation must surely lead us to understand why certain living beings are found in certain regions of the world and not in others.   The palm, as we know, will not grow in our climate, nor the oak in Greenland.   The white bear cannot live where the tiger thrives, nor *vice versâ*, and the more the natural habits of animal and vegetable species are examined, the more do they seem, on the whole, limited to particular provinces.   But when we look into the facts established by the study of the geographical distribution of animals and plants it seems utterly hopeless to attempt to understand the strange and apparently capricious relations which they exhibit. One would be inclined to suppose *à priori* that every country must be naturally peopled by those animals that are fittest to live and thrive in it. And yet how, on this hypothesis, are we to account for the absence of cattle in the Pampas of South America when those parts of the New World were discovered? It is not that they were unfit for cattle, for millions of cattle now run wild there; and the like holds good of Australia and New Zealand. It is a curious circumstance, in fact, that the animals and plants of the Northern Hemisphere are not only as well adapted to live in the Southern Hemisphere as its own autochthones, but are in many cases absolutely better adapted, and so overrun and extirpate the aborigines. Clearly, therefore, the species which naturally inhabit a country are not necessarily the best adapted to its climate and other conditions. The inhabitants of islands are often distinct from any other known species of animal or plants (witness our recent examples from the work of Sir Emerson Tennent, on Ceylon), and yet they have almost always a sort of general family resemblance to the animals and plants of the nearest mainland. On the other hand, there is hardly a species of fish, shell, or crab common to the opposite sides of the narrow isthmus of Panama. Wherever we look, then, living nature offers us riddles of difficult solution, if we suppose that what we see is all that can be known of it.

But our knowledge of life is not confined to the existing world. Whatever their minor differences, geologists are agreed as to the vast thickness of the accumulated strata which compose the visible part of our earth, and the inconceivable immensity of the time of whose lapse they are the imperfect, but the only accessible witnesses. Now, throughout the greater part of this long series of stratified rocks are scattered, sometimes very abundantly, multitudes of organic remains, the fossilised exuviæ of animals and plants which lived and died while the mud of which the rocks are formed was yet soft ooze, and could receive and bury them. It would be a great error to suppose that these organic remains were fragmentary relics. Our museums exhibit fossil shells of immeasurable antiquity, as perfect as the day they were formed, whole skeletons without a limb disturbed—nay, the changed flesh, the developing embryos, and even the very footsteps of primæval organisms. Thus the naturalist finds in the bowels of the earth species as well defined as, and in some groups of animals more numerous than, those that breathe the upper air. But, singularly enough, the majority of these entombed species are wholly distinct from those that now live. Nor is this unlikeness without its rule and order. As a broad fact, the further we go back in time the less the buried species are like existing forms ; and the further apart the sets of extinct creatures are the less they are like one another. In other words, there has been a regular succession of living beings, each younger set being in a very broad and general sense somewhat more like those which now live.

It was once supposed that this succession had been the result of vast successive catastrophes, destructions, and re-creations *en masse;* but catastrophes are now almost eliminated from geological, or at least paleonto logical speculation ; and it is admitted on all hands that the seeming breaks in the chain of being are not absolute, but only relative to our imperfect knowledge ; that species have replaced species, not in assemblages, but one by one ; and that, if it were possible to have all the phenomena of the past presented to us, the convenient epochs and formations of the geologist, though having a certain distinctness, would fade into one another with limits as undefinable as those of the distinct and yet separable colours of the solar spectrum.

Such is a brief summary of the main truths which have been established concerning species. Are these truths ultimate and irresolvable facts, or are their complexities and perplexities the mere expressions of a higher law?

A large number of persons practically assume the former position to be correct. They believe that the writer of the Pentateuch was empowered and commissioned to teach us scientific as well as other truth, that the account we find there of the creation of living things is simply and literally correct, and that anything which seems to contradict it is, by the nature of the case, false. All the phenomena which have been detailed are, on this view, the immediate product of a creative fiat and consequently are out of the domain of science altogether.

Whether this view prove ultimately to be true or false, it is, at any rate, not at present supported by what is commonly regarded as logical proof, even if it be capable of discussion by reason ; and hence we consider ourselves at liberty to pass it by, and to turn to those views which profess to rest on a scientific basis only, and therefore admit of being argued to their consequences. And we do this with the less hesitation as it so happens that those persons who are practically conversant with the facts of the case (plainly a considerable advantage) have always thought fit to range themselves under the latter category.

The majority of these competent persons have up to the present time maintained two positions,—the first, that every species is, within certain defined or definable limits, fixed and incapable of modification ; the second, that every species was originally produced by a distinct creative act. The second position is obviously incapable of proof or disproof, the direct operations of the Creator not being subjects of science ; and it must therefore be regarded as a corollary from the first, the truth or false-hood of which is a matter of evidence. Most persons imagine that the arguments in favour of it are over-whelming ; but to some few minds, and these, it must be confessed, intellects of no small power and grasp of knowledge, they have not brought conviction. Among these minds that of the famous naturalist Lamarck, who possessed a greater acquaintance with the lower forms of life than any man of his day, Cuvier not excepted, and was a good botanist to boot, occupies a prominent place.

Two facts appear to have strongly affected the course of thought of this remarkable man—the one, that finer or stronger links of affinity connect all living beings with one another, and that thus the highest creature grades by multitudinous steps into the lowest ; the other, that an organ may be developed in particular directions by exerting itself in particular ways, and that modifications once induced may be transmitted and become hereditary. Putting these facts together, Lamarck endeavoured to account for the first by the operation of the second. Place an animal in new circumstances, says he, and its needs will be altered; the new needs will create new desires, and the attempt to gratify such desires will result in an appropriate modification of the organs exerted. Make a man a blacksmith, and his brachial muscles will develope in accordance with the demands made upon them, and in like manner, says Lamarck, "the efforts of some shortnecked bird to catch fish without wetting himself have, with time and perseverance, given rise to all our herons and long-necked waders."

The Lamarckian hypothesis has long since been justly condemned, and it is the established practice for every tyro to raise his heel against the carcass of the dead lion. But it is rarely either wise or instructive to treat even the errors of a really great man with mere ridicule, and in the present case the logical form of the doctrine stands on a very different footing from its substance.

If species have really arisen by the operation of natural conditions, we ought to be able to find those conditions now at work; we ought to be able to discover in nature some power adequate to modify any given kind of animal or plant in such a manner as to give rise to another kind, which would be admitted by naturalists as a distinct species. Lamarck imagined that he had discovered this *vera causa* in the admitted facts that some organs may be modified by exercise; and that modifications, once produced, are capable of hereditary transmission. It does not seem to have occurred to him to inquire whether there is any reason to believe that there are any limits to the amount of modification producible, or to ask how long an animal is likely to endeavour to gratify an impossible desire. The bird, in our example, would surely have renounced fish dinners long before it had produced the least effect on leg or neck.

Since Lamarck's time almost all competent naturalists have left speculations on the origin of species to such dreamers as the author of the *Vestiges*, by whose well-intentioned efforts the Lamarckian theory received its final condemnation in the minds of all sound thinkers. Notwithstanding this silence, however, the transmutation theory, as it has been called, has been a "skeleton in the closet" to many an honest zoologist and botanist who had a soul above the mere naming of dried plants and skins. Surely, has such an one thought, nature is a mighty and consistent whole, and the providential order established in the world of life must, if we could only see it rightly, be consistent with that dominant over the multiform shapes of brute matter. But what is the history of astronomy, of all the branches of physics, of chemistry, of medicine, but a narration of the steps by which the human mind has been compelled, often sorely against its will, to recognize the operation of secondary causes in events where ignorance beheld an immediate intervention of a higher power? And when we know that living things are formed of the same elements as the inorganic world, that they act and react upon it, bound by a thousand ties of natural piety, is it probable, nay is it possible, that they, and they alone, should have no order in their seeming disorder, no unity in their seeming multiplicity, should suffer no explanation by the discovery of some central and sublime law of mutual connexion?

Questions of this kind have assuredly often arisen, but it might have been long before they received such expression as would have commanded the respect and attention of the scientific world, had it not been for the publication of the work which prompted this article. Its author, Mr. Darwin, inheritor of a once celebrated name, won his spurs in science when most of those now distinguished were young men, and has for the last 20 years held a place in the front ranks of British philosophers. After a circumnavigatory voyage, undertaken solely for the love of his science, Mr. Darwin published a series of researches which at once arrested the attention of naturalists and geologists; his generalizations have since received ample confirmation, and now command universal assent, nor is it questionable that they have had the most important influence on the progress of science. More recently Mr. Darwin, with a versatility which is among the rarest of gifts, turned his attention to a most difficult question of zoology and minute anatomy; and no living naturalist and anatomist has published a better monograph than that which resulted from his labours. Such a man, at all events, has not entered the sanctuary with unwashed hands, and when he lays before us the results of 20 years' investigation and reflection we must listen even though we be disposed to strike. But, in reading his work it must be confessed that the attention which might at first be dutifully, soon becomes willingly, given, so clear is the author's thought, so outspoken his conviction, so honest and fair the candid expression of his doubts. Those who would judge the book must read it; we shall endeavour only to make its line of argument and its philosophical position intelligible to the general reader in our own way.

The Baker-street Bazaar has just been exhibiting its familiar annual spectacle. Straight-backed, small-headed, big-barrelled oxen, as dissimilar from any wild species as can well be imagined, contended for attention and praise with sheep of half-a-dozen different breeds and styes of bloated preposterous pigs, no more like a wild boar or sow than a city alderman is like an ourang-outang. The cattle show has been, and perhaps may again be, succeeded by a poultry show, of whose crowing and clucking prodigies it can only be certainly predicated that they will be very unlike the aboriginal *Phasianus Gallus*. If the seeker after animal anomalies is not satisfied, a turn or two in Seven Dials will convince him that the breeds of pigeons are quite as extraordinary and unlike one another and their parent stock, while the Horticultural Society will provide him with any number of corresponding vegetable aberrations from nature's types. He will learn with no little surprise, too, in the course of his travels, that the proprietors and producers of these animal and vegetable anomalies regard them as distinct species, with a firm belief, the strength of which is exactly proportioned to their ignorance of scientific biology, and which is the more remarkable as they are all proud of their skill in *originating* such "species."

On careful inquiry it is found that all these, and the

many other artificial breeds or races of animals and plants, have been produced by one method. The breeder —and a skilful one must be a person of much sagacity and natural or acquired perceptive faculty—notes some slight difference, arising he knows not how, in some individuals of his stock. If he wish to perpetuate the difference, to form a breed with the peculiarity in question strongly marked, he selects such male and female individuals as exhibit the desired character, and breeds from them. Their offspring are then carefully examined, and those which exhibit the peculiarity the most distinctly are selected for breeding, and this operation is repeated until the desired amount of divergence from the primitive stock is reached. It is then found that by continuing the process of selection—always breeding, that is, from well-marked forms, and allowing no impure crosses to interfere,—a race may be formed, the tendency of which to reproduce itself is exceedingly strong; nor is the limit to the amount of divergence which may be thus produced known, but one thing is certain, that, if certain breeds of dogs, or of pigeons, or of horses, were known only in a fossil state, no naturalist would hesitate in regarding them as distinct species.

But, in all these cases we have *human interference*. Without the breeder there would be no selection, and without the selection no race. Before admitting the possibility of natural species having originated in any similar way, it must be proved that there is in nature some power which takes the place of man, and performs a selection *suâ sponte*. It is the claim of Mr. Darwin that he professes to have discovered the existence and the *modus operandi* of this natural selection, as he terms it; and, if he be right, the process is perfectly simple and comprehensible, and irresistibly deducible from very familiar but well nigh forgotten facts.

Who, for instance, has duly reflected upon all the consequences of the marvellous struggle for existence which is daily and hourly going on among living beings? Not only does every animal live at the expense of some other animal or plant, but the very plants are at war. The ground is full of seeds that cannot rise into seedlings;

the seedlings rob one another of air and light and water, the strongest robber winning the day, and extinguishing his competitors. Year after year, the wild animals with which man never interferes are, on the average, neither more nor less numerous than they were; and yet we know that the annual produce of every pair is from one to perhaps a million young,—so that it is mathematically certain that, on the average, as many are killed by natural causes as are born every year, and those only escape which happen to be a little better fitted to resist destruction than those which die. The individuals of a species are like the crew of a foundered ship, and none but good swimmers have a chance of reaching the land.

Such being unquestionably the necessary conditions under which living creatures exist, Mr. Darwin discovers in them the instrument of natural selection. Suppose that in the midst of this incessant competition some individuals of a species (A) present accidental variations which happen to fit them a little better than their fellows for the struggle in which they are engaged, then the chances are in favour, not only of these individuals being better nourished than the others, but of their predominating over their fellows in other ways, and of having a better chance of leaving offspring, which will of course tend to reproduce the peculiarities of their parents. Their offspring will, by a parity of reasoning, tend to predominate over their contemporaries, and there being (suppose) no room for more than one species such as A, the weaker variety will eventually be destroyed by the new destructive influence which is thrown into the scale, and the stronger will take its place. Surrounding conditions remaining unchanged, the new variety (which we may call B)—supposed, for argument's sake, to be the best adapted for these conditions which can be got out of the original stock—will remain unchanged, all accidental deviations from the type becoming at once extinguished, as less fit for their post than B itself. The tendency of B to persist will grow with its persistence through successive generations, and it will acquire all the characters of a new species.

But, on the other hand, if the conditions of life change

in any degree, however slight, B may no longer be that form which is best adapted to withstand their destructive, and profit by their sustaining, influence ; in which case if it should give rise to a more competent variety (C), this will take its place and become a new species ; and thus, by *natural selection*, the species B and C will be successively derived from A.

That this most ingenious hypothesis enables us to give a reason for many apparent anomalies in the distribution of living beings in time and space, and that it is not contradicted by the main phenomena of life and organization appear to us to be unquestionable, and so far it must be admitted to have an immense advantage over any of its predecessors. But it is quite another matter to affirm absolutely either the truth or falsehood of Mr. Darwin's views at the present stage of the inquiry. Goethe has an excellent aphorism defining that state of mind which he calls *Thätige Skepsis*—active doubt. It is doubt which so loves truth that it neither dares rest in doubting, nor extinguish itself by unjustified belief; and we commend this state of mind to students of species, with respect to Mr. Darwin's or any other hypothesis, as to their origin. The combined investigations of another 20 years may, perhaps, enable naturalists to say whether the modifying causes and the selective power, which Mr. Darwin has satisfactorily shown to exist in nature, are competent to produce all the effects he ascribes to them, or whether, on the other hand, he has been led to over-estimate the value of his principle of natural selection, as greatly as Lamarck over-estimated his *vera causa* of modification by exercise.

But there is, at all events, one advantage possessed by the more recent writer over his predecessor. Mr. Darwin abhors mere speculation as nature abhors a vacuum. He is as greedy of cases and precedents as any constitutional lawyer, and all the principles he lays down are capable of being brought to the test of observation and experiment. The path he bids us follow professes to be not a mere airy track, fabricated of ideal cobwebs, but a solid and broad bridge of facts. If it be so, it will carry us safely over many a chasm in our knowledge, and lead us to a region free from the snares of those fascinating but barren

The Darwinian Hypothesis 351

Virgins, the Final Causes, against whom a high authority has so justly warned us. " My sons, dig in the vineyard," were the last words of the old man in the fable ; and, though the sons found no treasure, they made their fortunes by the grapes.

XV

A LOBSTER; OR, THE STUDY OF
ZOOLOGY

NATURAL HISTORY is the name familiarly applied to the study of the properties of such natural bodies as minerals, plants, and animals; the sciences which embody the knowledge man has acquired upon these subjects are commonly termed Natural Sciences, in contradistinction to other, so-called "physical," sciences; and those who devote themselves especially to the pursuit of such sciences have been, and are, commonly termed "Naturalists."

Linnæus was a naturalist in this wide sense, and his "Systema Naturæ" was a work upon natural history in the broadest acceptation of the term; in it, that great methodizing spirit embodied all that was known in his time of the distinctive characters of minerals, animals, and plants. But the enormous stimulus which Linnæus gave to the investigation of nature soon rendered it impossible that any one man should write another "Systema Naturæ," and extremely difficult for any one to become a naturalist such as Linnæus was.

Great as have been the advances made by all the three branches of science, of old included under the title of natural history, there can be no doubt that zoology and botany have grown in an enormously greater ratio than mineralogy, and hence, as I suppose, the name of "natural history" has gradually become more and more definitely attached to these prominent divisions of the subject, and by "naturalist" people have meant more

and more distinctly to imply a student of the structure
and functions of living beings.

However this may be, it is certain that the advance
of knowledge has gradually widened the distance between
mineralogy and its old associates, while it has drawn
zoology and botany closer together; so that of late years
it has been found convenient (and indeed necessary) to
associate the sciences which deal with vitality and all
its phenomena under the common head of "biology";
and the biologists have come to repudiate any blood-
relationship with their foster-brothers, the mineralogists.

Certain broad laws have a general application throughout both the animal and the vegetable worlds, but the
ground common to these kingdoms of nature is not of
very wide extent, and the multiplicity of details is so
great, that the student of living beings finds himself
obliged to devote his attention exclusively either to the
one or the other. If he elects to study plants, under
any aspect, we know at once what to call him; he is a
botanist and his science is botany. But if the investigation of animal life be his choice, the name generally
applied to him will vary, according to the kind of animals
he studies, or the particular phenomena of animal life to
which he confines his attention. If the study of man is
his object, he is called an anatomist, or a physiologist, or
an ethnologist; but if he dissects animals, or examines
into the mode in which their functions are performed, he
is a comparative anatomist or comparative physiologist.
If he turns his attention to fossil animals he is a palæon-
tologist. If his mind is more particularly directed to
the description, specific discrimination, classification, and
distribution of animals he is termed a zoologist.

For the purposes of the present discourse, however,
I shall recognise none of these titles save the last, which
I shall employ as the equivalent of botanist, and I shall
use the term zoology as denoting the whole doctrine of
animal life, in contradistinction from botany, which signi-
fies the whole doctrine of vegetable life.

Employed in this sense, zoology, like botany, is
divisible into three great but subordinate sciences,
morphology, physiology, and distribution, each of which

may, to a very great extent, be studied independently of the other.

Zoological morphology is the doctrine of animal form or structure. Anatomy is one of its branches, development is another; while classification is the expression of the relations which different animals bear to one another, in respect of their anatomy and their development.

Zoological distribution is the study of animals in relation to the terrestrial conditions which obtain now, or have obtained at any previous epoch of the earth's history.

Zoological physiology, lastly, is the doctrine of the functions or actions of animals. It regards animal bodies as machines impelled by certain forces, and performing an amount of work, which can be expressed in terms of the ordinary forces of nature. The final object of physiology is to deduce the facts of morphology on the one hand, and those of distribution on the other, from the laws of the molecular forces of matter.

Such is the scope of zoology. But if I were to content myself with the enunciation of these dry definitions, I should ill exemplify that method of teaching this branch of physical science, which it is my chief business to-night to recommend. Let us turn away then from abstract definitions. Let us take some concrete living thing, some animal, the commoner the better, and let us see how the application of common sense and common logic to the obvious facts it presents, inevitably leads us into all these branches of zoological science.

I have before me a lobster. When I examine it, what appears to be the most striking character it presents? Why, I observe that this part which we call the tail of the lobster, is made up of six distinct hard rings and a seventh terminal piece. If I separate one of the middle rings, say the third, I find it carries upon its under surface a pair of limbs or appendages, each of which consists of a stalk and two terminal pieces. So that I can represent a transverse section of the ring and its appendages upon the diagram board in this way.

If I now take the fourth ring, I find it has the same structure, and so have the fifth and the second; so that in each of these divisions of the tail I find parts which correspond with one another, a ring and two appendages; and in each appendage a stalk and two end pieces. These corresponding parts are called in the technical language of anatomy "homologous parts." The ring of the third division is the "homologue" of the ring of the fifth, the appendage of the former is the homologue of the appendage of the latter. And as each division exhibits corresponding parts in corresponding places, we say that all the divisions are constructed upon the same plan. But now let us consider the sixth division. It is similar to, and yet different from, the others. The ring is essentially the same as in the other divisions; but the appendages look at first as if they were very different; and yet when we regard them closely, what do we find? A stalk and two terminal divisions exactly as in the others, but the stalk is very short and very thick, the terminal divisions are very broad and flat, and one of them is divided into two pieces.

I may say, therefore, that the sixth segment is like the others in plan, but that it is modified in its details.

The first segment is like the others, so far as its ring is concerned, and though its appendages differ from any of those yet examined in the simplicity of their structure, parts corresponding with the stem and one of the divisions of the appendages of the other segments can be readily discerned in them.

Thus it appears that the lobster's tail is composed of a series of segments which are fundamentally similar, though each presents peculiar modifications of the plan common to all. But when I turn to the forepart of the body I see, at first, nothing but a great shield-like shell, called technically the "carapace," ending in front in a sharp spine, on either side of which are the curious compound eyes, set upon the ends of stout moveable stalks. Behind these, on the under side of the body, are two pairs of long feelers or antennæ, followed by six pairs of jaws, folded against one another over the mouth, and five pairs of legs, the foremost of these being the great pinchers, or claws, of the lobster.

It looks, at first, a little hopeless to attempt to find in

this complex mass a series of rings, each with its pair of appendages, such as I have shown you in the abdomen, and yet it is not difficult to demonstrate their existence. Strip off the legs, and you will find that each pair is attached to a very definite segment of the under wall of the body; but these segments, instead of being the lower parts of free rings, as in the tail, are such parts of rings which are all solidly united and bound together; and the like is true of the jaws, the feelers, and the eye-stalks, every pair of which is borne upon its own special segment. Thus the conclusion is gradually forced upon us that the body of the lobster is composed of as many rings as there are pairs of appendages, namely, twenty in all, but that the six hindmost rings remain free and moveable, while the fourteen front rings become firmly soldered together, their backs forming one continuous shield—the carapace.

Unity of plan, diversity in execution, is the lesson taught by the study of the rings of the body, and the same instruction is given still more emphatically by the appendages. If I examine the outermost jaw I find it consists of three distinct portions, an inner, a middle, and an outer, mounted upon a common stem; and if I compare this jaw with the legs behind it, or the jaws in front of it, I find it quite easy to see, that, in the legs, it is the part of the appendage which corresponds with the inner division, which becomes modified into what we know familiarly as the "leg," while the middle division disappears, and the outer division is hidden under the carapace. Nor is it more difficult to discern that, in the appendages of the tail, the middle division appears again and the outer vanishes; while on the other hand, in the foremost jaw, the so-called mandible, the inner division only is left; and, in the same way, the parts of the feelers and of the eye-stalks, can be identified with those of the legs and jaws.

But whither does all this tend? To the very remarkable conclusion that a unity of plan, of the same kind as that discoverable in the tail or abdomen of the lobster, pervades the whole organization of its skeleton, so that I can return to the diagram representing any one of the rings of the tail, which I drew upon the board, and by adding a third division to each appendage, I can use it as a sort of scheme or plan of any ring of the body. I can give names to all the parts of that figure, and then if I take any segment of the body of the lobster, I can point out to you exactly, what modification the general plan has undergone in that particular segment; what part has remained moveable, and what has become fixed to another; what has been excessively developed and metamorphosed, and what has been suppressed.

But I imagine I hear the question, how is all this to be tested? No doubt it is a pretty and ingenious way of looking at the structure of any animal, but is it anything more? Does Nature acknowledge in any deeper way this unity of plan we seem to trace?

The objection suggested by these questions is a very valid and important one, and morphology was in an unsound state, so long as it rested upon the mere perception of the analogies which obtain between fully formed parts. The unchecked ingenuity of speculative anatomists proved itself fully competent to spin any number of contradictory hypotheses out of the same facts, and endless morphological dreams threatened to supplant scientific theory.

Happily, however, there is a criterion of morphological truth, and a sure test of all homologies. Our lobster has not always been what we see it; it was once an egg, a semifluid mass of yolk, not so big as a pin's head, contained in a transparent membrane, and exhibiting not the least trace of any one of those organs, whose multiplicity and complexity, in the adult, are so surprising. After a time a delicate patch of cellular membrane appeared upon one face of this yolk, and that patch was the foundation of the whole creature, the clay out of which it would be moulded. Gradually investing the yolk, it became subdivided by transverse constrictions into segments, the forerunners of the rings of the body. Upon the ventral surface of each of the rings thus sketched out, a pair of bud-like prominences made their appearance— the rudiments of the appendages of the ring. At first, all the appendages were alike, but, as they grew, most of them became distinguished with a stem and two terminal divisions, to which in the middle part of the body was added a third outer division; and it was only at a later period, that by the modification, or abortion, of certain of these primitive constituents, the limbs acquired their perfect form.

Thus the study of development proves that the doctrine of unity of plan is not merely a fancy, that it is not merely one way of looking at the matter, but that it is the expression of deep-seated natural facts. The legs and jaws of the lobster may not merely be regarded as modifications of a common type,—in fact and in nature they are so,— the leg and the jaw of the young animal being, at first, indistinguishable.

These are wonderful truths, the more so because the zoologist finds them to be of universal application. The investigation of a polype, of a snail, of a fish, of a horse, or of a man would have led us, though by a less easy path, perhaps, to exactly the same point. Unity of plan everywhere lies hidden under the mask of diversity of structure—the complex is everywhere evolved out of the simple. Every animal has at first the form of an egg, and every animal and every organic part, in reaching its adult state, passes through conditions common to other animals and other adult parts; and this leads me to another point. I have hitherto spoken as if the lobster were alone in the world, but, as I need hardly remind you, there are myriads of other animal organisms. Of these some, such as men, horses, birds, fishes, snails, slugs, oysters, corals, and sponges, are not in the least like the lobster. But other animals, though they may differ a good deal from the lobster, are yet either very like it, or are like something that is like it. The cray fish, the rock lobster, and the prawn, and the shrimp, for example, however different, are yet so like lobsters, that a child would group them as of the lobster kind, in contradistinction to snails and slugs; and these last again would form a kind by themselves, in contradistinction to cows, horses, and sheep, the cattle kind.

But this spontaneous grouping into "kinds" is the first essay of the human mind at classification, or the calling by a common name of those things that are alike, and the arranging them in such a manner as best to suggest the sum of their likenesses and unlikenesses to other things.

Those kinds which include no other subdivisions than the sexes, or various breeds, are called, in technical language, species. The English lobster is a species, our cray fish is another, our prawn is another. In other countries, however, there are lobsters, cray fish, and prawns, very like ours, and yet presenting sufficient differences to deserve distinction. Naturalists, therefore, express this resemblance and this diversity by grouping them as distinct species of the same "genus." But the lobster and the cray fish, though belonging to distinct genera, have many features in common, and hence are grouped together in an assemblage which is called a family. More distant resemblances connect the lobster with the prawn and the crab, which are expressed by putting all these into the same order. Again, more remote, but still very definite, resemblances unite the lobster with the woodlouse, the king crab, the water flea, and the barnacle, and separate them from all other animals; whence they collectively constitute the larger group, or class, *Crustacea*. But the *Crustacea* exhibit many peculiar features in common with insects, spiders, and centipedes, so that these are grouped into the still larger assemblage or "province" *Articulata*, and, finally, the relations which these have to worms and other lower animals, are expressed by combining the whole vast aggregate into the subkingdom *Annulosa*.

If I had worked my way from a sponge instead of a lobster, I should have found it associated, by like ties, with a great number of other animals into the subkingdom *Protozoa;* if I had selected a fresh-water polype or a coral, the members of what naturalists term the subkingdom *Cœlenterata*, would have grouped themselves around my type; had a snail been chosen, the inhabitants of all univalve and bivalve, land and water shells, the lamp shells, the squids, and the sea-mat would have gradually linked themselves on to it as members of the same subkingdom of *Mollusca;* and finally starting from man, I should have been compelled to admit first, the ape, the rat, the horse, the dog, into the same class, and then the bird, the crocodile, the turtle, the frog, and the fish, into the same subkingdom of *Vertebrata*.

And if I had followed out all these various lines of classification fully, I should discover in the end that there was no animal, either recent or fossil, which did not at once fall into one or other of these subkingdoms. In other words, every animal is organised upon one or other of the five, or more, plans, whose existence renders our classification possible. And so definitely and precisely marked is the structure of each animal that, in the present state of our knowledge, there is not the least evidence to prove that a form, in the slightest degree transitional between any two of the groups *Vertebrata*, *Annulosa*, *Mollusca*, and *Cœlenterata*, either exists, or has existed, during that period of the earth's history which is recorded by the geologist. Nevertheless, you must not for a moment suppose, because no such transitional forms are known, that the members of the subkingdoms are disconnected from, or independent of, one another. On the contrary, in their earliest condition they are all alike, and the primordial germs of a man, a dog, a bird, a fish, a beetle, a snail, and a polype are in no essential structural respects, distinguishable.

In this broad sense, it may with truth be said, that all living animals, and all those dead creations which geology reveals, are bound together by an all-pervading unity of organisation, of the same character, though not equal in degree, to that which enables us to discern one and the same plan amidst the twenty different segments of a lobster's body. Truly it has been said, that to a clear eye the smallest fact is a window through which the Infinite may be seen.

Turning from these purely morphological considerations, let us now examine into the manner in which the attentive study of the lobster impels us into other lines of research.

Lobsters are found in all the European seas; but on the opposite shores of the Atlantic and in the seas of the southern hemisphere they do not exist. They are, however, represented in these regions by very closely allied, but distinct forms—the *Homarus Americanus* and the *Homarus Capensis*, so that we may say that the European has one species of *Homarus ;* the American, another; the African, another; and thus the remarkable facts of geographical distribution begin to dawn upon us.

Again, if we examine the contents of the earth's crust, we shall find in the later of those deposits, which have served as the great burying grounds of past ages, numberless lobster-like animals, but none so similar to our living lobster as to make zoologists sure that they belonged even to the same genus. If we go still further back in time, we discover in the oldest rocks of all, the remains of animals, constructed on the same general plan as the lobster, and belonging to the same great group of *Crustacea ,* but for the most part totally different from the lobster, and indeed from any other living form of crustacean ; and thus we gain a notion of that successive change of the animal population of the globe, in past ages, which is the most striking fact revealed by geology.

Consider, now, where our inquiries have led us. We studied our type morphologically, when we determined its anatomy and its development, and when comparing it, in these respects, with other animals, we made out its place in a system of classification. If we were to examine every animal in a similar manner we should establish a complete body of zoological morphology.

Again, we investigated the distribution of our type in space and in time, and, if the like had been done with every animal, the sciences of geographical and geological distribution would have attained their limit.

But you will observe one remarkable circumstance, that, up to this point, the question of the life of these organisms has not come under consideration. Morphology and distribution might be studied almost as well, if animals and plants were a peculiar kind of crystals and possessed none of those functions which distinguish living beings so remarkably. But the facts of morphology and distribution have to be accounted for, and the science, whose aim it is to account for them, is physiology.

Let us return to our lobster once more. If we watched the creature in its native element, we should see it climbing actively the submerged rocks, among which it delights to live, by means of its strong legs; or swimming by powerful strokes of its great tail, the appendages of whose sixth joint are spread out into a broad fan-like propeller; seize it and it will show you that its great claws are no mean weapons of offence; suspend a piece of carrion among its haunts, and it will greedily devour it, tearing and crushing the flesh by means of its multitudinous jaws.

Suppose that we had known nothing of the lobster but as an inert mass, an organic crystal, if I may use the phrase, and that we could suddenly see it exerting all these powers, what wonderful new ideas and new questions would arise in our minds! The great new question would be "How does all this take place?" the chief new idea would be the idea of adaptation to purpose,—the notion that the constituents of animal bodies are not mere unconnected parts, but organs working together to an end. Let us consider the tail of the lobster again from this point of view. Morphology has taught us that it is a series of segments composed of homologous parts, which undergo various modifications— beneath and through which a common plan of formation is discernible. But if I look at the same part physiologically, I see that it is a most beautifully constructed organ of locomotion, by means of which the animal can swiftly propel itself either backwards or forwards.

But how is this remarkable propulsive machine made to perform its functions? If I were suddenly to kill one of these animals and to take out all the soft parts, I should find the shell to be perfectly inert, to have no more power of moving itself than is possessed by the machinery of a mill, when disconnected from its steam-engine or water-wheel. But if I were to open it, and take out the viscera only, leaving the white flesh, I should perceive that the lobster could bend and extend its tail as well as before. If I were to cut off the tail I should cease to find any spontaneous motion in it—but on pinching any portion of the flesh, I should observe that it underwent a very curious change—each fibre becoming shorter and thicker. By this act of contraction, as it is termed, the parts to which the ends of the fibre are attached are, of course, approximated—and according to the relations of their points of attachment to the centres of motions of the different rings, the bending or the extension of the tail results. Close observation of the newly-opened lobster would soon show that all its movements are due to the same cause—the shortening and thickening of these fleshy fibres, which are technically called muscles.

Here, then, is a capital fact. The movements of the lobster are due to muscular contractility. But why does a muscle contract at one time and not at another? Why does one whole group of muscles contract when the lobster wishes to extend his tail, and another group, when he desires to bend it? What is it originates, directs and controls, the motive power?

Experiment, the great instrument for the ascertainment of truth in physical science, answers this question for us. In the head of the lobster there lies a small mass of that peculiar tissue which is known as nervous substance. Cords of similar matter connect this brain of the lobster, directly or indirectly, with the muscles. Now, if these communicating cords are cut, the brain remaining entire, the power of exerting what we call voluntary motion in the parts below the section is destroyed, and on the other hand, if, the cords remaining entire, the brain mass be destroyed, the same voluntary mobility is equally lost. Whence the inevitable conclusion is, that the power of originating these motions resides in the brain, and is propagated along the nervous cords.

In the higher animals the phenomena which attend this transmission have been investigated, and the exertion of the peculiar energy which resides in the nerves, has been found to be accompanied by a disturbance of the electrical state of their molecules.

If we could exactly estimate the signification of this disturbance; if we could obtain the value of a given exertion of nerve force by determining the quantity of electricity or of heat of which it is the equivalent; if we could ascertain upon what arrangement, or other condition of the molecules of matter, the manifestation of the nervous and muscular energies depends, (and doubtless science will some day or other ascertain these points,) physiologists would have attained their ultimate goal in this direction ; they would have determined the relation of the motive force of animals to the other forms of force found in nature ; and if the same process had been successfully performed for all the operations which are carried on, in and by, the animal frame, physiology would be perfect, and the facts of morphology and distribution would be deducible from the laws which physiologists had established, combined with those determining the condition of the surrounding universe.

There is not a fragment of the organism of this humble animal, whose study would not lead us into regions of thought as large as those which I have briefly opened up to you ; but what I have been saying, I trust, has not only enabled you to form a conception of the scope and purport of zoology, but has given you an imperfect example of the manner in which, in my opinion, that science, or indeed any physical science, may be best taught. The great matter is to make teaching real and practical, by fixing the attention of the student on particular facts, but at the same time it should be rendered broad and comprehensive by constant reference to the generalizations of which all particular facts are illustrations. The lobster has served as a type of the whole animal kingdom, and its anatomy and physiology have illustrated for us some of the greatest truths of biology. The student who has once seen for himself the facts which I have described, has had their relations explained to him, and has clearly comprehended them, has so far a knowledge of zoology, which is real and genuine, however limited it may be, and which is worth more than all the mere reading knowledge of the science he could ever acquire. His zoological information is, so far, knowledge and not mere hearsay.

And if it were my business to fit you for the certificate in zoological science granted by this department, I should pursue a course precisely similar in principle to that which I have taken to-night. I should select a fresh-water sponge, a fresh-water polype or a *Cyanœa*, a fresh-water mussel, a lobster, a fowl, as types of the five primary divisions of the animal kingdom. I should explain their structure very fully, and show how each illustrated the great principles of zoology. Having gone very carefully and fully over this ground, I should feel that you had a safe foundation, and I should then take you in the same way, but less minutely, over similarly selected illustrative types of the classes; and then I should direct your attention to the special forms enumerated under the head of types, in this syllabus, and to the other facts there mentioned.

That would, speaking generally, be my plan. But I have undertaken to explain to you the best mode of acquiring and communicating a knowledge of zoology, and you may therefore fairly ask me for a more detailed and precise account of the manner in which I should propose to furnish you with the information I refer to.

My own impression is that the best model for all kinds of training in physical science is that afforded by the method of teaching anatomy, in use in the medical schools. This method consists of three elements—lectures, demonstrations, and examinations.

The object of lectures is, in the first place, to awaken the attention and excite the enthusiasm of the student; and this, I am sure, may be effected to a far greater extent by the oral discourse and by the personal influence of a respected teacher, than in any other way. Secondly, lectures have the double use of guiding the student to the salient points of a subject, and at the same time forcing him to attend to the whole of it, and not merely to that part which takes his fancy. And lastly, lectures afford the student the opportunity of seeking explanations of those difficulties which will, and indeed ought to, arise in the course of his studies.

But for a student to derive the utmost possible value from lectures, several precautions are needful.

I have a strong impression that the better the discourse is, as an oration, the worse it is as a lecture. The flow of the discourse carries you on without proper attention to its sense; you drop a word or a phrase, you lose the exact meaning for a moment, and while you strive to recover yourself, the speaker had passed on to something else.

The practice I have adopted in late years in lecturing

to students, is to condense the substance of the hour's discourse into a few dry propositions, which are read slowly and taken down from dictation; the reading of each being followed by a free commentary, expanding and illustrating the proposition, explaining terms, and removing any difficulties that may be attackable in that way, by diagrams made roughly, and seen to grow under the lecturer's hand. In this manner you, at any rate, insure the co-operation of the student to a certain extent. He cannot leave the lecture-room entirely empty if the taking of notes is enforced, and a student must be preternaturally dull and mechanical if he can take notes and hear them properly explained, and yet learn nothing.

What books shall I read? is a question constantly put by the student to the teacher. My reply usually is, "None; write your notes out carefully and fully; strive to understand them thoroughly; come to me for the explanation of anything you cannot understand, and I would rather you did not distract your mind by reading." A properly composed course of lectures ought to contain fully as much matter as a student can assimilate in the time occupied by its delivery; and the teacher should always recollect that his business is to feed, and not to cram, the intellect. Indeed, I believe that a student who gains from a course of lectures the simple habit of concentrating his attention upon a definitely limited series of facts, until they are thoroughly mastered, has made a step of immeasurable importance.

But however good lectures may be, and however extensive the course of reading by which they are followed up, they are but accessories to the great instrument of scientific teaching—demonstration. If I insist unweariedly, nay fanatically, upon the importance of physical science as an educational agent, it is because the study of any branch of science, if properly conducted, appears to me to fill up a void left by all other means of education. I have the greatest respect and love for literature; nothing would grieve me more than to see literary training other than a very prominent branch of education; indeed, I wish that real literary discipline were far more attended to than it is; but I cannot shut my eyes to the fact that there is a vast difference between men who have had a purely literary, and those who have had a sound scientific, training.

Seeking for the cause of this difference, I imagine I can find it in the fact, that, in the world of letters, learning and knowledge are one, and books are the source of both ; whereas in science, as in life, learning and knowledge are distinct, and the study of things, and not of books, is the source of the latter.

All that literature has to bestow may be obtained by reading and by practical exercise in writing and in speaking ; but I do not exaggerate when I say, that none of the best gifts of science are to be won by these means. On the contrary, the great benefit which a scientific education bestows, whether as training or as knowledge, is dependent upon the extent to which the mind of the student is brought into immediate contact with facts—upon the degree to which he learns the habit of appealing directly to nature, and of acquiring through his senses concrete images of those properties of things, which are and always will be, but approximately expressed in human language. Our way of looking at nature, and of speaking about her, varies from year to year ; but a fact once seen, a relation of cause and effect, once demonstratively apprehended, are possessions which neither change nor pass away, but, on the contrary, form fixed centres, about which other truths aggregate by natural affinity.

Therefore, the great business of the scientific teacher is, to imprint the fundamental, irrefragable, facts of his science, not only by words upon the mind, but by sensible impressions upon the eye and ear and touch, of the student, in so complete a manner that every term used, or law enunciated, should afterwards call up vivid images of the particular structural, or other, facts which furnished the demonstration of the law, or the illustration of the term.

Now this important operation can only be achieved by constant demonstration, which may take place to a certain imperfect extent during a lecture, but which ought also to be carried on independently, and which should be addressed to each individual student, the teacher endeavouring, not so much to show a thing to the learner, as to make him see it for himself.

I am well aware that there are great practical difficulties in the way of effectual zoological demonstrations. The dissection of animals is not altogether pleasant, and requires much time; nor is it easy to secure an adequate supply of the needful specimens. The botanist has here a great advantage; his specimens are easily obtained, are clean and wholesome, and can be dissected in a private house as well as anywhere else; and hence, I believe, the fact, that botany is so much more readily and better taught than its sister science. But, be it difficult or be it easy, if zoological science is to be properly studied, demonstration, and, consequently, dissection, must be had. Without it, no man can have a really sound knowledge of animal organization.

A good deal may be done, however, without actual dissection on the student's part, by demonstrating upon specimens and preparations, and in all probability it would not be very difficult, were the demand sufficient, to organise collections of such objects, sufficient for all the purposes of elementary teaching, at a comparatively cheap rate. Even without these, much might be effected, if the zoological collections, which are open to the public, were arranged according to what has been termed the "typical principle"; that is to say, if the specimens exposed to public view were so selected, that the public could learn something from them, instead of being, as at present, merely confused by their multiplicity. For example, the grand ornithological gallery at the British Museum contains between two and three thousand species of birds, and sometimes five or six specimens of a species. They are very pretty to look at and some of the cases are, indeed, splendid; but I will undertake to say, that no man but a professed ornithologist has ever gathered much information from the collection. Certainly, no one of the tens of thousands of the general public who have walked through that gallery ever knew more about the essential peculiarities of birds when he left the gallery, than when he entered it. But if, somewhere in that vast hall, there were a few preparations, exemplifying the leading structural peculiarities and the mode of development of a common fowl; if the types of the genera, the leading modifications in the skeleton, in the plumage at various ages, in the mode of nidification, and the like, among birds, were displayed; and if the other specimens were put away in a place where the men of science, to whom they are alone useful, could have free access to them, I can conceive that this collection might become a great instrument of scientific education.[1]

The last implement of the teacher to which I have adverted is examination—a means of education now so thoroughly understood that I need hardly enlarge upon it. I hold that both written and oral examinations are indispensable, and, by requiring the description of specimens, they may be made to supplement demonstration.

Such is the fullest reply the time at my disposal will allow me to give to the question—how may a knowledge of zoology be best acquired and communicated?

But there is a previous question which may be moved, and which, in fact, I know many are inclined to move. It is the question why should training masters be encouraged to acquire a knowledge of this, or any other branch, of physical science? What is the use, it is said, of attempting to make physical science a branch of primary education? Is it not probable that teachers, in pursuing such studies, will be led astray from the acquirement of more important but less attractive knowledge? And, even if they can learn something of science without prejudice to their usefulness, what is the good of their attempting to instil that knowledge into boys whose real business is the acquisition of reading, writing, and arithmetic?

These questions are, and will be, very commonly asked, for they arise from that profound ignorance of the value and true position of physical science, which infests the minds of the most highly educated and intelligent classes of the community. But if I did not feel well assured

[1] Since these remarks were made the Natural History Collection of the British Museum has been removed to South Kensington, and Huxley himself wrote later on: "The visitor to the Natural History Museum in 1894 need go no further than the Great Hall to see the realisation of my hopes by the present Director."

that they are capable of being easily and satisfactorily answered; that they have been answered over and over again; and that the time will come when men of liberal education will blush to raise such questions,—I should be ashamed of my position here to-night. Without doubt, it is your great and very important function to carry out elementary education; without question, anything that should interfere with the faithful fulfilment of that duty on your part would be a great evil; and if I thought that your acquirement of the elements of physical science and your communication of those elements to your pupils, involved any sort of interference with your proper duties, I should be the first person to protest against your being encouraged to do anything of the kind.

But is it true that the acquisition of such a knowledge of science as is proposed, and the communication of that knowledge, are calculated to weaken your usefulness? or may I not rather ask is it possible for you to discharge your functions properly, without these aids?

What is the purpose of primary intellectual education? I apprehend that its first object is to train the young in the use of those tools wherewith men extract knowledge from the ever-shifting succession of phenomena which pass before their eyes; and that its second object is to inform them of the fundamental laws which have been found by experience to govern the course of things, so that they may not be turned out into the world naked, defenceless, and a prey to the events they might control.

A boy is taught to read his own and other languages, in order that he may have access to infinitely wider stores of knowledge than could ever be opened to him by oral intercourse with his fellow men; he learns to write, that his means of communication with the rest of mankind may be indefinitely enlarged, and that he may record and store up the knowledge he acquires. He is taught elementary mathematics that he may understand all those relations of number and form, upon which the transactions of men, associated in complicated societies, are built, and that he may have some practice in deductive reasoning.

All these operations of reading, writing, and ciphering, are intellectual tools whose use should, before all things, be learned, and learned thoroughly; so that the youth may be enabled to make his life that which it ought to be, a continual progress in learning and in wisdom.

But, in addition, primary education endeavours to fit a boy out with a certain equipment of positive knowledge. He is taught the great laws of morality; the religion of his sect; so much history and geography as will tell him where the great countries of the world are, what they are, and how they have become what they are.

Without doubt all these are most fitting and excellent things to teach a boy; I should be very sorry to omit any of them from any scheme of primary intellectual education. The system is excellent so far as it goes.

But if I regard it closely a curious reflection arises. I suppose that fifteen hundred years ago, the child of any well-to-do Roman citizen was taught just these same things; reading and writing in his own and, perhaps, the Greek tongue; the elements of mathematics; and the religion, morality, history, and geography current in his time. Furthermore, I do not think I err in affirming, that, if such a Christian Roman boy, who had finished his education, could be transplanted into one of our public schools, and pass through its course of instruction, he would not meet with a single unfamiliar line of thought; amidst all the new facts he would have to learn, not one would suggest a different mode of regarding the universe from that current in his own time.

And yet surely there is some great difference between the civilization of the fourth century and that of the nineteenth, and still more between the intellectual habits and tone of thought of that day and of this?

And what has made this difference? I answer fearlessly: The prodigious development of physical science within the last two centuries.

Modern civilisation rests upon physical science; take away her gifts to our own country, and our position among the leading nations of the world is gone to-morrow; for it is physical science only, that makes intelligence and moral energy stronger than brute force.

The whole of modern thought is steeped in science; it has made its way into the works of our best poets, and even the mere man of letters, who affects to ignore and despise science, is unconsciously impregnated with her spirit and indebted for his best products to her methods. I believe that the greatest intellectual revolution mankind has yet seen is now slowly taking place by her agency. She is teaching the world that the ultimate court of appeal is observation and experiment, and not authority; she is teaching it to estimate the value of evidence; she is creating a firm and living faith in the existence of immutable moral and physical laws, perfect obedience to which is the highest possible aim of an intelligent being.

But of all this your old stereotyped system of education takes no note. Physical science, its methods, its problems and its difficulties will meet the poorest boy at every turn, and yet we educate him in such a manner that he shall enter the world, as ignorant of the existence of the methods and facts of science, as the day he was born. The modern world is full of artillery; and we turn out our children to do battle in it, equipped with the shield and sword of an ancient gladiator.

Posterity will cry shame on us if we do not remedy this deplorable state of things. Nay, if we live twenty years longer, our own consciences will cry shame on us.

It is my firm conviction that the only way to remedy it is to make the elements of physical science an integral part of primary education. I have endeavoured to show you how that may be done for that branch of science which it is my business to pursue; and I can but add, that I should look upon the day when every schoolmaster throughout this land was a centre of genuine, however rudimentary, scientific knowledge, as an epoch in the history of the country.

But let me entreat you to remember my last words. Mere book learning in physical science, is a sham and a delusion—what you teach, unless you wish to be impostors, that you must first know; and real knowledge in science, means personal acquaintance with the facts, be they few or many.

EVERYMAN'S LIBRARY

A LIST OF THE 973 VOLUMES
ARRANGED UNDER AUTHORS

Anonymous works are given under titles.

Anthologies, Dictionaries, etc. are arranged at the end of the list.

NOTE—The following numbers are temporarily out of print:

4, 5, 8, 26, 28, 30, 37, 39, 43, 47, 52, 65, 66, 85, 89, 100, 109, 110, 111, 126, 127, 129, 130, 136, 137, 139, 140, 143, 144, 146, 147, 157, 158, 161, 164, 167, 174, 175, 210, 228, 244, 245, 246, 249, 250, 262, 263, 275, 279, 282, 289, 309, 323, 332, 346, 348, 350, 357, 363, 364, 369, 376, 377, 390, 391, 392, 410, 418, 420, 421, 446, 470, 473, 493, 507, 508, 512, 514, 518, 53, 540, 541, 557, 560, 567, 569, 574, 581, 590, 597, 598, 607, 610, 615, 63, 641–52, 658, 664, 675, 679, 682, 689, 693, 695, 703, 716, 717, 719, 72, 726, 731, 738, 740, 749, 766, 767, 769, 777, 789, 805, 813, 818, 824, 830, 831, 856, 920

LONDON: J. M. DENT & SONS LTD
NEW YORK: E. P. DUTTON & CO. INC.